D1291740

Explorations in Freedom

Explorations in Freedom: Prose, Narrative, and Poetry from Kultura

Leopold Tyrmand, Editor

THE FREE PRESS, NEW YORK
in cooperation with
THE STATE UNIVERSITY OF NEW YORK AT ALBANY
COLLIER-MACMILLAN LIMITED, LONDON

Translation from the Polish by permission of *Institut Littéraire*

Printed in the United States of America

The Free Press
A Division of The Macmillan Company
866 Third Avenue, New York, N.Y. 10022

Collier-Macmillan Canada Ltd., Toronto, Ontario

Library of Congress Catalog Card Number: 76-99731

printing number
1 2 3 4 5 6 7 8 9 10

Contents

Foreword

IN winter, 1968, I watched as Leopold Tyrmand began what seemed at that time the Herculean task of extracting a sample of articles from twenty-two years of *Kultura.* The result of his efforts, gathered in the two companion anthologies, *Kultura Essays* and *Explorations in Freedom: Prose, Narrative, and Poetry from Kultura*, testify to the journal's scope and vitality. *Kultura*'s *raison d'être* is made explicit in several places, but the simple answer I came to give my colleagues who asked "What is *Kultura?*"—that it was "a Polish émigré journal"—is neither sufficient nor, indeed, correct.

The phenomenon that is *Kultura* must be viewed in some larger context to grasp fully the implications of these volumes that reflect its quarter-century of growth. As a sociologist, I find it useful to consider *Kultura* as a *social movement.* I am convinced that, looked at under this rubric, those characteristics that make it much more than just another "émigré journal" come sharply into focus. Further, delineating *Kultura* in this sense may make some contribution to an understanding of modern social movements in general.

Cameron, in *Modern Social Movements*,[1] presents a short, useful definition which I shall adopt here.

> A social movement occurs when a fairly large number of people band together in order to alter or supplant some portion of the existing culture or social order.[2]

1 Cameron, William Bruce, *Modern Social Movements: A Sociological Outline*, Random House, New York, 1966.

2 Cameron, p. 7.

Cameron is quick to point out ambiguities in several of the terms he uses, but stresses that the main characteristic of a social movement is its emphasis on changing the culture or the social structure, or redistributing power within a society. Certainly it is to this end that *Kultura* came into being and continues to exist.

This is not to say that *Kultura* serves no other purpose For the Eastern European specialist, the journal may be no more than a source of otherwise unavailable data; for the student of contemporary Polish literature, only a good resource; but many human institutions and associations have more than one function. To examine *Kultura* as a social movement I shall take a brief look at its *origins* and stated *purpose*, consider some of the characteristics of its "*leader*" and its "*followers*," and attempt a description of its *structure* and *mode of action*. I shall not attempt to assess its significance. That task exceeds the scope of this paper, and must lie with others who are better qualified.

Emigré journals and papers have played an important part in helping displaced nationals (of whom the world has known many in the past century) to adjust to new life styles. Few have persisted for any length of time. Many have been "reactionary," in the sense that they were oriented to a restoration of old regimes, and others have frankly served as a medium for introducing readers to a new culture. Few have had clearly stated the long-range goal of altering the existing culture—with some notable exceptions.[3]

Kultura began with a man and an idea: The man was Jerzy Giedroyć, a Polish publisher and editor, and the idea was a revisionist approach to the problems of eastern Europe. Serving with the Polish Army in the Near East and Africa, he found himself, after Yalta, a man without a country—at least, without a country to which he could willingly return. He begins his "Manifesto" with the words:

3 For example, *The Bell*, a Russian émigré paper, edited by Hertzen and Ogarev. It lasted for ten years, and was designed to bring about social and political changes in eastern Europe. See Edward Carr's *The Romantic Exiles*, Beacon Press, Boston, 1961, for a good account of exiles in mid-nineteenth-century Europe.

La revue *Kultura* a été fondée en 1947, c'est-à-dire l'année ou l'on faisait table rasé des derrières traces laissées par les accords de Yalta . . .[4]

and goes on to argue that it is not sufficient that exiles only stand and wait; they must, he insists, make their presence and their positions known. Their positions must begin by a realistic appraisal of what exists and a clear analysis of the factors needed to bring about change. He maintained that the most potent force for change in Eastern Europe was *l'intelligentsia*, and from this group he sought both his writers and his audience.

Beginning in Rome, but moving soon to Paris, he established the *Institut Littéraire* (a publishing house) and the journal *Kultura*. In this venture he was joined by a few collaborators: Zofia and Zygmunt Hertz, and later by Juliusz Mieroszewski, Józef Czapski, Gustaw Herling-Grudziński, and by his younger brother Henryk Giedroyć. All of them served with Polish forces in the Near East and Africa. These composed *Kultura*'s "inner circle."

Giedroyć was a man obsessed with a feeling of "mission." Penniless, in exile, at a time when war had shattered the Europe he knew, he held to a faith that through *Kultura* Poland—and the world—could be saved.[5] Giedroyć had a love of independence from reliance on others (which is beautifully illustrated in *Kultura*'s independent and individualistic stance). He believed *Kultura* could succeed only if it were supported entirely by its readers. The first issues appeared thanks to loans accorded to him and repaid scrupulously (and through subsidies provided by old friends). The first issue ran to 1,000 copies and was mailed all over the world as a sample. With time the number of subscribers grew and permitted the regular publication of the review. Its circulation continued to grow every year.

4 The "Manifesto" is a long statement of *Kultura*'s rationale, circulated by Giedroyć after the Hungarian Revolt in 1956. For a formal analysis of *Kultura*, see Mieroszewski's article (in *Kultura Essays*) "The Political Thought of Kultura."

5 I am indebted to my colleague, Alicja Iwańska, and to other American contributors to *Kultura* for sharing their personal knowledge of Giedroyć and the "Inner Circle." The interpretation is mine. Compare with Tyrmand's "Preface" in this volume.

Giedroyć rapidly developed a structure composed of "contributing editors" around the world: mostly Polish exiles who both contributed and solicited articles. He persuaded a number of "stars" to write for *Kultura*, drawing on many of the best minds in Europe. Believing that *Kultura* should create opinions and shake up existing views, he enlisted a variety of talents, literary, political, economic, and philosophical, and offered a spectrum of ideas—all, however, subject to his personal editorial rule.

A second circle of *Kultura* supporters thus grew: both writers and faithful readers, mostly Polish, many living in Poland, but other eastern European exiles in both Europe and America were included.

Many of this group are frequent visitors to Maison Laffitte, the house outside of Paris where *Kultura* is put together. Here, the editor, his staff, and visitors gather around the table and talk. Ideas are exchanged, argued, fought; and routine business transacted. A constant stream of letters and articles pours in from all corners of the world. Giedroyć reads all, and sends out long letters to each correspondent. These are the "believers" who support *Kultura* through their faith and works.

The outermost circle is made up of *Kultura*'s readers: an uncountable aggregate. Some of their characteristics can be inferred from the nature of the journal itself: they can read Polish, they have some special interest in or relationship with the disciplines represented in *Kultura*'s articles, many are in the academic world, some are Eastern European specialists in universities or in government posts, some are language students, and others are perhaps reading *Kultura* as an assignment from their superiors. It is rumored, repeatedly, that *Kultura* is required reading for certain levels of government officials throughout Eastern Europe. Some support for this comes from the official and public condemnation of *Kultura* in Poland, where the government has denounced it as an "opposition" journal!

Many young writers are represented in current issues, and one suspects younger readers are being attracted for whom the historical context out of which *Kultura* developed represents ancient times. This receptive attitude promotes, without overt proselytizing, a source of continuing commitment to *Kultura*'s goals, and helps to prevent the isolation of an aging group of early supporters.

From time to time an article in *Kultura* will explicitly restate its objectives, and thus its rationale is kept in constant view. Also, as its influence is reaffirmed by other articles, both in *Kultura* itself, or through references in other media, the appeal and legitimacy of *Kultura* is reinforced. *Kultura* is in every sense an ideological journal which, one might claim, has come to be both the carrier for and the symbol of the belief-systems of its readers.

The listing of *Kultura*'s editorial staff and its contributing editors on its masthead makes at least the "inner" and part of the "second circle" highly visible. This suggests, as Cameron notes,[6] that public opinion exerts more control over it, as a social movement, than would be the case if it were less visible. Its healthy economic status tends to support this inference.

None of this implies that *Kultura* is a democratically organized institution in the conventional sense. It does not have voting members, or a formal set of by-laws, but its position is clear, without being rigid, and the charismatic quality of its leadership is so balanced by the rationality and consistency with which it deals with world problems that *Kultura* appears to be a truly "open-ended" movement, ever ready to adapt itself to changing conditions. And, in a way, this is a reflection of Giedroyć, the man who prefers "to remain in the shadows," to work through others, who strives to avoid becoming an "organization," but whose presence speaks on every page.[7]

Perhaps *Kultura*'s chief strength as a movement comes from its choice of nonviolent means to achieve its end: change. For intellectuals, whether truly so or self-defined, appeals based on reason still are cherished. *Kultura*'s long and open opposition to the use of force or violence is well documented. *Kultura*'s major premise, that change must be first affected in the minds of men, is testified to in its own pages.

All of these things that I have touched upon reinforce my own feeling that *Kultura* is indeed a social movement of some importance. Recent events in Eastern Europe (even tragic events) can be seen as supportive of *Kultura*'s position. Whether the association is coincidental does not really matter.

6 Cameron, p. 83.
7 See Note 5.

Because *Kultura* makes no claim for its unique role, and has no pretentions to organize itself more formally as an instrument to *control* power, but is content to let the power of ideas bring about change in a variety of ways, it may be the most effective social mechanism for promoting a *rapprochement* of East and West that we have yet tried. After twenty-two healthy years, it would appear that the ultimate measure of its success might be its disappearance as a distinct voice calling for "revision" of world policies. Paradoxically, one might wish it a speedy success, while at the same time foreseeing another quarter-century of vitality.

Paul F. Wheeler
Professor and Associate Dean, College of Arts and Sciences
The State University of New York at Albany

Preface

THE companion anthologies, *Kultura Essays* and *Explorations in Freedom: Prose, Narrative, and Poetry from Kultura*, are the result of a cooperative effort between the State University of New York at Albany (SUNYA) and The Free Press.

Early in 1967, SUNYA's College of Arts and Sciences began to take a special interest in the activity of the *Institut Littéraire*—a Polish émigré institute in Paris. For the past two decades, the *Institut Littéraire* has been publishing books by noteworthy authors. Its reputation, however, rests above all upon its monthly review *Kultura*, whose impact upon the Polish intelligentsia, at home and abroad, has been both striking and unique. It represents a rare case of political and cultural opposition originating in exile but influencing the ideological scene in the home country. Moreover, during the past ten years, the *Institut Littéraire* has expanded its range and, by defying the means of suppression at the disposal of a modern police state, has become a challenging outlet for all those from behind the Iron Curtain who either fled their countries, or remained there but found it impossible to publish except under a pseudonym and in the West, thereby pursuing the heroic path of clandestine opposition. The *Institut Littéraire* gained world-wide recognition by publishing some Russian manuscripts rescued from the hands of censors and the secret police, although their authors, above all Andrey Sinyavsky and Yuri Daniel, did not escape, unfortunately, the most cruel punishment meted out to all of those who want to be free in the Soviet Union.

The reader of these anthologies certainly will discover why Russians, Ukrainians, Hungarians, and others have chosen the modest

Polish émigré publishing house as the means of channeling to the free world their flaming protests and superb artistry.

Recognizing *Kultura*'s literary merits and its unusual position in the contemporary ideological struggle, the Dean of SUNYA's College, Dr. O. William Perlmutter, together with the Chairman of its Sociology Department, Prof. Paul F. Wheeler, and the Professor of Sociology and Anthropology, Dr. Alicja Iwańska, joined forces with The Free Press in a decision to publish two selections of writings from *Kultura* in English.

As editor, my principal task was to choose appropriate texts. My general approach was based on three premises:

• Eastern Europe, including Russia, today presents a boiling kettle of ideas. The shapelessness and immediacy of many of them, and their dialectical complexity, often molded on the spur of the moment by political situations, appear confusing to Western observers. From the lack of understanding and the routine superficiality of press reports, biased and fallacious conclusions are drawn. I have tried to permit the most competent, involved, and committed spokesmen to comment on ideas and facts which are so frequently misinterpreted. My hope remains that these anthologies, as conceived and completed, will clarify and create a truer image of issues and events in an area which, incontestably, bears a good deal of responsibility for mankind's future.

• *Kultura* is distinguished by a significant trait of ecumenism. It is difficult to subordinate narrow, national priorities to more general ends within a geographical heritage where ethnic diversities and animosities have made history. Yet, in keeping with the tradition of Polish universalism, *Kultura* has attempted to overcome the hardships of Eastern European particularism and build an awareness of a common destiny and vital interests. Its fundamental political postulate is a commonwealth of nations which have entered the road to socialism but must free themselves from the oppressive totalitarianism of the present Communist state. I consider it especially important to convey this.

• Finally, these anthologies should produce testimony of Polish and Eastern European involvement in the crucial problems of our epoch. It should determine the notion of totalitarian communism and its trend toward the ruthless extinction of human and humanistic values, not only as an endemic Eastern European issue, but as a universal condition of our time. The literary part of the anthology should also reflect the artistic skills of several writers whose spirit of innovation is jeopardized both by their situation as exiles without a vast audience and by the language barrier.

It remains for readers, students, and critics to judge whether these aims have been satisfied. None could have been achieved, however, without help from the twenty-three competent translators, to whom I hereby extend my thanks for their efforts.

As the result of the preparatory work in Albany, SUNYA's library is now in possession of a collection of the *Institut Littéraire* publications, including a complete set of *Kultura*. Some of its early issues are presently collector's items. In the future, they may be able to reveal to scholars and researchers many aspects of our time that are commonly overlooked by contemporaries.

But the greatest credit has to be given to the person to whom *Kultura* owes its very existence. Undeniably, *Kultura*'s strength derives from the coalescence of gifted intellects and pens. Yet, despite its abundance of heterogeneous elements, it is essentially a one-man enterprise—the fruit of his individual talent, perseverance, intransigence, and untiring labor. That man is Jerzy Giedroyć.

Giedroyć was born in 1906 in Poland into an old family of mixed Polish-Russian-Lithuanian descent. He was educated in Moscow and Warsaw, and studied law and history at Warsaw University. He worked first with the official Polish news agency, and then in the ministries of agriculture, industry, and commerce. In 1929 he started publishing a bi-weekly, which later became a weekly, which under the title of *Polityka* succeeded in gathering together a number of outstanding young writers and intellectuals and aroused much interest in Warsaw at that time. That circle cradled many figures still influencing Polish political and intellectual life.

With the outbreak of World War II, Giedroyć worked in the Polish Embassy in Bucharest, then enlisted as a private and took part in 1941 in the battle of Tobruk during the Libyan campaign. Later he was transferred to the press bureau of the Polish Corps in Africa, then to the Ministry of Information in London.

After the war, when Communist rule over Eastern Europe became a grim reality, Jerzy Giedroyć decided to continue fighting on the ideological and political levels. He organized a publishing enterprise in Rome, and then transferred it to Paris, where he established the *Institut Littéraire*. In 1947 he began the publication of *Kultura* with the help of his brother Henryk Giedroyć and Zofia and Zygmunt Hertz, who have remained his most faithful collaborators over the past twenty years. In 1968, the prestigious French academic lexicon, *Dictionnaire des Littératures*, wrote in its *Kultura* entry:

> Kultura (Culture).—Revue mensuelle polonaise paraissant depuis 1947 à Paris. Elle groupe les écrivains émigrés qui suivent avec objectivité les transformations opérées en Pologne et publie dans une collection spéciale les œuvres marquantes des écrivains émigrés. A l'heure actuelle elle est une des meilleures revues européennes.

I hope that the pages of this anthology will serve as adequate evidence of Jerzy Giedroyć's intellectual and ideological pilgrimage and quest.

Leopold Tyrmand

Explorations
in
Freedom

Józef Wittlin

The Splendor and the Squalor of Exile

THE reflections set down here form an introduction to an essay on which I have been working, off and on, since the end of World War II. The essay I have in mind will outline the physiology of émigré literature.

When I say "essay," I deliberately use that word in its literal sense. We have fallen into the habit of calling an "essay" any study of literary or artistic criticism. Yet in the strict sense of the word, an "essay" is no more than an "attempt," and an essayist is a writer who is only trying to do something. What he is trying is to discover the inner meaning of the subject he is investigating. And, as we all know, it is a long way from attempt to achievement. Even the work of Montaigne, which is something much greater than its title indicates, or John Locke's memorable *Essay Concerning Toleration* or his *Essay Concerning Human Understanding*, do not absolve us from the obligation of modesty and from the duty of restoring to the word "essay" its original meaning.

Thus in the essay to which these reflections are an introduction, I am only trying to establish certain principles and laws governing the life and death of literary creativity in exile.

Ours is not a voluntary emigration. Writers have been driven to it by bitter necessity, by a catastrophe, a national calamity—or else by the need to act, to oppose defeat in the hope of ultimate victory. In any event, the type of emigration to which we belong was produced by a set of circumstances which threatened a writer's creativity, if not his physical safety. That is why we have adopted the somewhat melodramatic name of *exiles*. The word need not connote the grim image of men brutally driven out of their country.

There are many among exiled writers who left of their own free will, refusing to submit to conditions they could not endure.

One of the reasons why it is so difficult to determine under what conditions émigré writing will flower or wither is the resentment a writer feels toward events and people responsible for his exile. In some cases this understandable rancor acts as a potent stimulant to creativity, much like a poison will often quicken the functions of a sluggish organism. But just as often it has a deadly effect on creative powers, blocking them altogether, or leading to their perversion. And, now and then, an overdose of this venom kills the writers themselves. In the long run life in an alien world proves too much to bear. They find that they have completely exhausted their store of illusions, and illusions in exile sustain the will to live far more than they do in one's native land.

In many cases, the suicides among exiles are struck by a bolt of panic. Even before World War II several renowned German writer-exiles departed this world by their own hand. For instance, Kurt Tucholsky, associated for many years with the liberal weekly *Die Weltbühne*, committed suicide shortly after Hitler came to power; this happened in Stockholm where Tucholsky had many friends. Another German writer who was well known in Poland, the playwright and left-wing activist Ernst Toller, hanged himself in a New York hotel just before war broke out. The talented (although not as well known as he deserved to be) writer from Prague, Ernst Weiss, took poison in Paris shortly before the Germans entered the city. In one of the concentration camps in which the government of Daladier, to its eternal shame, kept distinguished German refugees under lock and key during the so-called "phony war," Walter Hasenclever, one of the most brilliant dramatists of the expressionist period, killed himself. And the charming Stefan Zweig, whose popularity was world-wide, committed suicide, as did his wife who was thirty years his junior. The time was 1942, a dark year for the Allied forces. But the place was Brazil, a safe haven, friendly to Zweig.

Granted that without this venom, this poison that stirs up the psychological processes of exiles, we would not have the Dresden sequel of Mickiewicz's *Dziady* nor his *Pan Tadeusz*. However, one must not rely on this venom in the hope that it will produce of itself, as it were, some new *Dziady* or another *Pan Tadeusz*. It is a sobering thought to recall that Mickiewicz's productivity as a poet ended when he was only 36. From then on, for the remaining 21 years of his life, he only thought to improve and convert the world from the chair he held at the Collège de France, or used the pages of his French journal, *Tribune des Peuples,* to arouse, recruit, and organize hotheads, and lead them into foolhardy ventures. I have often wondered what might have happened to Mickiewicz had he, after writing *Pan Tadeusz* in 1836, returned to Poland and settled, say, in Cracow or in Lwów. Would he there, too, have gone into decline as a poet? Or would his genius have continued to flourish into the fullness of old age as did that of Count Alexander Fredro? This veteran of the Napoleonic wars never had any trouble with foreign censors as he continued to turn out his masterpieces of comedy, completely devoid of bitterness and rancor. These, however, are idle speculations. We will do better to turn our attention to contemporary developments. Perhaps upon closer scrutiny they will give us a clue to at least some of the laws that govern creativity in exile.

I have used the phrase "physiology of literature." This phrase is not my invention. I owe it, as I owe many other things, to the French critic Albert Thibaudet, who died in 1936. If memory serves me correctly, he was the first to use the word "physiology" in connection with literature.

However, before discussing literary creativity in exile, before considering the specific laws that cause émigré literature to differ from the literature developing in the exiles' countries of origin, let us ponder the word exile itself.

Toward the end of World War II, in the spring of 1945, Thomas Mann was celebrating his seventieth birthday in New York. During the celebration held in his honor, he delivered an address in which he explained the common roots of the English word "alien" and the German word *Elend. Elend* once meant the same as alien land. Today it means exclusively misfortune, misery. And yet to be an alien is not necessarily a misfortune, nor does every alien feel a pauper, either in the material or moral sense of this sad word. There is nothing pitiful about staying in a foreign country on the strength of a regular visa in one's passport or, indeed, without a visa (a privilege enjoyed by U.S.A. citizens in almost all European countries). On the contrary, it often provokes envy on the part of native inhabitants who cannot afford to travel abroad.

In the beautiful antiphon *Salve Regina* sung in Catholic churches, we twice find the word "exile." The author of the antiphon first calls the whole of mankind "*exules filii Haevae*," and then describes our earthly life as "*exilium*." From where have we been exiled? Since early childhood I have been haunted by the image of an angel brandishing a fiery sword. The picture was a reproduction of some steel or copper engraving, I don't remember which, dating from the rococo period. Obviously, the angel was expelling Adam and Eve from Paradise, and the devout author of the antiphon had in mind just that kind of exile.

If we accept this premise, then we owe it to our first parents that our stay on earth, regardless of where we live, and regardless of whether we are happy or unhappy, is an exile—an exile from a country where we have never been ourselves. On the other hand, the same doctrine that requires us to believe that our earthly existence is exile, also gives us the hope that when the exile will pass we will be permitted to return to the place from which our first parents had been banished—provided, of course, we first fulfill on this earth some unavoidable, if difficult, conditions.

Today, and not only today, the majority of people do not want to consider temporal life as exile, either from Paradise, or from anywhere else, although this life is not full of charm and sweetness for everyone. And yet it is precisely people whom temporal life never spares disappointments and miseries, people who should hate that life, who are most strongly attached to it. Many persons also see nothing heartening in the thought that some day, when the exile is over—*post hoc exilium*—they will be able to stay in their true country, not only temporarily but forever. One cannot expect these people to long for Paradise; they do not know it. They regard only their stay on Earth as real; here, and only here, is their home, no matter what kind—a splendid palace or a squalid shack. Only here on earth do their lives go on, no matter what, good or bad. And often they sacrifice their lives to restore and embellish their home, if not for themselves then for their descendants. And even if they do not succeed in this, if their whole existence is only a series of disappointments and failures, they have no intention of giving up their earthly citizenship. They do not at all try to obtain their first citizenship papers for eternity. Such people know well, or if they do not know, they feel, that their stay on earth is limited. Nevertheless, they act as if it were to last forever, as if the purpose of life were life itself. Consciously or unconsciously such people are existentialists of various non-religious shades.

But let us assume that they are wrong, while the author of the antiphon *Salve Regina*, as well as numerous authors of other texts, in verse and prose, expressing a kindred view of the world and of the beyond, are right. Could it be that a seed of the splendor of our status of exiles lies concealed in such awareness?

We have been told often that every truly original artist is an alien in his own land. The very fact of being different, his perverse lack of common sense, the fact that all he offers is unusual, often odd, and for the most part utterly foreign even to those closest to him, turn him into an exile. He is an exile, even if he lives in the same home from birth to death. We will spare you the long list of names of those heroic or tragic solitary minds who only after their departure from this world have become close and dear to this world, and who only after *hoc exilium* have ceased to be exiles in their own society. Almost every nation takes pride in its "*poètes maudits*," in its Edgar Allan Poe, Baudelaire, Rimbaud, Hart Crane. Every nation has its Van Gogh or Cezanne. No, in my humble opinion, exile need not be pure misfortune. It can also be a challenge. Certainly no one can deny that only artists, that is exiles, can throw fresh light on many problems of our earthly existence. Only poets can view the human condition in true perspective. And the loss of country can provide them with a splendid vantage point. (I am speaking of "Country Lost" because I don't want to encroach upon Milton's territory.)

But let us come down to earth where political exile is mostly a misfortune. Anyone who turns this misfortune into a religion will never be saved. And he who, unable to overcome it, looks upon exile as a normal form of existence—with no prospect but non-existence beyond—falls far short of glory.

E. M. Cioran, a Rumanian émigré who lives in Paris, the author of two fascinating books *Précis de décomposition* and *Syllogisme de l'amertume*, and winner of the Prix Rivarol for foreign writers writing in French, offers some penetrating insights into the subject. Reflecting on the fate of a poet in exile, for instance, he expresses the fear that a poet might acquire a taste for his status of exile. "No one," Cioran says, "can preserve the youthful poignancy of his sorrow. Sorrow wears off. So does nostalgia for one's country. Any nostalgia, in fact. Inspiration dries up in a poet for lack of variety in what he experiences and for lack of authentic anguish."

Obviously, exile in its primary, brutal sense afflicts not only writers who, as previously noted, are already exiles on account of their vocation. Artists are not the only ones to feel the splendor and squalor of exile.

In the third scene of Act I of Shakespeare's "Richard II," the Duke of Norfolk is sentenced by Richard to life-long banishment. Norfolk, as far as we know, was not a man of letters. Yet upon hearing the royal verdict he bursts forth:

> The language I have learned these forty years,
> My native English now I must forego;
> And now my tongue's use is to me no more
> Than an unstringed viol or a harp,
> Or like a cunning instrument cased up,
> Or being open, put into his hands
> That knows no touch to tune the harmony:
> Within my mouth you have en'gaoled my tongue,
> Doubly portcullissed with my teeth and lips,
> And dull, unfeeling, barren ignorance
> Is made my gaoler to attend on me.
> I am too old to fawn upon a nurse,
> Too far in years to be a pupil now:
> What is thy sentence, then, but speechless death,
> Which robs my tongue from breathing native breath?

If the prospect of being cut off from his native language can fill Norfolk with such bitter regret, how cruelly painful it is bound to be for an exiled writer. Even writers who find refuge in countries where the common language is the same as their own—Spanish writers in Latin America, for instance—never feel quite at home. Unfortunately, we no longer live in a world where Latin and Greek are the common instruments of poetry and prose of the intellectual elite of many nations, large and small. Today we live in a world where even Icelandic makes the same demands of the contemporary writer in Iceland, and produces in his fellow-citizens the same response, as does English in Great Britain or in the United States. And yet Icelandic is used by only a hundred thousand people.

To uproot a writer from the soil on which he lived for years in a symbiosis with the language of that soil can be a cruel act of violence. To be cut off from one's native stem is painfully felt, even by writers who stay outside their country temporarily and by choice. For instance, Dostoevsky wrote from Vevey in Switzerland to Nikolay Nikolaevich Strakhov: "With regard to my work here, I obviously will lag behind as far as the lack of knowledge of what is happening at home (although I know better about this than you do because every day I read three Russian newspapers and get two periodicals). But I will lose touch with the living flow of existence—not the thought of existence but its very essence—and how this can affect one's literary work!"

Dostoevsky, of course, is not a true example of a writer who bears ill the effects of uprooting. He did not write the words quoted above as an exile but as a traveler in Western Europe, which he intensely disliked. He spent four years there, yet very little of that part of the world found its way into his novels. Dostoevsky walked the streets of Berlin, Dresden, and Florence as if he were wearing blinkers. He could not stand the Germans. Nor did he wish to become more intimately acquainted with their life, civilization, and culture. His opinion of western culture—an unfavorable one—had been formed even before he left Russia. It is true that in Dresden he visited museums and art galleries. But he felt attracted by gambling casinos more than by museums. Purportedly to improve his health the author of *The Gambler* went to Wiesbaden and to the Swiss spa of Saxon-les-Bains, where there were not only therapeutic waters but also a famous casino. Roulette tables and silhouettes of gamblers aside, the most important "echoes" of Dostoevsky's four-year stay in Western Europe to be found in his great novels are the guillotine in Lyon and the last moments of a condemned man, as related by Prince Myshkin in *The Idiot.* It goes without saying that Dostoevsky was far more interested in what a man thinks a few minutes before his head is cut off than in the city of Lyon or, generally, in France. Dostoevsky the novelist shed his four-year stay in Western Europe like a duck sheds impure or brackish water. And yet, perhaps without those four years we would have had neither Ivan Karamazov nor "The Story of the Grand Inquisitor," despite the fact that the author had brought his dislike of the West and of the Catholic Church from Russia.

Whatever sustenance his imagination drew from what went on

around him during these years abroad was rather in the nature of "negative vitamins," because even in Western Europe Dostoevsky lived by Russia, and in the Russian way probed the depths of Russian souls. The scene of the criminal's execution which, like Myshkin, the hero of *The Idiot*, Dostoevsky saw in Basle in some illustrated magazine and which made such a shattering impression on him, was not merely a memory of his visit abroad. The author of *The Idiot* had himself once stood on a scaffold as a convict, not in Lyon but in Russia, and he was not to be guillotined but shot. Thus from the West Dostoevsky brought to his works themes that had been properly his long before. He was never threatened by the barrenness of which he had such nervous fear when writing that letter to Strakhov.

Barrenness caused by uprooting threatens rather the artist who easily and willingly yields to the fascination of a foreign world but is unable to assimilate it in such a way that the foreign environment becomes viable material for him. Some artists deliberately avoid in their work all elements that are indigenous to their own country. They roam the world in search of exoticism, foreign color, and foreign *condition humaine*. We do not speak here of professional travel-book writers. Let us look, for instance, at Hemingway's work. In his major books the characters operate mostly in non-American lands, if they are Americans at all. We see them in Italy, Spain, France, Africa, Cuba. Hemingway himself probably spent a major portion of his exuberant life outside the United States. For many years he resided in Cuba, from where he set out to various parts of the globe in search of unusual impressions. He doubtless found it useful to remain outside his native land from which, as far as we know, no one expelled him.

The Polish author Witold Gombrowicz has been living for the past twenty years in Argentina, but he has not stopped to think in his own highly individual manner about Poland and the Poles. In an interesting polemic with the previously mentioned Rumanian émigré Cioran, Gombrowicz rightly says that "it hardly matters in which particular spot of the world writers toil," because "every prominent writer as a result of his prominence was a foreigner even in his own homeland." The bitter taste of this truth is familiar to all creators of new values in art, even if they are members of Academies, or Nobel Prize winners.

In Spanish there is a special term to describe an exile: *destierro*

—a man deprived of his land. I would like to coin still another description: *destiempo*—a man deprived of time, the time that is still going on in his country. Time in exile is something completely different, something abnormal, almost insane—because an exile lives simultaneously in two different time levels: the present and the past. Living in the past is sometimes more absorbing than living in the present, and can exert a tyrannical influence on an exile's whole psyche. Such influence may be good or bad. Let's start with the latter.

An exile living in the past runs many risks: for instance, the risk of pining after trivial things whose real or imaginary charms have gone forever. He even runs the risk of falling under the spell of stage props once used in the comedies and dramas of a world that no longer exists. Such props in the course of normal, pre-exile existence would have been below his notice. Let me give you an example drawn from my own experience. In 1950, in New York, I often stopped before the window of an antique shop on Lexington Avenue. The window displayed ancient armor, weapons, helmets, and shakos. What riveted my attention was the shako of an officer of the Imperial and Royal Austro-Hungarian 4th Regiment of Uhlans. Before World War I that regiment was stationed in Lvov, my home town. Don't imagine that I ever served in it. I was but a simple infantryman. In a normal existence, daydreaming at the sight of such a shako would be dangerous infantilism. But in 1950 in New York, after World War II, and during the Korean War, I confess it without false shame, that shako produced nostalgia. Nostalgia for what? For the Austro-Hungarian cavalry? For the army in general? Nothing of the kind. Simply nostalgia for the past, for a world that ceased to exist in 1914, and which, perhaps, was better than our present one. Or was it? Was that, too, an illusion? That shako evoked a longing for the Europe of bygone days, for its colorful life, its sense of security, false as it proved to be, and last but not least, for my own youth. Such fixation on a useless stage prop is one of the dangers lurking for a writer in exile. Each of us is threatened by some shako or another, and consequently runs the risk of a false evaluation of bygone events and forgotten people—false, because we see them through a sentimental mist.

Another threat to the writer in exile is the loss of his ability to select among his reminiscences those suitable as material for his literary work. The life of the exile, like the life of any other person, speeds onward, but an émigré writer professionally tends to retreat further and further back. This often leads to serious, sometimes even tragic conflicts between his private and literary life. Occasionally an émigré artist lives in a complete vacuum which his imagination fills exclusively with phantoms of a dead world. Not every writer in exile is a Proust or a Joyce or a Polish Mickiewicz. These great writers bravely plunged *à la recherche du temps perdu* not to glorify the past but in order to unmask it mercilessly or, like Mickiewicz, to toy with it with fond forbearance. Let us, therefore, call this segment of our research in the physiology of émigré literature "the boon and the curse of retrospection."

The boon is as great as the curse. In his book on James Joyce, Professor Harry Levin says: "The first principle of artistic economy was isolation. Joyce had detached himself from his nationality and his religion, but he found his medium, his language, pointing back to them." Joyce was a voluntary émigré, an expatriate, and who knows whether it was not precisely because he spent the greater part of his life in Paris, Trieste, and Zürich, and not in his native Dublin, that he created an authentic great style and a language of his own. And from the various elements of his poetic vision he produced a new Dublin.

More often, however, a writer who cuts himself off from his nation for a longer period of time pays for it dearly. Take Turgenev: His two novels *Smoke* and *Virgin Soil* in which, during his long stay in Paris, he tried to depict contemporary life in Russia, were failures—the price of his uprooting.

An exiled writer lives in a restricted community in which it is not easy to create, and especially to publish, precedent-shattering works. Such a confined society would rather listen to what it already knows, and it demands from artists primarily a confirmation of its own views. Thus it is hard for an émigré writer to impose his own choice, his newness, on the émigré society. Nevertheless, he cannot yield. Because the desire to please, that greatest enemy of any artist even in a normal society, is a hundredfold more dangerous in a constricted, ghetto-like community, condemned to rely on its own strength and resources. In émigré circles there almost always occurs a confusion of concepts and criteria. Because there is no real yardstick to measure the true value of a writer's work, that value is often determined by sentimental considerations. As the duration of the exile becomes extended and the émigré literature moves further away from the life of the home country, even comparatively young writers run the risk of turning into delightful *raconteurs* of trivia.

Separation from the problems of his time may, however, be salutary for a writer, even for one who lives in his own country, because anyone who is too passionately rooted in his time may become its slave. Woe to the writer sentenced to a life-term of imprisonment in his own NOW. Only a *destiempo* can be really free, and judge his epoch from outside. Almost every writer—even one whose ambition is to reflect his time—strives to leap out of its confines and to produce "timeless values." A *destierro-destiempo* writer should start his career with such a leap, even at the risk of breaking his neck.

The question of language: Because the language of a people changes as the life of that people changes, we, living in exile, have at our disposal only those elements of language (a) that we have brought from home, (b) that have been produced abroad by former émigrés, and (c) that we create ourselves in exile. Thus our language no longer comprises new elements born at home during our absence. No matter how diligently we follow what is written there, we know the living speech of our country only at second hand, from reading.

On the other hand, in exile we can observe an interesting phenomenon which I would call the return of words. Words forgotten, no longer used in our present life, come to the surface of our consciousness. They return as memories. Only their purely sonorous form, from which life has evaporated, remains. A word of this kind is no longer the voice of life, but its echo. It is an empty shell in which now and then one can hear the hum of life. If we put it to our ear it still rings, sometimes even more beautifully than when a living organism dwelt inside. Such a word often means something else than it once meant in our native land. Thus the imagination of the exile is not only filled with memories of places and people left behind, but also with memories of words heard in the distant past. Such words haunt the writer like shadows, like ghosts. After a while those shadows begin to live a life of their own and become myths. Every writer in exile possesses a whole store of such verbal myths. There also begins to operate in a writer, and especially in a poet, a peculiar magic of words that in everyday life mean nothing or almost nothing. At this point I would like you to remember James Joyce who, far from Ireland, far from England, built whole worlds from words he invented or transformed.

Should an exiled writer switch to another language? The aforementioned Rumanian writer, Cioran, who writes in French, ponders the fate of a writer who attempts the shift. "He who abandons his language," he writes, "changes his personality, and commits treason on a heroic scale by breaking with his past, and—in some measure—with himself." Cioran sees only two forms of release for a poet in exile. In his opinion these forms are radically opposed: either humor or faith. "Depending on his temperament," says Cioran, "a poet turns to either faith or sarcasm."

Frankly, I do not see why humor cannot be reconciled with faith. Leon Bloy, for instance, was a man of profound faith, and yet in his works there is no lack of bitter sarcasm. Nor do I see why we should leave humor exclusively to the Devil. It is one of the spurious legends of the end of the nineteenth century that Heaven is hopelessly boring, while Hell is an exceedingly interesting intellectual club, a super P.E.N. Club, as it were. G. B. Shaw's brilliant play *Man and Superman* had a lot to do with the spreading of this legend. Personally, I think boredom *is* Hell.

Nor can I share Cioran's view that exile is a school of insanity. Admittedly, all of us émigrés are slightly mad, but many an émigré writer has found himself, his mission, his proper role, and has created truly outstanding work, precisely in exile.[1] Consider the literary output of German émigrés in the period 1933 to 1945. No, exile need not be a school of insanity. On the contrary, it can

1 The truth of this statement was recently confirmed by one of the most gifted Polish writers in exile, Piotr Guzy, the forty-year-old author of *The Short Life of a Positive Hero*, a novel published in Paris in 1966. Guzy is a fairly recent political émigré from Poland. In the January, 1966 issue of the Paris monthly *Kultura,* he is quoted as saying: "I could never have written *The Short Life* while there [in Poland]. It's the first honest book I've ever written. What use, then, have I for a fatherland? It is precisely here, in a foreign land, that I feel free: no taboos, no need to kowtow to anyone. I can insult whomever I please. I am paying—because one must pay for everything—by assuming full responsibility for what I am doing. Can any writer in Poland even dream of such things?" [Author's footnote, 1968]

be a school of sanity, of a clear and penetrating view of the world. In his own country, at home, in the hubbub of public life, a writer is constantly hampered when he tries to evaluate impartially whatever is going on. Sometimes he is even personally involved. How can he perceive the truth? Only in exile does he discern between form and content. It is often only in prison that a man acquires a sense of freedom, because he has at last severed the bonds that bound him to the outside world. As Guillaume Apolinaire, alone in his cell in the Paris Santé Prison, expressed it in his poem "A la Santé":

> Nous sommes seuls dans ma cellule
> Belle clarté, chere raison

Even Sartre, when he was seeking *Les Chemins de la Liberté*—the roads to freedom—in the second volume of his cycle, in the novel *Le Sursis,* had one of his heroes exclaim: "*La liberté c'est l'exile et je suis condamné à être libre.*" All of us in exile can repeat after Mattieu Delarue, that hero of Sartre's novel: "I am condemned to be free." Indeed, an exile, unless he voluntarily succumbs to the dictates of the émigré community, can make solitude the very foundation of his creativity. Solitude cools our passions, but it also sharpens our perspicacity. It is a miraculous soil which brings forth the ability to view temporal affairs in the light of the timeless.

Admittedly, few writers are ready to renounce fame and to suppress their vanity. Nonetheless, an émigré writer must realize that one may be a star only in an authentic, not in an artificial, firmament. And exile lets him shine only in a make-believe sky, a stage backdrop representing the sky.

Distance often helps to re-evaluate one's own country and one's own people. On the other hand, it forces a writer to divine when dealing with events of which he has no first hand knowledge. And this brings us to the question: What is more important in writing fiction—the art of divination, or the art of recreating authentic facts drawn from one's own experience? Who knows better what actually happened—the man who in the midst of fire, in the turmoil of battle, in the panic of the moment lost his bearings and his ability to observe, or the man who dares to divine, and reconstructs the total picture on the basis of varied, often contradictory accounts of eye witnesses? World literature contains a unique description of the battle of Waterloo, seen through the eyes of a participant, Fabrice del Dongo (in *The Charterhouse of Parma*). It is unique because it so vividly renders the chaotic vision of a great event. Stendhal knew from his own experience what Napoleon's battles looked like, although he took part only in the victorious ones and was not present at Waterloo. On the other hand, Tolstoy never witnessed a Napoleonic battle, yet he divined them from the material he had at hand: family tradition, letters, and documents. Thus for the sake of our creative work it is perhaps better to follow historic events from a distance in both time and space, instead of getting embroiled in them up to our ears. It's a point to ponder.[2]

"How do you spell your name?"—a foreigner is constantly asked this question. It is not one to please a writer. A writer as a rule is fond of his name. He values it, and feels it ought to be at least known, if not loved and admired. Some authors consider the question "How do you spell your name?" nothing short of an insult. It is true that we know émigré writers whose names have won fame only in exile. But as a rule exiled writers have an anonymous status and feel it as part of the squalor of exile. We are not going to analyze this fact. Let us, instead, turn our attention to the positive side of a writer's anonymity. Exile, where he is little known or even unknown, gives him a wonderful opportunity of comparing his opinion of himself with what he really represents. He can, first of all, compare his writings with those of indigenous writers. This may lead to lethal megalomania, or produce an

2 Why reach so far back? We have a far more recent example in support of the thesis that one need not be an eye-witness of events in order to describe them effectively and with a high degree of accuracy. In 1966 there appeared in New York a novel written in English by W. S. Kuniczak: *The Thousand Hour Day*. It is a novel about the German–Polish war in September, 1939. The author was still a child at that time, and he was brought up in England, where his family had settled after the war. His father was a high-ranking officer in the Polish army, and had participated in the campaign. From what his father told him and on the basis of the recollections of hundreds of other veterans of the campaign, the young author's imagination reconstructed pictures of battles which, as both Polish and American critics agree, from the most successful part of Kuniczak's ambitious novel. [Author's note, 1968]

equally lethal inferiority complex. On the whole, however, it helps him form a fair assessment.

Let us now consider the part played by those great artists who centuries ago adorned the Byzantine basilicas with mosaics, built Romanesque and Gothic cathedrals, and filled them with stained glass windows, and carved figures of saints and martyrs. Not only do we not know the names of those inspired artists today, but they themselves did not seem to care whether posterity would or would not discover their identity. They worked for the sheer beauty of their work, for the very—please excuse me—holiness of their work.

Anonymity offers an artist many advantages; there is even something charming about it. All too often writers and artists mold their work, even their ideas, to fit the name they have made for themselves thanks to previous works. This can be a great handicap in creating something new. The artist becomes a slave of his own name. Now, if he bases his work on the principle of anonymity he never need look back to what he has already done. With each new work he can begin a new life, as if in a state of virginity.

"To forget its creator is one of the functions of the creations," writes F. M. Foster in his beautiful essay *Anonymity*, "because the poet wrote the poem, no doubt, but he forgot himself while he wrote it, and we forget him while we read." "It was not the speaker who was in the beginning but the Word."

When speaking about the advantages and attraction of anonymous creation, I do not recommend that any of my fellow-writers in exile publish their books anonymously. God forbid! But I do wish for them, as I wish for myself, that our writings might be as well known as *Lorelei*, although the name of the author of that lyrical work was for twelve years taboo in his own country.

To be frank, the fact that what we create in exile lacks a wide field of radiation and no longer has that special aura which surrounded our name in the past, tends to hamper creativity. It is difficult to feel useful where no one needs us. The creators of cathedrals and stained glass windows knew that crowds would worship in these shrines. It is hard to be even a shoemaker where people prefer to walk barefoot. And a shoemaker who makes shoes for imaginary feet may in time lose interest in his trade, and take up another. Every émigré writer, at one time or another, has been confronted by a similar situation. Yet few will abandon their shoemaking. Apparently, some hope or illusion wins out in the end. A writer who writes without immediate response lays up a store for the future in the hope that some day his books will be widely read. It was so with Stendhal, who in a way was an exile too, in Civitta Vecchia. He deliberately dedicated his *Charterhouse of Parma* "to the happy few" and predicted accurately how many years it would take before he would be discovered by the general public, and how many before he was properly understood and appreciated. Many a novelist without a following, either in his own country or in exile, hopes that he will become a new Stendhal.

Such maximalistic expectations also impose maximalistic duties. Anyone who wishes to be read in fifty or one hundred years must write differently than an author who caters to present-day tastes. We have no idea what the reading public will be like in fifty or one hundred years. Nevertheless, we assume that their number will still include people sensitive to certain moral, aesthetic, and perhaps also religious values, just as we, in spite of the lightning-swift advance of barbarity, still retain a sensitivity to the universal and timeless elements handed down to us by the literature of antiquity and by the writings of the fifteenth, sixteenth, and seventeenth centuries.

In the twenty-second century people perhaps will no longer play football, and the tragedy of a football player will attract the reader only if he finds in it "purely human" elements independent of the game itself. No general today conquers a besieged city with the help of a wooden horse with soldiers hidden in its belly. And yet even in this atomic-hydrogen bomb era, people follow with breathless interest the well-told story of that siege. This is what should lure an artist in exile. Here is our chance for splendor. We can make shoes for feet which will tread this earth a hundred years from now, provided the earth still exists.

But let us return to where we started these random digressions. If, as the author of *Salve Regina* wants us to believe, it is true that our life is exile, we are bound to bring to this exile some hazy recollection of Paradise, the homeland we lost thanks to our sinful first parents.

Amidst the horrors of life, amidst hell on earth, we feel, time and again, a sudden longing for something that is neither Hell, nor horror, nor exile. Who knows? Perhaps it is the artists' mission in life to grasp and express these very longings and presentiments.

It seems to me that working in exile under conditions of more or less forced anonymity, we may come close to those artists who in the Middle Ages were preparing men's souls for another, no longer an exile's existence, where no one asks "How do you spell your name?"

1957–1959

Translated by Rulka Langer

Stanisław Vincenz

A Rarity

THE inn at Javorovic was filled before the wedding began. A variety of vehicles and horses stood next to one another on the paved driveway, in the courtyard, the stables, the carriage houses, and the barns. The wooden porch that went around the whole inn, the big guest rooms, and even the small private rooms were swarming with people. The guests were not exactly grouped according to their social class. Almost half the people in and about the inn were Jewish drivers or musicians. One big room housed the Kolomyski musicians and the passengers from the hackney coaches. People were already trying to dance in there. As a result, the guests, trying to avoid the bustle, moved out to the little garden in the back, where benches and tables stood in the shadow of some beech trees.

In spite of the overcrowding, as always at the inn, everyone was well served. Wildhorn, who was quite old, stood by the tavern serving-window and almost without uttering a word took care of the business. His family was bustling about the rooms and garden. The special guests, if they asked, were served various tasty tidbits: marinated salmon, trout from Rybnica, the sour waters from Burkuc with raspberry jam, slices of honeycomb filled with dark honey, and coffee with cream. The drivers drank beer and ate fresh Bryndza cheese. Everyone was constantly being served white rolls, more white rolls, and still more white rolls. The whole inn smelled of rolls, and outside was the smell of cut hay.

The air was filled with gaiety—the wedding had already begun. With the exception of the owner of the inn and his family, everyone else was a guest. This one and that one were busy doing something the way children at play are busy doing something. One man was giving his horse a little more feed to get him ready for the rest of the trip, but because there was plenty of time, most people waited to hear the end of a story someone was telling, or they watched for the arrival of new guests who were all coming from around Kosova.

It was noon. The wind had not let up. In a warm corner, however, under the hill, the wind was barely noticeable. It rustled only in the tops of tall, strong beeches and maples. Every so often it spread about the bright rainbow-colored fall leaves.

In a warm and completely shaded part of the backyard, on the high bank of the little stream called the Rybnica, that well-known old talker Bjumen sat on a bench on his sheepskin. He found himself among the "gentlemen." Everyone knew him. More new people kept coming outside and they greeted him and stopped to chat with him. Someone might even crack a joke or maybe get out a good story.

"What a rarity old Bjumen is," one of the young students said aloud over his beer. He said it so that Bjumen would overhear him.

Bjumen smiled playfully over his pint of beer. "A rarity? Today every road is loaded with these rarities. Every ragged jacket is filled with these rarities. But do you know, ha! ha! ha!"—once Bjumen began to talk he at once fell into form—"I know a true story, not some wild story, about a poor Jew who was really a rarity. I'll tell it to whoever buys me a beer."

On all sides people began shouting—"Beer! Beer! Beer!"

"Not all at once," said Bjumen quietly. "It's not necessary. Just one pint. Right. Fine."

"Long live Bjumen! Tell the story now!"

And this is how Bjumen told it: "It took place a long time ago. That doesn't matter—it's the truth. This is a story that made a lot of smart heads shake. It was the time, to be frank, when the only ladies and gentlemen were Christians and I was still a rarity—ha—ha—ha! Well, the talker gets to be smarter from the ladies and gentlemen. It was that time when the great Rabbi of Ostre was living—there is such a little town near Cracow. Well, maybe it was two hundred years ago. I really am not good enough to talk about this Rabbi. Ask someone who is better to tell you—how about old Bercunia? Oh yes, he's dead. Well, ask the Rabbi or Mr. Wildhorn here. But this story is really for another time. It's not to be told at a bar over beer. And this great man, this Rabbi, has as much to do with this whole story as God himself. He wound the whole thing up mechanically and secretly like a clockmaker winding his clocks. Ha! Ha! My God, what harm did all that do.

"Anyway, in Ostre there was this quiet little Jew. A tailor named Pinkas. Pinkas believed in the Rabbi. Pinkas was always asking his advice about some Sabbath regulations so that the Sabbath would be important. Sometimes he bored the Rabbi. The great Rabbi was patient because he knew that Pinkas was a pious man. He answered Pinkas with yes—no or no—yes. He didn't lift his head from his book when he spoke.

"Everyday Pinkas went from his little street to the castle on the manor and back again. He went to sew for his excellency the Count. On Saturday he went to the end of his street for a walk. I forgot to tell you that in Ostre there was a country gentleman, his excellency the Count, as they say. Pinkas was his excellency the Count's tailor. The Count was a good man and was satisfied with Pinkas. He praised him and even lent him out to other gentlemen. Later he stopped lending him out because he wanted him all to himself.

"Pinkas did well. What's supposed to go well for a Jew? He was married, he had a lot of children, and he always thought only of his work. He was always thinking about how, what, and from what he was going to make clothes. If a suit turned out well for him, or a Polish overcoat, or a Hungarian fur coat, or whatever they call them, he was so happy, as if I don't know what kind of luck met him. He walked home singing. He almost began to dance sometimes, but by the time he was in the mood he was in his own house with the kids.

"Pinkas was very satisfied with his Count. What does 'satisfied' mean? Pinkas had him to himself. He didn't have to worry that the Count would go to some other tailor. But what was most important was that this Count had a perfect shape. He could have been a tailor's model. Gold, not a model! Tall, straight, a fine figure of a man, a perfect size! Pinkas would quietly smack his lips with satisfaction everytime he measured the Count or had the Count fit his clothes.

"And when the Count tried them on—the Count was a sort of a daydreamer—he sometimes would ask politely: 'Dear Pinkas, maybe it should be this way—the German cut? Or maybe—a Spanish puff? Or, maybe?'

"Pinkas gave short answers: 'Yes—no or no—yes.' He never raised his head from his material.

"The Count understood. A master craftsman is a master craftsman.

"And you could say that they were friends, even though one was a Count and the other a wretch. One served faithfully, as was right, night and day. The other walked, rode, danced, also faithfully, whether it was necessary or not, night and day. And he was always dressed up! What does 'dressed up' mean? He shone with elegance. He paraded all over Cracow and boasted about his clothes in foreign countries, until his fame went around the world: 'to be as fashionable as the Count of Ostre.'

"But where did this come from? I must tell one important thing here. Pinkas was not only faithful. He had a special, a keen eye for putting things together. He knew where such a fold had to go, or a pleat. Even if a frock coat had a tiny wrinkle, he found it immediately and knew how to fix it. So his frock coats looked like they came from a mold.

"The Count, like all gentlemen, had relatives everywhere. Even the Emperor, who, as it says in the book, lived at that time somewhere in Spain, was his relative.

"And what happens? One time the Emperor writes to his excellency the Count and sends his special messenger with this letter:

" 'My dear Cousin, God be with you! I have a great favor to ask you. The word here is that you have a Jew. A real Jew! I don't know if it's true, and it probably isn't, but I am assured here that you yourself told one of my courtiers. If it's true bring him with you and I'll be very indebted to you. For me and for all my subjects it will be very important. It will be a great rarity. For a long time now we haven't had a Jew to cure us. We need one very much. More than one grace will fall upon you for this favor and upon your Jew. Gifts won't be lacking either. God be with you.' That's how the Emperor wrote from Spain."

* * *

The rumblings of new arrivals and the commotion all over the inn broke into Bjumen's story. Some long-expected guests had arrived. A great many young men poured into the garden. They were mainly brothers and cousins of the groom and their friends. Mr. Karol, the brother of Mr. Eusebius and a judge in training, held sway among them. Others looked to him and waited to hear what he'd say. They hung on his every word. They pampered him.

Mr. Karol was a young man with dark eyes, sharp features, and a bold look on his face. With a serious mien, as if grumbling over something, he mocked or continually poured out jokes. He had already arranged his life so that then, and later even more, jokes, amusement, and anecdotes followed him endlessly. He forced others to be this way. His friends changed to a group of mockers and jokesters. He was able to gain privileges from his superiors by telling anecdotes and he could conduct business with jokes. In turn, his companions and acquaintances, waiting for his jokes, encouraged him, almost forced him, to make jokes. They shook hands with Bjumen as though they were old friends. In his school days Mr. Karol sometimes rode to Kosov with Bjumen and listened to his stories.

The arrivals immediately received steaming, fragrant coffee and raspberry jam. And again there were white rolls, lots of white rolls. After the newcomers looked about the garden, after they talked about what happened on the road, they noticed that those present were waiting for the next part of Bjumen's story.

"What's Bjumen telling about today?" asked Mr. Karol.

"Ha! Ha! Ha!" chortled Bjumen. "No luck, Mr. Karol. But maybe I should say Mr. Adjunct? I drank that beer for nothing. You know the story better than me. You already told me some new jokes about that rarity. You know what? You finish it. You can really tell the part about the gentlemen and how they greeted him better than I can. I got to the part where the Emperor wrote the letter to the Count about bringing the Jew."

"Please tell it, Mr. Karol. Long live Mr. Karol. Three cheers for the Adjunct!" shouted the guests from their tables.

These shouts brought new listeners and the garden began to fill up. Mr. Karol, not finishing his coffee, got pulled in and began to tell the story:

"From my point of view, in this story, which I heard for the first time years ago from Bjumen—later I spoke to several specialists of this 'literature,' for so it is called—what is astounding is not, as Bjumen would have it, that the Jew was a rarity. It's something entirely different: it is that there are unpleasant individuals, really annoying and unbearable, quite frankly bad types, whose very presence forces others to exercise so much control, to swallow so much perpetual bitterness, to digest so much awkwardness that those who can take it are really saints. That is how the Emperor and all his court thought of it—the Jew, that is. They imagined that a Jew must be some kind of horrible thing, some monster. They needed him for their self-mortification.

"So let us listen to what the story says further. Where were we? Oh yes, the Emperor wrote to the Count. This 'Count' was really only a Polish nobleman. What does it mean for a Pole to be a Count? One way or another, he rules the same way, title or no title. Maybe he got his title from the Emperor later. Maybe because he brought the Emperor the Jew. Anyway, from this time on he wore some old ribbon or other, like an ornament, on his elegant clothes. Princes call him Count. . . . After he read the Emperor's letter he was satisfied. He was almost happy.

"The Christian Emperor and his court already knew about Pinkas. Ha! Probably the fame of his clothes has traveled far and wide. Now he'll have a chance to show himself before the world.

"He orders Pinkas to come to the manor immediately, at an unusual hour. 'Dear Pinkas,' he says, 'listen, the day after tomorrow we are going to Spain together. The Emperor has invited me, and he asked me especially to bring you. Look over my wardrobe one more time and get yourself ready for the trip. Farewell.'

"Pinkas was struck dumb. First he got very red, then he went pale. He wanted to say something, but the nobleman nodded and left. Pinkas's legs were giving way under him. Not able to think and carried on a wave of fear, he runs to the Rabbi.

"And how does it go from here, Bjumen?"

"What do you mean? Now *he* speaks. That's what it says in the old book."

"Aha. *He* is the great Rabbi. He knew about everything already. He didn't lift his head from his book. He smiled and said: 'Go!'

"Pinkas despaired. How was he to go? To strangers? To Spain? Who doesn't know what Spain means? They torture people there. The Jews are wiped out there. 'I have little children. . . .'

"*He* interrupted Pinkas: 'Take your funeral shirt with you!'

"He made a sign with his hand and went back to his book. Pinkas left, but he was barely alive.

"Eventually he told his wife everything and said good-bye to his family. They cried all night, sure that they would never see each other again.

"The nobleman set out for Spain with a beautiful train of coaches. Close behind the nobleman's coach came the baggage wagon, packed with Pinkas' help, carefully covered with sheets, and carrying only clothes—all made by Pinkas. And somewhere at the very end of the train rode the Jew, the tailor Pinkas, on a rattling old wagon with the wagon hands. Everyday the nobleman had Pinkas called out to check to see that he didn't have, God forbid, some pleats or folds or creases on his frock coat that ought to be taken care of. He didn't care about anything else.

"I ought to describe this journey, but it's difficult even to imagine what it was like for Pinkas. We can't really know what that trip—through strange countries, over mountains and even, I'm afraid to say it, over the water, through sinkings at sea—was like for him. Never in his life had he gone beyond Ostre. He had been nowhere beyond the street of the Jews and the manor of his excellency. Only once a week, on Saturday, he went to the end of the street.

"After many weeks of difficult traveling, after crossing the sea, they arrived in Spain. The shores were crowded with people waving flags and banners. There was absolute silence. The Emperor waited on the shore on his throne, dressed in satin and gold, surrounded by the clergy and his Lords and Ladies. The nobleman, dressed in his best garments, approached the Emperor and knelt before him. Close behind him stumbled Pinkas. No one greeted the nobleman; no one paid any attention to him. The fidgety Emperor, amid universal silence, asked very quietly: 'Where is the Jew?' The nobleman turned around and pointed to Pinkas.

" 'There is my tailor, Pinkas, the Jew.'

" 'Ah, that's a Jew?' The Emperor got up quickly from his throne and went up to Pinkas.

"He looked at him for a long time. Finally he turned away. His face was completely changed and filled with happiness. He greeted the nobleman politely.

" 'Do you understand now, cousin? You have done us an invaluable service for the saving of our souls. You certainly know that Jews are the greatest enemies of us Christians. Our faith teaches us to love our enemies. But where do we find them? Now I've looked at him and now I love him. I feel that I'm saved. And you, my dear Jew, tell us what you want for this.'

"Pinkas was dejected and didn't know what to say to him. At first he stood like a post. Then he began to sway back and forth and kept bowing without stopping. He scraped first his left foot as he bowed, then his right. In the meantime, the Emperor himself hung a string of pearls around Pinkas' neck and ordered that a large number of ducats be set aside for him. They brought in expensively saddled camels and horses for him. In addition, the Emperor had brought in for him lengths of rich cloths and samite and God knows what other splendors.

"Standing in rows in readiness behind the Emperor were the dignitaries of the Church and the candle bearers. The first to approach Pinkas was the Archbishop of Spain, then came the archbishops of individual provinces, then the Spanish magnates, then the ministers and dignitaries from the Emperor's court, and the government officials from the Emperor's dominions approached in order according to the fame of their birthright and their importance. Each one in turn took a long look at the exhausted Pinkas. Little by little, each one began to melt like the snow that melts on the mountains in the spring. Each one melted as if from sunbeams of universal love, and from Pinkas's own current of love that flowed from his eyes. Each one left lifted up a little, a little happier. Each one offered Pinkas what he could. Gifts were bequeathed him. Already a special place was set aside where Pinkas could store all the gifts and treasures that he got in this short time. In spite of all the universal love, armed guards were set about to protect Pinkas.

"But poor Pinkas also melted. He fell down from fatigue. He tottered. He tottered some more. Finally he fainted. General panic followed. A doctor was called. A stretcher was prepared. He was carried to a bed in the Emperor's palace. Everyone finally understood that the Jew was frankly exhausted from his journey; he was so tired that he was barely alive. A gloomy fear weighed upon the throng. It had seemed that good fortune was so near! What would happen if the Jew died?

"Nevertheless, Pinkas, under the thoughtful care of the doctors, the Emperor's chief steward and the ladies of the court who watched over him night and day, slowly came to himself. When he was finally completely cured, joy overcame the whole town. Later it spread like a glow over all of Spain. All work stopped and there was a constant holiday. It was something like a plague of joy sweeping in all directions and running through the whole country. Pilgrimages from all over the country jammed the coastal town to see the Jew, to love the Jew, to be sure to be saved.

"When Pinkas was really fully recovered, he was dressed richly and shown from that time on upon the Emperor's dais or next to the throne. Anyway, his health was spared. The gentry, the burghers, the artisans, the soldiers, crowds of peasants, and beggars, as well as gypsies and tramps, paraded before the Jew. The masses of humanity stared at him with love and soaked up the feeling of being saved. When they left him, they were moved and flushed with joy. In order to store the gifts that endlessly poured in from all over Spain, he was given one of the biggest palaces in town.

"During this time the nobleman had closely looked over the clothes of the first and foremost Spanish magnates, princes, and rich men. He would laugh to himself. All of them were, to be sure, brand new, sumptuous, even laden with velvet, gold, and other riches, but somehow they were pretentious and could not compare with Pinkas' work with regard to cut, taste, smoothness, concept, and imagination. During this time no one ever thought what Pinkas was worth as a tailor. Why should anyone bother! They wanted a Jew. What a nation without taste! Without wit!

"In the meantime, this whole story got about to the neighboring countries. It finally got to Rome. The Pope listened attentively to the story. He was obviously upset. He sped to Spain himself. Surrounded by his most holy train, amid the ringing of bells and the shooting of cannon, he approached Pinkas. In his hand he had a magic amethyst before which everyone bowed. He looked at Pinkas with such black, sharp eyes that they seemed to stab Pinkas down to his liver.

" 'This is supposed to be a Jew?' he asked in a sharp, dry voice.

"The harsh sound of these words suddenly reminded Pinkas of his children, his wife, and his mother, as though he saw them before him. Soon, however, the Pope brightened up. He approached Pinkas and offered him the amethyst. Then all heads bowed before Pinkas.

"Up to this time Pinkas just sat sadly, eating his heart out, not himself at all. Now Pinkas became happy. He smiled for whatever reason. Were these honors amusing to him? I would like to know if that mighty and formidable Pope—*der Pojbst*, as the old Jewish books call him—was happy and calm, and if he maybe knew that this signaled the end of the torment. Pinkas smiled for the first time and the last. The Pope brightened up again. He was thinking about something and weighing it in his mind for a long time. He finally called out:

" 'Stand Christians! This is no Jew! He is an ordinary raspscallion, most certainly a fraud, a tinkling cymbal that plays with you and your salvation. Your precarious salvation! It's no game to love someone like him. If you had seen a real Jew, a real enemy, you would understand what it is to love an enemy. And you, you poor soul, because you dared to expose the salvation of so many Christian souls, you will perish immediately at the stake.'

"The crowd surged with a groan of terror. Pinkas was seized and tied. He was recalling *his* words (those of the Rabbi of Ostre), and under his new clothes he was wearing his funeral shirt. Now he knew why. Now he spoke up for the first time. He swore that he was the truest Jew and that he could prove it. But no one in Spain knew any Jews; no one remembered the Jews. There was no one to verify that he was a Jew. Pinkas was led to the dungeon where tortures awaited him before he was to go to the stake.

"The Emperor wanted to soften the punishment. He fussed about like someone who doesn't know what to do. Finally, no one paid any attention to Pinkas. Many were not sure now that he was a Jew, that maybe. . . . Only our friend the nobleman fretted. If something happened to his man, to his very own tailor, all of Ostre would convert to Calvinism! He threatened further: his relatives would raise the alarm in the Sejm of the Republic, for his, the Polish nobility had been tricked. If all this wouldn't help, he said with great exasperation and a few curses, he and the men in his train would free the tailor, and he wouldn't be liable for all the Christian blood that would be shed for the Jew's cause. Maybe he was sure of the backing of the Emperor, his cousin.

"In the meantime, mobs of people, each group seemed poorer than the last, began to gather and to mutter to themselves. They began to get excited and it wasn't a joke any more, this crowd. 'The Jew, the Jew—give us back the Jew! We want the Jew. We want salvation!!!'

"Like waves hitting the huge sea dikes, those voices reached the dignitaries. Maybe as a result of all of this the gentlemen divided into two camps. The higher ecclesiastics asked the Pope for mercy.

The Pope thought about it, then ordered Pinkas to be brought from the dungeon and said to him:

" 'My man, I'm giving you a last chance to prove you are a Jew. Thirty miles to the West of here is a very high mountain and on that mountain another one. You must climb the first mountain and the second one to the very top. Remember that! If you return from there well and tell the truth about what you saw, then you are a Jew. Then everything is fine. Go with God, if you are a Jew.' That's what the Pope said.

"Shortly after, after Pinkas had already left, the doctors who were caring for Pinkas's health rushed in. They warned earnestly that he could not survive such a difficult journey. The doctors were scorned. It would be a different story if Pinkas were a Jew, they said. Now it is not his body that is threatened but his Christian soul. It's none of your concern."

* * *

Mr. Karol stopped and ordered some more strong, fresh coffee. In the meantime, through the garden filled with guests, squeezed an old, venerable artisan, a potter from Pistynia named Januncia. He was dressed in his Sunday best in a dark gray coat trimmed with galloons like the country squires used to wear. Although he had an ordinary name, a country name, he was of the gentry on his mother's side. He considered himself gentry.

In spite of his age, this master craftsman still moulded his own pots, and what is more important, he painted clever and fantastic designs on his pots in secret, all alone, in the only way he knew how. Sometimes he read the newspapers. He always read the lives of the saints, dream books, as well as collections of ballads. He owned a few thick books himself. During the week he was a man of few words. He got talkative on Sunday. He would gladly philosophize with his grandchildren. The journey to the wedding was obviously a holiday for him. Maybe he was even able to see some of his family that he ordinarily didn't get a chance to see otherwise.

Through his glasses, with rims so flimsy that they barely held in the glass, Januncia's deeply set gray eyes looked out cautiously and searchingly. With his beautifully long head he was able to conquer a bulging, wrinkled little forehead. He added to his nobility with a strong, sharply etched face, although his nose was not so narrow. And finally, with impatience in the midst of peaceful fantasy, his bold mustache waved in the air. When Januncia was about to speak there appeared on his face, against a background of immaculate naïveté, something like a painful effort at independent thought. Januncia had known Mr. Karol since the latter was a child, but since his own childhood he had learned how to be dignified.

"I beg your indulgence," he said slowly and very clearly, "and I hope to be excused with honor by the Judge (it was a Galician custom to raise the ranks and titles of people spoken to). The Judge is telling the story to us so nicely, about how the Spanish gentlemen were worried about their salvation. But we are dying to know what the tailor had to say. What was the tailor thinking? Tailor? That—if you'll excuse my calling him such a name—it's some hard word—" Januncia was embarrassed.

"Rarity," prompted Mr. Karol.

"If you'll excuse my calling him such a name and I beg the honor of the Judge—a rarity," repeated Januncia with resignation. "Judge, councilor, when a pot turns out good for me, me and my family give it a nice name, but if it doesn't turn out so good, we don't give it a bad name. And I beg your honor, but just as it is with the pot, so it is with this tailor, this Pinkas—this whatever word that is. Well all right, but what was he thinking? It seems to me that he did not pay them back for their love: he wasn't grateful for the presents. He wasn't even grateful for the great favor of His Holiness of not sending him to the burning fire but to the cool mountains. We must understand that! What was he thinking?"

Mr. Karol laughed: "But wait a minute, was he thinking at all?"

Januncia answered even more respectfully but with a little irritation: "Mr. Councilor, Mr. Chief Councilor, who else is supposed to think?"

A young student with reddish-blond hair interrupted: "If this keeps up, in a little while Mr. Karol will become the President of the National Court of Appeals."

Mr. Karol gave him a hard glance. The student giggled and hid his head. Januncia pulled himself together and answered very slowly: "I beg your indulgence and hope to be excused by your honor Mr. Scholar. We potters are not scholars, and you scholars are not potters, and even less tailors. Mr. Scholar is educated, is always learning, is in a hurry and doesn't have to think. A potter has a little more time while he is making his pots. Later, he must work the bellows, scramble around, paint, and be careful—the thinking has to be dropped. And the tailor? He sinks onto a bench. He sits and sits like some owl in the place of honor. A tailor is all thought. I beg you with honor and excuse myself, but someone else is supposed to think?"

Mr. Karol became lost in melancholy thought.

"Ha! What did the rarity think? What could he think?" Mr. Karol was thinking, deeply impressed, until everyone laughed out loud. "A good question, but probably Bjumen will know. I don't."

Bjumen answered patiently: "Pinkas, good sir, and this is how it is written in the books, he was always thinking about his work, about needles, thread, the cut of frock coats, and of folds! God forbid there should be any! On Friday he thought about the Sabbath, and then he thought the same things all over again. So nothing bothered him. What did he think then, beyond the sea, in Spain? He probably thought about something and probably about *tachles*, as they say—about his family, wife, and children. And what else was he supposed to think about? You understand these things better that I do, my dear potter. Before, he was a tailor, but what is he now? A Jew, an enemy—only an enemy. And later what was he? Not even a Jew. But what? It's terrible. Good thinking. He probably didn't think just then—he was just afraid. . . ."

"How's that? He was afraid all the time? Day and night?"

"Why not? Every hour. Every minute. He was afraid so long that he was really afraid. And about all that help and gratefulness, well, that's what we'll talk about now."

"Well fine, let Bjumen finish the story himself," said Mr. Karol, drinking his fresh coffee. "I told my part about the 'gentlemen' already."

Bjumen stood on ceremony. A new pint of beer came his way, and fresh white rolls.

The old man laughed and finished the story this way: "I'm an old vagabond, but I'll admit to you, so help me, that when I'm alone at night, I sometimes think about how that Pinkas went to the mountain in that deserted place. There he was a rarity. Aha! A real rarity, absolutely one. There a Jew was not only a rarity but any man was. There aren't even any robbers, not even wolves. At the bottom of the mountain there were some scrawny fir trees that beckoned him on. They looked like they went up higher than he had to go, but they didn't. Higher up there were bare cliffs reaching to the sky and farther. Pinkas was scratching up those cliffs one day and a second. His funeral shirt was already soaked. When it dried it got thick and heavy like a door mat. But Pinkas was not dying. The higher he goes the scarier it is, for he can see that there is no return. He went on like this for a few days—who knows how long. When he got to the top he thought he'd rest. And what's at the top? A few sharp stones like knives. You can't sit or stand. And higher up there is another mountain, sticking up like a needle, covered with ice. People say there is a country here and that it's warm. Pinkas goes on. But how? He keeps crawling up that cliff. He's all scratched up himself, covered with black and blue marks, almost wounded. He had twisted his feet and frozen his hands—that's how it goes with this climbing. But once he got so scared that he didn't get scared any more. Now, everything was all the same to him—nothing bothered him. Little by little, foot by foot, he keeps crawling, like an ant on the wall. And it's not going too badly for him after all. What? You're laughing at all the fresh air he's getting up there. Well, that's not the point. Maybe he's far away from human madness, from the whole human lot and that's the point. Well, no one knows how long he was climbing up there. What is strange, though, is that up there on the mountain it was level and there was plenty of room. He looks around a little bit and sees something that has something human about it. Some stones are piled up in such a way that they look like a table. He comes closer to them and can hardly believe his eyes. There was Hebrew writing on them that said that this was the grave of the ancient high priest Aaron. Also written on the stone was a holy word. And something else was written there, too: it said that the word could be spoken by the person who would come to this place. . . . He fell on his knees to pray and raised his eyes to heaven. Then he saw somewhere far away, at a great distance, something only for his eyes. It was a huge, terrible, frightening pleat turned over itself and it hung over all of Spain and over the whole world.

"There was a pleat, brother. Just in time, too. It was black! What do I mean by black? In comparison, coal is as white as that roll. But coal is really like an Easter Matzoh. Some red! What kind of red? In comparison, red hot steel is like the rosy cheeks of a baby. There was a main pleat. From that one came all the other pleats.

"Then he was terrified. He cried, prayed, pleaded, and begged that God remove the pleat. Let happen to him and to his family what would, whatever God granted, but only let that pleat disperse and be ironed out. And—just how it happened no one knows—but the books written over two hundred years ago say that God looked in on the poor tailor and answered his prayer. Did *he*, the Rabbi Ostre, have something to do with this? The pleat dispersed; it smoothed out; it was bright, happy, and good on the Earth. You could see a long way from there—far into God's world.

"The tailor quietly walked down on the other side of the mountain on a good wide path. He returned to the Emperor, the Pope, and the Count. The Count was very happy with his tailor and the Emperor was kind to this rarity. The Pope looked long and deeply at him. He waited for the Jew to speak. When Pinkas told the Pope everything, exactly as it happened down to the last crease, the Pope became thoughtful. He finally said to Pinkas: 'My dear Jew, yes, it's all true. You are a Jew. Everything is fine now. You may go to your palace and live quietly. But tell us what you especially want. Everything will be done for you, so that you will not be left without a great reward!'

"Pinkas felt freer than he had ever felt before. He was as happy as if he had made the best possible suit perfectly for his Excellency the Count. He wanted to sing. Maybe he would dance. Instead, he told them: 'Dear sirs, God be with you, Pope, Emperor, and my Excellency the Count! I really do love you and now I understand all. Now I have a favor to ask of you from the bottom of my heart. Take back these treasures that you gave me, you gentlemen here and those good people—the palaces, camels, horses, diamonds and pearls, clothes, velvets, and all those wonders. Do with them what you want, but send me back to my country as soon as possible, back to Ostre and my Rabbi! Peace be with you. Shalom Aleichem!'

"Maybe this request was a little awkward for all those great gentlemen, but they gave their word. Once again Pinkas traveled over the seas, over the mountains, through distant lands, back here to Poland, to our country. Pinkas wasn't at all afraid now. Even though he was exhausted he sang to himself. When he finally got to Ostre, even though it was night, he didn't go straight home to his family or to the manor, but to *him*, to the great Rabbi.

"*He* wasn't sleeping. *He* knew everything. *He* tore his eyes from his book and raised them to heaven. In *his* chamber it became bright as day. *He* said quietly: 'Why didn't you wait? Do you know that when that pleat is over the world the Messiah is closest to the world?'

"Then he made a sign with his hand and the chamber became dark.

"Pinkas went home to bed. That's what the old book says and that's the true story of the rarity, my dear sirs."

Bjumen did not laugh out loud as he usually did; he was thoughtful and silent for a moment, looking into his empty glass. Then he suddenly stood up and looked at the sky: "Hey! It's past noon already. Bukoviec is before us yet. We'll have to get under way slowly. I'm going to call together my passengers and friends. Thank you for the beer, and I thank Mr. Karol for helping me with this story. Ha! Ha! Ha!"

"We thank you, Bjumen, for this rarity and may God give you health."

Bjumen put his heavy sheep's skin over his arm and turned his big steps toward the door. The light-haired student took this opportunity to make a joke. He called after Bjumen: "All that's fine, Bjumen. A rarity is a rarity, but Baron Rothschild and Baron Hirsch are not so poor."

Bjumen turned around and laughed out loud: "Hey, my boy, those are things one must understand. They are not Jews."

The student was taken back a moment, but then the wind changed. "What are you talking about? Who built the hospital in Chernovsa and the Hebrew School in Kolomyl? The Jews did and they are better for it."

"Better or not, they are not Jews. They call themselves that only as an honor."

"What kind of honor?" continued the student. "Quite the opposite. Those are educated people. They are elegant. They patronize the Jews. They are considerate and charitable."

"I'm not saying anything," laughed Bjumen. "They are good people, but to God, who knows? Ha! Ha! Ha!"

He waved his hand and left immediately.

Translated by Hubert Babinski

Kazimierz Wierzyński

The Gardeners

The gardeners sculpture the earth
Improve its features:
They want to beautify my most beautiful,
Caress my anxious one,
Heal my poisoned one.

But History rolled over the earth,
In schools they teach writing it with a capital H,
They build palaces of marble to History,
They bring electricity to History's huge provinces,
They play violin for History,
Dreadful performances
On deaf and dumb instruments:
The sound has been lost in their cases.

The gardeners weed.
The Japanese in rain, under umbrellas,
The French old men in little gardens by a river,
The Spanish hags among beggars' stones,
They weed in Israel's kibbutsim,
They weed in Ceylon.

They want to weed a tiny field under the sky-reaching wall of
History,
A green square under the all-seeing eye of History,
Plant mushrooms in the cellars of History,
Place flower pots on the terrace of History,
Sculpture an instrument lost in History.

What are you doing, nothing will change,
It's only a drawing pin under an elephant's foot.

But they keep on weeding.
They want to beautify my most beautiful,
Caress my anxious one,
Heal my poisoned one,
The gardeners, the geo-humanists.

Translated by M. Czajkowska

Kazimierz Wierzyński

The Roof and the Walls

I am obsessed by the roof
Not letting the rain in
I am obsessed by the walls
For the wind not blowing right through
I want to stay away, hide, and write
But I cannot leave the street
And I stand in the rain which blows into my eyes
Holding tightly soaked books under my arm
I can feel the thinnest book slipping,
And watch it fall mouth first in the mud,
The wind tearing at its pages,
And I cannot pick up this unhappy one,
And I cannot pick up this helpless one,
And I cannot pick up this dearest one,
I stand there amidst rain and wind
Being obsessed by the roof and the walls.

Translated by M. Czajkowska

Kazimierz Wierzyński

By the River Housatonic

The river Housatonic overflowed. Flood in the forest.
Water embraced the feet of the trees
Rising up higher to the knees, to the waist.
If it should reach the throat? Who will cry out?
The trees tied to the earth could not move.
Deer and foxes run away, footprints in the snow,
An exodus of all creatures.
For them—salvation.
For the trees—death.

Then frost came at night, the waters froze up,
And under the ice floated away to God knows where.

From the floods the trees emerged dressed anew
In ballet dancers' skirts on the hips of tree trunks,
Little aprons of heavy damask silk,
A ladies' court in white crinolines,
Queens in Velasquez lace
And ruffles round their necks.

Thus a fancy dress ball began in the forest:
The winter carnival.

The wind drove swiftly past in sledges filled with straw.
The horses went white round the mouth,
Their breath turned green in the moon
And ice cracked and burst.

A volley of shots from young men firing in salute.
Young ladies and men burst out laughing, laughing,

Quite rightly, freedom was returning to the trees.
The carnival raced past, the last carnival,
And in a forest hut sat a short-sighted man
Peering over papers, over books,
Seeing nothing, his blindness grew,
Writing nothing, his loneliness grew,
Only scribbling slowly one line after another:
If it should reach the throat? Who will cry out?
If it should reach the throat? Who will cry out?

Translated by M. Czajkowska

Kazimierz Wierzyński

There Is No Such Thing

There is no such thing as was
(Faulkner)

There is no such thing as was
There is only such a thing as is
Begun yesterday drawn into tomorrow
Through the past and present tenses
In the irregular conjugation
Of man and the world

But the most important thing is everything
The greatest unity not to be shared
The only common possession to be given away
Justification of being
Unsurpassed in grief as NEVER
Warm with hope as ALWAYS

(R.I.P. 6.7.1962)

Translated by M. Czajkowska

Gustaw Herling-Grudziński

The Bridge:

A Chronicle of Our City

I

HERE is Kafka's story *Die Brücke:*

"I was stiff and chilled, I was a bridge over a chasm—my toes on one side, my fingers clinging to the other, and my teeth sunk into the crumbly clay. The wind fluttered the tails of my overcoat. The trout-filled stream roared far below. No tourists ever came up so far, and the bridge was not yet marked on any map. So I lay there and waited. All I could do was wait. Once a bridge has been erected, it cannot stop being a bridge. Unless it falls down.

"It happened toward evening one day—the first day? the thousandth?—I couldn't say. My thoughts were blurred and constantly went round in circles. Toward evening—it was summer, when the roar of the river grew louder—I heard the sound of human steps! They were coming toward me, toward me. Straighten up, bridge! Unrailed planks, get ready to receive the wanderer who has been entrusted to you! If his steps are uncertain, stealthily give them strength, but if he stumbles, show him what you can do: like the God of the Mountains, hurl him into the abyss!

"He stepped onto me, rapped on me with the steel tip of his walking stick. He impaled my coattails, lifted them, and put them down in place. He sank the tip of his walking stick into my thick hair and left it there a long time, evidently forgetting all about me as he cast his aimless glance around him. But suddenly—I had been mentally following his glance over mountains and valleys—he jumped with both feet onto the middle of my body. I shuddered with the staggering pain, not knowing what was happening. Who was he? A child? A dream? A wanderer? A suicide? The Tempter? The Destroyer? I turned over to look at him. A bridge turning over! I had not turned over completely when I began to fall. I fell and in a minute the jagged rocks that had always looked up at me so peacefully from the rushing stream tore me to pieces and pierced my body."

II

In De Sterlich's *Cronaca Giornaliera delle Province Napoletane* the entry for June 3, 1869, reads: "A young man jumped off the *Ponte della Sanità*." Six days later, June 9: "Again today someone jumped off the *Ponte della Sanità*. There have been a great number of suicides in Naples lately, and many of them choose the *Ponte della Sanità*. We have always had suicides, but never in such numbers as there have been lately. It seems that since March, when I started keeping this chronicle, I have counted more than ten. No sooner was the bridge built than it became the ideal place for anyone who had known utter despair and sought release in death. Those who irrevocably long to die prefer it to other places. They leave their houses and do not turn aside along the way, certain that falling from that height death is sure and quick. I do not know, and I do not think anyone does, how many unfortunate beings have put an end to their lives there. But everyone must know that it would be a very good thing to erect a strong, high iron grating on or against the parapet. In Delcarett's time there was also a period in Naples when the mania for jumping off that bridge attracted people's attention: two policemen were stationed at either end to restrain the impulse. The result was that nothing more was heard of suicides from that bridge. One night, however, some poor wretch again thought of the forgotten bridge. But just as he was preparing to take the dreadful step, the police caught his arms in time. Taken to the *Questura*, he had to sign a pledge that he would not make another attempt on his own life."

III

The *Ponte della Sanità* is located in the vicinity of the National Museum on the street that forms the continuation of the former *Via Toledo*. That street leads up to the hill called Capodimonte, where the *Pinacoteca* was recently transferred to the former royal summer palace. Our picture gallery's chief attraction for tourists, of course, is Breughel's painting of the blind leading the blind. Having looked their fill at the Flemish artist's masterpiece, visitors usually go out on the roof of the palace. The view of Naples from there is just like the old panoramic engravings. Naples rises from the sea toward the hill by layers of streets and houses, like the cluttered steps of a staircase long worn away by the erosion of the capricious waves. On a clear day the vitreous air of the bay somewhat relieves this vortex of lines.

The bridge is a veritable passage from lower to upper Naples. Beyond it a broad street runs flat for a while, but soon begins the sharp turns of its climb up to the top of the hill. As one comes down from Capodimonte between houses lichened with misery, the bridge seems even more like a boundary point. But it is not that the churning misery vanishes like a picture cast aside. It simply goes straight down.

For the bridge is a bridge over something. Not over a river, not over a chasm, not over a stream full of trout, not over a gorge, not over a subway crossing. But over a street of lower Naples. The lowest? It often occurs to us who live here that Naples has no natural barrier holding people back from continually digging into the depths. Until the fires of hell are uncovered, people will descend lower and lower seeking shelter from the sun in summer, the rain in autumn, and the cold in winter. Only in the springtime are the heavens more benevolent from the rooftops.

Be that as it may, a street runs under the central part of the bridge. A few stories—five? six?—separate the bridge from the stone pavement swarming with people, where carts rumble and cars bounce along, and stalls are crammed up to the very brink of the roadway. The wings of the bridge spread just above the top terraces of the tenements, where washing hangs out to dry, discarded furniture is dumped, cats doze, and television aerials protrude.

IV

By day the bridge, because it is a boundary point, attracts no particular attention. The rushing flood of the streets on both levels inundates it with its waves and deafens with its roar.

But by night! By night, silent and deserted the bridge comes to life—solitary, clean, and naked. Even from a distance one can almost see it rise on its crutch-like support, buttressing the sleeping town.

Every step of the late passer-by seems to enhance its bulk. And it is not even a grand or imposing bridge. Night rouses it from the half-life of day with this broad and fantastic gesture.

The chronicler was heeded: a tall iron barrier was set into the parapet on both sides of the bridge. Close-set pointed bars hedge off the bridge from the abyss. They are set so closely together that one can barely squeeze a hand between them. From above and from below one now sees the arch of death through a grating—bound and rendered harmless.

From above, at night, one has a broad view of the black street, illuminated here and there by the weak glow of street lamps, like the moonlight pallor of waterflowers on a marsh. The windows of the houses are shuttered. The stalls are bare. The pavement, washed down in the evening, glimmers like the tarnished scales of a dead fish.

From below, one looks up at the limitless desert of the sky. Stars glitter like hard quartz crystals. Over the bridge the sky is creased with dark vertical lines.

Not far from the *Ponte della Sanità* a church of the same name was built: its crypt preserves the skulls of people who died of plague. The nameless skulls are venerated by the people in the neighborhood. About the church door is a table already worn with age, *Aut mori, aut pati.*

V

These words contain the essence of the bridge. The two *aut*'s are its only supports. Between them the bridge lies and waits.

Several years ago the bridge acquired a tenant in the shape of a beggar no one had ever seen before. People called him *Il Pipistrello,* and that nickname perfectly suited his appearance. Small and thin, with protruding ears and a black-stubble beard, the man did not move like a living being but like a wind-up toy, continually lifted off the ground as if jerked by a spring. Hopping from one foot to the other, with his long feet pointing outward, he balanced his slight body with arms that looked like bat wings in the sleeves of his loose overcoat.

The nickname of the Bat also suited his behavior. He spent his days fastened to the parapet or to the grating of the bridge. Fastened by an invisible thread, he hid his head in his coat collar and rarely lifted his glance to passers-by, just like those night birds sunk in their diurnal lethargy. He did not beg with the insistency of his Neapolitan fellows: on the sidewalk beside him lay his cap, and coins were tossed into it. Their sound did not rouse him from immobility. Often, instead of money, scraps of food wrapped in paper were dropped in the cap. It wasn't long before it would have been hard to imagine the bridge without him.

But, despite appearances, he did not drowse. His eyes stared incessantly at the street below the bridge. Observing him looking down with such persistence, I sometimes suspected that it was not the street that absorbed his attention, although he must have glimpsed at all the minutiae of its life—not the street, but the abyss separating it from the bridge—and even more: the bridge reflected in the mirror of that abyss. His glance melted and softened, involuntarily and certainly without its wonted intensity, only when it rested briefly on the cupola of the church and then, brushing against the tablet on its façade, again slid slowly down to the bottom of the street.

VI

When night fell he wrenched himself from his post, took the coins out of his cap and put them in his pocket. He gathered up the paper-wrapped scraps and went to the nearby tavern. He swayed from side to side, taking up the whole sidewalk and forcing everyone to step aside, drunk before he crossed the threshold of his evening haven.

The tavern is out of sight to the passer-by hurrying down the street. Before the entry to the bridge, on the side of the continuation of the *Via Toledo*, several steps lead down to a little garden, where on the slope, nay, on the very edge of the precipice, a wooden chalet sprang up soon after the war. Beyond the bushes and pitiful flower-beds stands a wire fence almost adjoining the outer parapet of the bridge. Two primitive little rooms, pasted over with pictures of movie stars cut out of magazines and oleographs *con vedute panoramiche di Napoli*, constitute the whole of the establishment. There is an old and rarely used billiard table in one of the rooms. In the other is served the cheapest wine, rough and sour, produced in the environs of Naples. It looks like black blood in the light of the faint bulbs and goes right to the head. The poor of the neighborhood come here, chiefly porters and peddlers, who pass the evening hours with a liter of wine and scraps of cheese, tripe sold on street barrows, or rice cakes fried in oil. From the barrels in the corner comes the smell of mold mixed with the stench of frying, dirt, sweat, and urine discharged behind the bushes in the garden. The din of shouts, arguments, and drunken songs swells continually, but it is only toward midnight that it explodes with angry vehemence. The door opens then and slams with a crash, and on the narrow path and steps bent shadows, their arms linking them by twos and threes, step cautiously and gropingly toward the street, as in Breughel's painting.

VII

He was usually the last to leave, now really drunk. His resistence to wine was amazing. He managed to drink glass after glass, to the very bottom of his beggar's pocket, slowly and with the same persistence with which he was accustomed to observe the street for days at a time from his perch on the bridge. During these evening hours, sitting at his table, he spoke rarely and, unless he was approached, never. It was usually a mumbled assent, uttered at if he were begging not to be tormented by an effort too great for him. But no one bothered him. He was generally left in peace, and with the passing of the years he seemed nothing more than a part of the poor furnishings of the tavern. Meanwhile he sat in the corner, now fastened by a thread to the little table. His wide-open eyes became cloudy the more he drank—even more densely and gloomily fogged. He seemed continually to wait; he could but patiently wait, as if he had been created exclusively for waiting. Perhaps his Creator knew for what.

The fresh air that struck him as he left immediately released the long-delayed effect of the wine. That was the moment when his melancholy disappeared without a trace. Yes, he revived at night, just like the bridge and the bird from which he took his nickname! He ran zigzag in the direction of the National Museum, light, free, grinning, and almost happy, as he glided over the pavement of the street and soared up the hill with the flutter of his outspread arms. Then he would slow his pace, tired and panting.

Before him opened the *Via Foria,* broad and unpeopled at that hour.

It was said that he hurried to Poggioreale and slept in the cemetery, where now and again the grander family vaults provided the homeless man with a roof over his head. The legend sprang up later that he helped the gravediggers to sort out the corpses. Our city is also threatened by the asphyxiation of death; hence the dead are no longer buried in church crypts, and night after night at Poggioreale the feverish work of exhumation goes on, to see which earthly remains still merit that name and their own patch of valuable ground, and which can be consigned to final annihilation in the communal grave.

VIII

We became accustomed to him in the course of those years. I often stopped next to him on the bridge and looked with him into the depths of the street below, as if after almost a century the bridge were suddenly sounding the gloomy echo of its past. And its old name sometimes cropped up in conversation, the *Ponte della Morte*, the name coined after the events described by De Sterlich and used until the beginning of this century, that is, until the erection of the iron barrier.

Autumn last year was exceptionally rainy and cold. The rain lashed or drizzled incessantly, a dark cloud settled on the city; the sea, the color of churned swill, spilt over the seaside promenade, and from the surrounding areas came news of floods and landslides on unforested hills. In the narrow back streets water rushed in torrents. Doorways were crowded with fleeing people, and small fires burned on basement thresholds.

The beggar's figure did not disappear from the bridge. He sat hooded under an old sack, crouching, livid with cold, and shivering. People tried to drag him to one of the nearby doorways, but in vain: he clung to the iron grating with a strength that none of us could have imagined in that miserable body. And it seemed that from under his squinting eyelids he stared down below even more avidly than usual.

One day, toward the end of autumn, the police took him away from the bridge.

IX

He reappeared on the bridge at the beginning of winter. There was a change in his behavior. Clearly weakened by illness, he did not resume his place on the parapet but sat on the sidewalk. During the day he slept. At night he rarely looked in at the tavern, and when he did, one glass of wine was enough for him. After the place closed he would return to the bridge and sleep some more, almost disappearing into his too-ample coat. At a distance one might have thought that someone had dumped a pile of rags against the low wall.

Winter was frosty but pleasant. Children basked in buggies by the sea, and the snow-sprinkled peak of the volcano glinted happily in the sun; the "Mediterranean red" of the buildings acquired the hue of clotted blood on butcher stalls, and the palms in the city garden took on the same shade of green as the waves along the shore; and in the streets and back alleys silver stars and festoons and barrels of snake-like black fish heralded the approach of Christmas, while the churches beckoned the faithful to their stalls.

We were constantly passing the bridge, but now one saw a sleeping face. He must have been dreaming what he used to feel when he left the tavern drunk, for he often smiled in his sleep, and sometimes he even jiggled his legs and the arms of his coat, like a disjointed puppet worked by a string from below.

X

The *Cronaca cittadina* of our leading newspaper, *Il Mezzogiorno*, carried the following article on January 2 of this year, under the title *La morte del Pipistrello:* "People whose daily activities take them across the *Ponte della Sanità* have long been acquainted with the beggar familiarly known as *Il Pipistrello*. In the course of these last years his life was bound day and night to this notorious"—*malfamato* was the word the journalist used—"point of our city. (Is there anyone who does not know the fame this bridge once enjoyed? There was a time when our forefathers spoke of it as the *Ponte della Morte*.) Yesterday at dawn two policemen found the poor man's body on the lower street below the bridge. It is not known whether it was an accident caused by abuse of alcohol or an impulse of utter despair. It has been ascertained that during the night a hole was cut in the wire fence that separates the tavern next to the bridge from the outer parapet. One of the customers who stayed late in the tavern has testified that several times by the light of the New Year's fires he noticed a long dark shadow just about the center of the bridge, up against the protective iron barrier as if it were stuck to the grating. But he thought that it must have been some cats frightened by the fireworks who had fled there from the nearby roofs. So he did not think of calling the authorities. It is believed that the unfortunate man must have spent three or four hours lying in this position, convulsively clinging to the bars with his hands and feet, until his stiffened and frozen limbs failed him. If he called for help his voice could not have been heard in the din of the explosions that continued to greet the New Year until almost three o'clock in the morning. Whatever the truth is—an impulse of total despair or an accident caused by an abuse of alcohol—one thought irresistibly comes to mind. Perhaps the day is not far off when Naples' new city plan will render the bridge superfluous, and one more of our city's achitectural anachronisms will be removed. But until that happens, we are obliged to demand that the authorities erect an iron barrier to secure that section which until now has been so poorly protected by a rusty wire fence."

Because no one knew his real name or where the dead man came from, he was buried, after all the formalities of the law had been attended to, in the communal grave at Poggioreale. Later someone in the tavern said that he had been tossed into the hole like a dog.

1963

Translated by Ronald Strom

*Witold Gombrowicz**

Diaries

I. The Paris Diary

I HAD little time for walks; there were friends new and old, French writers to meet, negotiations with publishers, translators . . . but whenever I did manage to get out into the streets of Paris, I looked about for ugliness and found it. The search for it was an act of love toward Argentina, my Deserted—I still wanted to wear her beauty—but I also remembered that I had to make myself felt here, in Paris . . .

Watching the street crowds, I sought out the deformed; I looked for sunken chests, for goose necks, for hunchbacks, for twisted bodies and desperate limbs. I gazed so intently at all this flesh that I had no eyes for palaces and churches, squares and vistas, arches, domes, and bridges. I followed with particular insistence a certain look of incompleteness and inelegance that hovers around so many, but by no means all, French noses and mouths. It was unpleasant, but forgivable; on the whole, the Paris crowds looked no worse than those of other cities. But their real ugliness lay deeper and was all of their own making: they were intelligent and self-aware. In the Avenue de l'Opéra, in the Rue de Rivoli . . . they know themselves so well . . . there are too many mirrors, too many hairdressers, too many tailors, hat shops, and beauticians . . . the Parisians drink deep of the cup of ugliness, they drain it to the last drop. I saw the anguish of faded women, the bitterness of exhausted young poets, the laborious stylization of goateed men, the gross resignation of the obese, the oddest efforts at sublimation

* W. G. left Buenos Aires, where he had lived since 1939, for Paris in 1962. [Translator's note]

into beauty with the aid of hats and umbrellas. The fierce battle against ugliness went on everywhere, and everywhere it ended in defeat (in that I rejoiced—their defeat served to enhance the beauty of my Argentina). I saw distaste in the faces of *Messieurs—Dames*, as if they were always sniffing at something unpleasant, and the air of Paris seemed to me redolent of the *déshabillé*, and of the morning hour devoted to dressing, of creams and powders and eau de cologne, of negligées and pyjamas. Even that was bearable. But behind it was something even more unpleasant: an annoying layer of gaiety. I could forgive them sadness and despair, but I could not forgive their ugliness for being gay and well equipped with humor, *l'esprit*, and *la blague*.

An old oaf at a street corner was eyeing the thighs of a doll boarding a bus and there was *tout Paris* in his smutty delight. I watched with loathing a pink-lipped, bloated chef in the doorway of a restaurant, trickling out spicy *bon mots* for the benefit of *Madame*, so full of twists and curves that she almost amounted to a labyrinth . . .

So they still wanted to enjoy life . . .

Such scenes naturally inspired no enthusiasm and no wish to approve of them with a "*Voilà Paris!*" Indeed, it seemed to me that only Susannah and the Elders deserved such greeting. I wasn't alone, of course, and I wasn't the first to feel a profound distaste at the sight of their ugly greed. The Parisian sensuality, unable to express itself directly any longer, all went into the make-up, the corsets, the elaboration of dress and manner, into song and art, into wit and conversation. The sociability that made the sum total of desperate deficiencies into a brilliant whirl, the *esprit* that made pinching glamorous—and that horrible gaiety, laboriously cultivated for centuries to enable them to savor life, come what may! The ugliness so self-aware and yet a-dancing. Their repulsive aesthetics contained also a fatal naïveté, based on an illusion that one can cheat age and transfer one's pleasures onto some higher plane, where they become realized in another dimension.

Paris, the old tenor, the wizened ballerina, the hoary joker . . . what is your mortal sin against Beauty? Is it perhaps that you devour it? *Mais permettez-moi donc, cher Monsieur!* Could *Monsieur*, who with the years has ceased to be a *beau garçon*, a blissfully gratuitous, generous, and graceful adornment of the world, still have any connection with beauty? But of course! Life was still full of delights! He could still walk into a well-chosen restaurant and order *Veau à la Crevette Sauce Moustache* or *Sautée Velay Mignonne Asperges* . . . or, for that matter, those excellent dishes *Fricassé de Jeunes Filles en Fleur* or a *Beau Garçon Rôti à la Bordelaise*.

The meaning of my culinary metaphor is that to consume beauty one must first break with it completely. Not only must it come from outside, served, as it were, on a plate, but one must also re-arrange oneself inwardly in such a way that one's ugliness does not interfere with one's enjoyment. But this operation is bound to be so painful that I doubt whether any civilized person could perform it on himself. It requires a shift from the individual to the collective, to the social. It needs the participation of others. One must first have a community, a civilization where the meanness of its own atrophied nature is replaced by such substitutes as *belles manières*, *élégance*, *distinction*, *esprit*, *bon goût*, etc., etc. In that civilization one dons a top hat in the manner of Swann and becomes a *gourmet sans gêne*.

The great and real beauty of humanity, a beauty both young and naked, has been relegated by the Top Hats to the statues standing silently amongst the trees of Paris, which they have to regard simply as legitimate objects of a highly expert pleasure. Now, although it may be admirable to sacrifice beauty on the altar of purity and contemplation, it is repulsive to see it offered up to lust and greed. I paced the Parisian avenues feeling that if there was anything I found loathsome it was a gourmet . . . It was Paris.

This city filling its aged mouth with ambrosia! I wandered through Paris with my head bowed, dispirited and silent. All that was needed—I thought—was that they should creep up one night to the naked statues and dress them in the latest fashion . . . Diana in a Dior dress—yes, that was it, that was the spirit of their *mondanité*, providing palatable substitutes for beauty! And yet, I kept repeating to myself, the real beauty was naked still. One could be constant to it only by remaining naked oneself, or by preserving the nakedness of the past, whether real or potential, but appropriate to one's age.

The nakedness of Paris has been dressed by the couturiers.

The Top Hats swoon into ardor at the sight of *une belle femme*, their ecstasy knows no bounds, they fall in love and they subject their emotions to subtle analysis, but they never, never undress.

The roles have been so distributed that only one of the partners is to remain naked . . . I don't know if it was true, what I was told about their way of making love . . . that they put on gloves and that, feverishly undressing *la belle*, they quickly button up their own clothes.

* * *

I went to see the little Rue Belloy, between Avenue Kléber and Place des États Unis. I wanted to see the house where I had lived thirty-five years before.

Returning from the house of Alain Kosko (who was out), I took a look at the Boul Mich to refresh old memories.

It really is extraordinary that my anti-Parisian reaction has remained stubbornly the same over thirty five years—my emotions were exactly the same.

Silence.

* * *

Hector Bianchotti took me to the Louvre. The walls were crowded and the paintings hung stupidly, touching one another. The hiccoughs of accumulation! The cacophony! A low tavern where Leonardo and Titian were punching each other!

The squint ruled overall. When you looked at one thing, another poked you in the eye . . . you moved from one to another, stopped, gaped, stepped back, drew nearer, stopped, and gaped again . . . a moment earlier, outside you had enjoyed the light, the shapes, and the colors, but here they all crossed and broke in so many variations that you simply felt sick. They crept into your throat and tickled like the flaming feathers at the end of a Roman banquet.

But in the end, you reached the holy of holies, the abode of divine Gioconda. Hail Circe! You are as hard-working and vigilant as when I watched you last, steadily transforming men, not into swine, admittedly, but into fools. I remembered with what horror Schopenhauer thought of the perennial mechanisms which for centuries has made some tortoises each year climb out of the sea to lay their eggs on an island—and to be devoured by wild dogs as soon as they had done it. For the last five hundred years, crowds have been collecting daily in front of this painting, only to undergo each time the same besotting experience. And each day the celebrated face obliged . . . Snap! An American with a camera. Some in the crowd smile indulgently, full of forbearance, and blissfully unaware that in their superior tolerance they were no better than the rest.

Stupidity surrounds you . . . it emanates from the rooms of the Louvre. It really is one of the stupidest places in the world . . . and the rooms are so large . . .

There are forty thousand painters in this town, just as there are forty thousand cooks. Everyone dabbles in beauty, everyone pokes into it. Because they manufacture beauty on canvas with their subtle fingers, they seem to cultivate in themselves a deliberate ugliness. Some stylized themselves into monsters, confining beauty to the fingertips. To come into the world of their painting is to join in an enormous perversion, a gigantic masquerade where an artificial artist creates artificially for an artificial consumer, with the accompaniment of dealers, snobs, drawing rooms, academies, riches, luxury, criticism, and commentaries. In that world, supply and demand create an abstract system based on fiction . . . Is it surprising that Paris should be its center?

A model undressing for the painter is an exact equivalent of a woman dressing at Dior or Fath. In an instant they will both cease to be naked: the nakedness of one will become the pretext for a dress; that of the other will melt into a painting. One will become "elegant," the other will become "art."

* * *

Since my arrival in Paris the most peculiar things started to happen so far as Sartre was concerned.

I had long admired him in Buenos Aires.

Alone with his works I had the reader's advantage of being able to dismiss him with a shrug of the shoulders, and yet even then I was afraid of him as of someone stronger than myself. But it was only in Paris that he grew in my mind to the proportions of the Eiffel tower, overshadowing the whole of the Parisian panorama.

It all began when I tried to find out how much the French mind had absorbed of the Sartrian existentialism. By steering the conversation to the subject of Sartre, I discreetly explored the knowledge of *L'être et le néant* among various writers and non-writers. My researches brought some odd results. In the first place, although Sartre's ideas rambled and wandered through French minds, they remained amorphous, plucked at random from anywhere, more often than not only from his novels and plays. It didn't surprise me that they appeared vague and fragmentary, concerned chiefly with the absurd, freedom, and responsibility. It was clear that *L'être et le néant* was practically unknown in France. Sartre's ideas, loose, disjointed, deformed, torn to pieces, left in tatters, grown wild, fearful, and weird, floated in the air. They served to undermine the existing intellectual order, but nothing more. Further inquiries led to some interesting conclusions. It struck me that they spoke about him with dislike or, rather, with a latent desire to finish him off. Sartre? "Well, yes, only he is so repetitive." Sartre? "Oh, yes, but his days are over." Novels? Plays? "They serve well enough to illustrate his theories." His philosophy? "It is but the rationalization of his other writings." Sartre? "Well, of course, but really there is too much of him and he doesn't wash. He is not a poet; besides, there are his politics, and he is finished in fact! Sartre, you know, is finished."

I wondered . . . There is a certain amount of avuncular kindness in our admiration for the artist, the kindness that makes us praise the child in order not to distress him. The artist has also managed to win our favor and sympathy, so much so that we are happy when admiring him, and that not to admire him is hardly bearable. You can see this in the French attitude to Proust—they still feed him with *bonbons* even in his grave—he won them over. But Sartre is, I think, perhaps the only eminent contemporary writer who is personally hated. When compared with the Sartrian outpouring of revelation who is the Argentinian Borges, that tasty broth for the *littérateurs?* And yet they coddle Borges and they pummel Sartre . . . and is it only because of politics? That would be unforgivably petty. Petty? But perhaps it is not because of politics at all. Perhaps this hatred is pettiness itself. Perhaps they hate Sartre simply because he is too great.

My thoughts followed a chaotic and haphazard course, yet one of a peculiar extremism . . . as a result of the chance confrontation of Sartre and Proust the whole of France broke for me into two parts, that of Proust and that of Sartre. When I went, one day, on a pious pilgrimage (I the natural anti-pilgrim!) to meditate before the windows of Sartre's flat in the square next to *Deux Magots*, I no longer had any doubts about the choice of the French. They had chosen Proust against Sartre. They had chosen the restaurant *Du côté de chez Swann* where they were served with subtle delicacies prepared by a gourmet chef who well knew how to flatter the palate. I was once told that the finest cooks used to kill turkeys with a pin inserted very slowly—it was supposed to make the meat taste even better. But to return to Proust, I do not deny that he has a certain tragic quality, severe and even cruel but, nonetheless, edible. Just like the tortures of the turkey, it has a gastronomic purpose, it is tied to the dish, the vegetables, and the sauce . . . And on the other side. *Du côté de chez Sartre*, the fierce and tense mind, the most creative French thinking since Descartes, demolishes the culinary delectation . . . I stopped; what made me stop? A little group of two or three boys, two girls, bubbling with high spirits and gaiety, that other France, young, enchanting, equal to nakedness, brusquely interrupted my meditation. They crossed the square and disappeared around the corner—and, in a flash, I saw Sartre as something hurtful, as the ruin of that youth. But when they vanished out of sight and I was left with *Messieurs—Dames* of gastronomic age, I understood that the young could not be saved except by Sartre. He was the only liberating energy capable of wrenching them away from ugliness. I would even say that French ugliness itself, accruing for centuries in their flats, behind their curtains, and among their ornaments, finding itself unbearable, gave birth to Sartre, the awesome Messiah . . . Only he could demolish the restaurants and the drawing rooms, destroy the top hats, the galleries, the music halls, the newspaper columns, the theaters, the carpets, and the scarves. Only he could sack the Louvre and the Champs Elysées and wreck the statues at sunset in the Place de la Concorde. And the Bois de Boulogne! The fact that the Frenchman who conceived my favorite philosophy was himself very plain didn't shock me in the least. I felt that with his passionate responsiveness to art he had a better right than anyone to demand retreat beyond the object, beyond the substance, even beyond the region where one exists for oneself. To bring nothingness into a man is to cleanse him of his ugliness. Yes, Sartre, and not Proust! Proust's feebleness and Sartre's force—what a contrast! Can't they see the difference? True, I myself can't accept half of his conclusions in *L'être et le néant;* they just don't tally with my experience of life, and I am convinced that his "cogito" cannot survive in its present absolute form. Its single-mindedness stands in need of a complementing principle, equally fundamental but diametrically opposed. At present a kind of dismal one-sidedness becomes apparent as soon as one applies his system specifically. Like a two-faced god with one face removed, it represents only a half-truth. Sartre as moralist, psychologist, aesthete, and politician is, for me, only a half of what he should be. (Should I add that I don't know Sartre well myself, that I have not read all his works, and that even in *L'être et le néant* there are chapters I have only scanned?) Yet I am sure that he alone is capable of breaking open the bolted doors. Things that in Proust and in all French writing are only a sequel to what has gone before, and is about to come to an end, become in Sartre a new beginning. The consciousness of Proust is greedy (but even the greed has declined in intensity since Montaigne!); the consciousness of Sartre has regained the pride of a creative force.

I, a Pole . . . I, an Argentinian . . . a Slav and a South American . . . a writer lost in Paris, searching for a sting with which to leave his mark. . . . I, a melancholy lover of a dead past . . . I was trying to form an alliance with Sartre against Paris. It was a tempting opportunity to demonstrate to the Parisians that someone they had already confidently classified was, in fact, unique.

* * *

I am not going to attack Paris on any other front in settling our accounts. I confine my field to beauty. Perhaps because, up to a point, I am still an artist; perhaps because I still feel a part of that other deserted, transoceanic beauty; perhaps because as an argument beauty itself hurts?

But what cult of nakedness do I have in mind when I say that Paris has lost it? Could I be more specific?

I do not expect them to worship flesh and nature, and I do not demand from them songs in praise of nudity.

But I expect a man (be he as ugly as a monster) to have in him the idea of human beauty—this let him not forget: "I delight in the beauty of my race" and "through human beauty I worship the beauty of the world."

This is why inwardly we must never break with youth, the only time in life when beauty is attainable. Beauty gained later in life is imperfect, incomplete, and tainted with the absence of youth; only the young have a naked beauty that has no need of shame.

One who stays young will never take to the masquerade of

clothes. This for me is a fundamental aesthetic principle. The dislike of clothes is important! That is why I cannot come to terms with Paris, where trappings are religion.

* * *

I was still infatuated with the Argentine, and in Paris I felt younger (which confirmed both the youthfulness of Argentina and mine as her lover). I also felt younger as a Pole, an ambassador of younger civilization. All this gave strength to my denunciation of Parisian senility and propelled me further into nakedness. And yet, in fact, I was middle-aged, almost elderly, and in any case I did what I could to become, in a way, older than they, the Parisians, more cunning, more subtle, so that they would not find me out as a naive provincial . . . I was serving up my youth garnished with old age *à la Parisienne* with all the skill I could muster.

In the end I no longer knew whether I was young or old. There was plenty of discord in the cacophony . . .

* * *

I asked them who was X, whom I only knew by reputation. I was told that he was an eminent writer. I said yes, a writer, but who was he? They explained that he started as a surrealist, but was now an objectivist. I approved of objectivism, but still asked who was he? I was told that he was a member of the Melpomene group. I agreed with Melpomene, and still asked who was he? They said that his style was a mixture of *argot* and a kind of fantasticated metaphysics. I agreed with the mixture, but who was he? And I was told that he had won the *Prix St. Eustache* four years earlier.

We were in a small but delectable restaurant on the banks of the Seine at the time, and I was happily engaged in eating a particularly idyllic *mouton*. I realized how tactless I had been. What did it matter who your cook was? You didn't feed on him, only on his dishes. I had been tactless not only toward cooks but also the couturiers: to ask who you are is to strip you (it also happens to be an anti-phenomenological question). A French writer does not parade naked—the air is full of elaborate cloaks; he has only to reach out to find one that suits him and to become a *romancier*, *historien d'art*, a Catholic, or a *Phataphysicien* . . . The air teems with techniques, directions, solutions, platforms, and points of view. The air of Paris is full of old junk. Their literature does not use raw materials; it relies on rehashes and reproductions.

When I said that basically I was not a writer or a member of anything, neither a metaphysician nor a journalist, but a man, free and alive, they promptly concluded that I was an existentialist.

My own transatlantic nakedness (essential to my love affair with the Argentine, conducted so much against my age) urged me to strip them too.

The eminent writers dining with me that night were aghast at my naive and passionate attempts to see through their clothes. An embarrassing situation arose. My question (still transatlantic—particles of the remote Indian lands) were met by mute melancholy, absolute discretion, and a tactful withdrawal. My hosts remained dressed from head to foot, wrapped up although it was May, their faces stylized by hairdressers . . . and each of them kept in his pocket a little naked statuette to be examined at intervals with expertise.

This city is ruled by modesty and good sense. Nobody intrudes. Everyone minds his business. They function, they produce, they are culture and civilization. They are imprisoned in their clothes, they move like insects covered in a gluey mess. When I started to take off my trousers, they fled like mice through doors and windows. Even the cooks got away and I was left alone in the restaurant gasping . . . Good God, what was I up to, what was it about . . . and I stood there with one trouser leg on and another in my hand.

At that moment Kot[1] came in and saw me. He asked, flabbergasted, whether I had gone off my head. Feeling cold and embarrassed, I said that when I started to undress they had all scampered away . . .

"You are mad; why should they be put off by stripping? There is no place in the whole world where they would be more used to it than in Paris. You must have got hold of the mice, but I will invite for you such lions that if you decide to dance on the table naked, I promise they won't bat an eyelid." We made a wager there and then, a wager both Polish and old-fashioned, in the nineteenth-century manner. (With Kot I felt Polish and not Argentinian, because we had discovered a grandmother in common.) All

[1] Gombrowicz's translator into French, Konstanty Jeleński [translator's note]

was agreed, and he asked all the best people, all the intellectuls ready to strip themselves at will. I kept quiet till the dessert was brought in and then I started. How they ran! Full of apologies, must go and all that. Leonor Fini and Kot stayed and said that, surely, they couldn't have been put off. It was impossible, they specialized in that sort of thing. I was thoroughly sick of it, unhappy, and so sad that I was close to tears.

"The whole point is," I said—"even when they take their clothes off, they are in fact clothing themselves. Their nakedness is just another pair of pants. And when I let my pants down, it terrified them, chiefly because I didn't do it in the manner of Proust, or à la Jean Jacques Rousseau, or after Montaigne. I didn't do it in the spirit of existentialist psychoanalysis, I just took them off."

* * *

I said in an interview that they were rather like the Pavlov dogs. I wish I had never said it. Since that day their artificiality became a condition and the howling of affected hounds resounded in the silent streets at night.

When an adult has finally broken with his youth, nothing can stop him from becoming more and more artificial.

His relationships—with anything—are conducted in coded symbols, as if by telegraph. Any form of directness is strictly out. The whole secret is the conditioned reflex. To make a Pavlov dog salivate you don't show him a piece of meat, you play the trumpet. To throw a Frenchman into raptures you have only to quote Cocteau or show a Cezanne: he is enchanted, he associates this with beauty, and he salivates or, rather, his hands prepare to applaud. Unquestionably to let one's youth go is to loose lightness, applaud.

I had some very odd adventures in that magical world, full of signs, symbols, passwords, rituals, ceremonies, and gestures.

I knew, of course, even before I came to Paris, that the French had some difficulty in expressing themselves; one could sense it in their books, getting less and less articulate . . . but I had no idea how far it went. I was asked to dine with some writers . . . I went, looking forward to a brilliant evening (they had great reputations). The initial reflexes were well up to the mark and we went through the greetings, the compliments, and the courtesies as expected. So long as our conversation stayed within that framework, all went well. Someone made a joke, I laughed, they laughed. And all the time the hounds tormented me, they were getting at my throat, howling in my gullet, I was literally being choked by the conditioned dogs. In the end I tried to say something. Good God, was that such a dreadful sin? I simply expressed a thought . . . about art or about life . . . as I have done many times in Buenos Aires, in the Fragata. It silenced them. They said nothing and gave themselves to eating and the rest of the symposium was confined to food and silence. Thoroughly nonplussed, I imagined that they felt insulted in some way and I asked Wladimir Weidle, with whom I dined next evening, what I had done. We got to the cheese, and I described what had happened. His explanation was that no one talked in Paris any longer . . . even when they did, it was only to avoid saying something . . . he gave me as an example the banquet for the *Prix Goncourt* which takes place annually in a rather superior restaurant. There they talk of food to the exclusion of everything else, and so they avoid any danger of saying something about art . . . Unquestionably to let one's youth go is to lose lightness to accept the unease of being gradually weighed down by time. It is the same with them: they have been invaded by a horrible malaise and they can no longer express themselves. Even when they have something to say, they can't do it—it's too difficult, too profound, too lofty, too subtle . . . so they pay homage to their unease in silence. I met Butor at a party and I mentioned that as we were going to be in Berlin about the same time, we would have the chance to talk to our heart's content about most things, perhaps even about the *nouveau roman français*. Instead of replying, the leader of the *avant-garde* laughed. His laughter was a polite formality, an impenetrable barrier, the laughter of a tin of sardines in the Sahara . . . Good God!

The genius of Paris is still in a state of feverish activity—it still produces ideas and books—the boldest of cities is as much in the *avant-garde* as ever . . . but I would say that between the city and the inhabitants there is nowadays something agonizingly amiss. Their genius has become an anti-genius; they are intimidated by their own daring, afraid of their own courage, tamed by their own revolt, made mediocre by their own techniques . . . so they tend their Genius as well as they can, rather like farm hands looking after a cow: they tend it, they milk it, and they sell the milk. Paris is still a palace, but the Parisians are only palace servants.

Yes, palace servants. In that city of conditioned dogs that salivate at the sound of a trumpet, I had some extraordinary adventures . . . One night on my way back from an agreeable bistro, I saw an exquisite baroque palace with the doors ajar . . . I decided to walk in . . . I found vast rooms, sculptures, painted ceilings, coats of arms, and masses of gilt. I was met by a little man, neatly dressed, but so quiet that I took him to be a servant, a majordomo perhaps. I asked him to show me around and he called for his wife and sons. When they came out, they all took me around the house, pointing out the sculptures, brushing off the dust . . . as I was about to leave, I put my hand in my pocket, but the little man protested and then introduced himself and his family: I am Prince so-and-so, this is the Princess, my sons the Marquis, the Count, and the Viscount. Overcome, I left the house in silence.

I walked about the streets for a long time and in the end I found myself among the statues in the *Jardin des Tuileries*, encircled by supple, pliant, willowy nudity, lithe, slender, and slight . . . but made of stone, a paradox of static movement, inanimate life, rigid softness, and chilly warmth, stillness alive in the light . . . The magical paradox! Its power over me grew and grew until it swelled beyond itself. It seemed better not to stay within that stony gallery too long and I decided to leave. I started walking off, at first slowly, then faster and faster, but the statues multiplied into a forest of stone . . . I tried to dodge some and by-pass the others . . . then I stopped dead! Dogs in front of me! I looked again: a marble Akteon was fleeing from nude Diana . . . his own dogs after him, their teeth bared, ready for the kill.

The horror of it! The fierce pursuit of the transgressing mortal *stood still*, motionless like a stream frozen forever. The sin was dead! I heard the Pavlov dogs howling all over Paris in the dead of night—and I went home.

* * *

In France the visual arts encroach more and more on literature. The style of the literary critics has been formed in art galleries and would be better fitted to the description of paintings and sculpture. After all, in painting period, school, and style tend to dominate the individuality of the artist (able to express itself infinitely more freely in words than in images), and the present ascendency, in literary criticism, of the collective and the abstract is quite striking. The visual arts are closer to things than to people; painters and sculptors manufacture objects and nowadays critics tend to regard a literary work as just another object. They compile catalogues, enumerate, classify, and try to write objectively. Their criticism is full of theories; they are less and less like artists and more and more like research workers, erudite and expert disseminators of information.

A critic of painting or sculpture has to write about them from the outside, as they are basically alien to words—as distinct as pen and brush. But literary criticism? It is literature about literature, words about words. It is clear that a literary critic must be an artist and a co-creator. He cannot *describe* literature as one must, regrettably, describe paintings; he must participate, and criticism from outside, criticism of literature as an object is quite unacceptable.

But because they have stifled youth in themselves, with its divine ability to embrace and to attract, their world is becoming more and more external—or objective. *The nouveau roman français* is a sad sacrifice of humanity to the external world . . . it has become alienated from poetry.

Or rather, its poetry is one-sided. It lacks all the essential qualities of youth: the overwhelming attraction, the ability and the wish to please, the immediate warmth that draws together but does not classify. The poetry of youth is attainable even today, but only to a writer who remembers that he is writing also for the young. And that an adult exists—also—for the young.

Beauty and poetry created exclusively by the middle-aged sound most unlikely. Surely to make real music, it is better to have all the ages playing within us. To achieve beauty divorced from the only age to which it belongs by nature is well-nigh impossible.

Without youth, writing may retain all its qualities but one—attractiveness. Without its allure the literature may still be superb, but it is bound to be *cold*.

Do I mean French literature, or literature in general? I still tend to mistake Paris for the world.

* * *

Dinner. *Truffles à la Soubise* and *Crème Languedoc Monsieur le Duc*. I talked and they listened. I didn't like that. In Argentina when I went to Santiago del Estero, I listened and let the local writers speak . . . it's always the provincial who talks; he has to prove himself.

Genet! What a nuisance! That pansy attached himself to me, followed me all the time. I might be walking with friends—and there he was, standing at the corner under the street light, giving me signs of some sort. As if we were of the same fraternity! The disgrace . . . And also the danger of blackmail. Before leaving the hotel, I peered through the window to make sure that he wasn't there . . . but he always was. Even with his back turned, he was still making eyes at me.

I knew nothing of Genet before coming to Paris, I must stress that I never read him in the Argentine and my *Pornography*, good or bad, is my own, and not the fruit of a love affair between myself and Genet. A week after my arrival in Paris, somebody lent me his *Pompes funèbres*.

I opened it. My first impression? This was the real war; never have I read anything so full of the ghastly taste of 1939–45, of its distilled essence. Second impression. That he managed to fuse beauty and ugliness into one, a single angel, looking through the same eyes. The boldness of it! The audacity! Third impression? That the amazing and terrifying genius of France has given us again a burglar capable of forcing a locked door! The fourth? Poetry! The fifth? How well this burglar sensed the priceless and forbidden treasures under lock and key! And the sixth? That this book, difficult and inevitable, was like a dream or like Golgotha, born of fate, linked with destiny.

My seventh impression was that Genet was my own invention, that I had conjured him up and that, if he surpassed me, I have been surpassed by my own creation.

But I felt uneasy. Genet, the kindred spirit, was somewhat embarrassing and not only that; his hand under the street light, extended obscenely toward me, was so *cold!*

I was deeply impressed—and yet I rushed through the *Pompes funèbres* (I didn't even dip into his other writings). There were the usual distractions, appointments, visits, telephone calls, the whole daily whirl . . . and in the end I only flicked through its pages.

But I did buy Sartre's study of Genet, *Saint Genet, comédien et martyre*, a book of 578 pages, and any time I had I devoted to swinging from Sartre to Genet and from Genet to Sartre. But I didn't read Sartre's study through either, despite my deep conviction that his existentialist analysis was a discovery more important than a dozen Prousts. But you know how it is . . . nobody reads books properly . . . I read like everybody else. While I was reading I asked myself what it was in Genet, and in Sartre's interpretation of him, that made me feel I had to defend myself against them both. What was it that repelled me?

Reading Genet the poet was a shattering experience, and I admired the way in which Sartre makes this homosexual lose his quality of apartness, his "abnormality," and reunites him with the "normal" in a common humanity. In Sartre's interpretation, Genet only "became" a homosexual and a thief in the same way as others "become" sportsmen or salesmen. Sartre dealt humanly with the inhumanity of Genet; the way he managed to disarm his ghoulishness by taking it to the extreme appeared to me as no mean intellectual achievement. And yet . . . my final impression was that Sartre had been taken in. Genet, according to Sartre, turns against his own freedom in an act of free will, he chooses to "become" bad, a homosexual and a thief, simultaneously confirming freedom and destroying it. Following a dialectic line of reasoning the attempt to destroy freedom leads to the destruction of all existence. Existence becomes an illusion, and the inherent contradiction of Evil which is Negation makes the existence even of Evil impossible. . . . In the end, Genet regains through nothingness the freedom he has rejected. This sounds fine. But somehow this argument, without ever leaving the ground, seemed to hang in the air. . . . Why?

And why did Genet, announcing that he had chosen Evil and that he desired Evil, seem to me as untrustworthy as a pickpocket telling tales to the judge and jury? Someone has been taken in. Sartre by Genet? Or Genet by himself? Behind the ominous gate leading supposedly to hell there was no hell; something else lurked behind. It was the *ease*, the *facility* of it all. This is how it had happened: Genet as a boy began to steal, simply to get hold of money, then he became a homosexual to fulfill his physical need. It occurred in quite an ordinary way, slowly and naturally. It grew with time, with the progression of imperceptibly short moments of existence. It happened smoothly, of itself, through thoughtlessness and irresponsibility, in the turmoil of life lived amongst men as easy-going as himself. The absolute Evil attached itself to his existence much later when he started writing and needed it as a literary alibi. It was then that he announced he had chosen Evil. But he never added that he had chosen it after the event. Thus the study by Sartre was not a study of existence itself but of an interpretation of existence. . . . He started on the life of Genet when Genet himself has already made it into a myth.

How easily the temple of the Devil has fallen before me! And it has fallen into *facility!*

Some people might have felt uncomfortable, I suppose, at such a simple explanation. But I knew that it wasn't an accident. This facility was indeed the obstacle most likely to trip up both Genet and Sartre.

So what finally repelled me in Genet? He was trying, as I did, to make the young beauty into the beauty supreme, and to put the young on a pedestal. But he never caught the essence of youth. Youth is essentially disarming, light, dependent, and therefore incapable of a separate existence, something intermediate, both helpful and absolving. For Genet, youth was crime—cruelty—sin—sanctity—torture . . . that monk, sinner, saint, criminal, and executioner approached youth with a drawn knife to make it into an atrocity and to force it to the utmost.

How typical of Paris, the capital of the world, that its most daring attempt to defy youth ended in casting it into hell and into sin, and so into morality and civilization. Not for a moment did Genet allow youth to free him from centuries of French morality. On the contrary he made it tense and rigid, and in the end he succeeded in hardening the supple twig into murderous steel. So the youth to which Sartre applied his middle-aged analysis had already been worked on and tampered with by an aged mind. . . . Will we never (Paris and I and Sartre and Genet) be able to stop on the increasingly stony road to Mastery? Will we never look back? Not once? Oh, Argentina! Is the past irretrievable? Now I simply must add something to obliterate the bathos of these words: I met Winczakiewicz. I spoke on the radio. I ran into Antonio Barni on the Quai de la Tournelle.

II. The Berlin Diary

I landed in Tegel Airport in Berlin on the sixteenth of May a year ago.

A representative of the Ford Foundation, Professor von Bomhard, put me and my suitcases in a beautiful black car and drove us through the city. I was an extra suitcase, unloaded in front of a building in the middle of a park, taken up in a lift, then along a passage into a large room with an enormous window, and then up a stair to another room: a balcony, a wardrobe, a table. Unpacking.

I went out on the balcony: the rectangular blocks of fifteen storey buildings among the trees, a garden town. I delighted in the spaciousness, after my claustrophobic room in Paris.

The first person I made friends with was Ingeborg Bachmann, an Austrian poet and another guest of the Ford Foundation. She was also staying in the Akademie der Künste and we walked together, both surprised and bewildered by that island in the communist ocean; or was it something else? We knew little or nothing about Berlin, and I remember that we were amazed at its emptiness, so that when we saw someone we cried "man on the horizon!" In strange, exotic, unusual places one tends to suffer from difficulties of perception. . . . I remember when in Upper Paraná I saw a full moon right under my nose only a few steps away. It was no good pinching myself; it was there—the ball of light above the water—it was there and it was the moon, and it was no good trying to explain it away. . . . The lack of understanding is with us everywhere, of course—at home, in a room of our own—but it grows more insistent in places so out of the ordinary that they seem to be hidden behind a code. Why did Berlin appear to me almost empty in those early days? After all, although the Akademie building was in a park, I was often driven through the center of the city. I still don't understand it. Was it a mirage? A week later I realized that there were quite a lot of people in Berlin.

After the whirl of Paris, quiet and silence were bliss. Nothing urgent to do except for a few calls. Later Professor Höllerer took Miss Bachmann and me to Lake Wansee and somebody filmed us. I gave a few interviews. A holiday . . . and a cooling down of all that had been happening to me; the Argentine, the journey, and my stay in Paris were all falling asleep. . . .

But just then I caught (in the Tiergarten) a certain scent, a mixture of herbs, water, stone, and tree bark. I wasn't sure what it was . . . but it was Poland, a Polish smell of childhood, of Małoszyce and Bodzechów . . . the same smell. Well, after all, it wasn't far, just over the border; the essence of nature was the same. The nature I had deserted a quarter of a century before. Death. The cycle was closed, I was back to the same scents, and it meant death. I have met my death before in various circumstances, but there was always in those meetings a certain obliqueness, and therefore some hope of life. That time in the Tiergarten, I met my death eye to eye—and it has not left me since. I should never have left America. Why hadn't I understood that Europe meant death to me? In my situation the return to childhood and youth was bound to end in self-destruction. Later I sometimes felt "surprised" that something as ephemeral as a scent could suddenly end my life, but from that moment death sat on my shoulder, light as a bird, during the whole of my stay in Berlin.

The Argentine period, now closed, was acquiring the brilliance of a myth. Walking in the Tiergarten, I remembered the incredible moment of finding myself in Argentina. There I was, a Pole of 1939, alone in a land lost in an ocean, a land spreading like a fish tail toward the Antarctic. On the map the Argentine appeared alone amidst the waters, pushed far down, drowned in the distance. I too was alone, lost, cut off, alien, unknown, drowned. My ears were still filled with the tearing noise of the European loudspeakers, my mind tortured by the war cries of the newspapers. And already I was immersing myself in the unknown language and in the remote life of the new land. It was a thoroughly weird moment. There was silence as in a forest; one could hear a fly buzzing, and its solitary hum was music after the din of the immediate past. The silence grew and two extraordinary and rare words flew out: Witold Gombrowicz. Witold Gombrowicz. Originally I had left for the Argentine by chance and then only for a fortnight's stay. Had the war not broken out, I would have been back in Poland—but I had to admit that when the door slammed and when the

Argentine closed in around me, I felt that here at last I could hear myself.

For twenty-four years I lived free of history. Buenos Aires was like a camp of six million people, a nomadic crowd of Italians, Spaniards, Poles, Germans, Japanese, Hungarians, a stirring cauldron, changing from day to day. . . . The native Argentinians said openly *que porquería de país* (the beastly country) and their freedom sounded marvelous after the choking fury of nationalism. It was marvelous in those first few years not to know anything about the Argentine, about its parties, programs, leaders, not to understand its newspapers, to live like a tourist. But being a tourist is a sterile thing in the long run. What saved me was that as a writer I was accustomed to make use of form. In my new situation I was able to undertake the task of transforming myself. But hadn't the Argentine, in fact, been my fate always, even when as a child in Poland I did everything to avoid marching with others to a military tune?

The blessing of the enormous waves breaking into eternity, keeping me away from the history of Europe! And suddenly . . . the return, the swing over to Europe, and in Europe to this city, more painful and stained with history than any other. I guessed, or perhaps I knew, that I was not going to have a smooth passage, but from the first my journey became something far more dangerous than I could have imagined when packing in Buenos Aires. Something very desperate attached itself to the expedition. Even so, I was not prepared for death in the Tiergarten. Was it make-believe? And cant on my part? Of course it was, but of the kind that never lets go once it gets hold of you. . . .

* * *

I was still chewing through Paris and I was thinking of Sartre.

Who was more provocative, Sartre or Voltaire's Pangloss? It was a little as though smoke rising from the crematoria and the cinders of war rose up to the sky and formed itself into the word "freedom."

But such a proclamation of freedom would have been a provocation everywhere and at any time, not only in the war and over the camps. Telling us, the victims, the martyrs, the slaves, up to our necks in disease, vice, passion, forever in harness, in toil, in fear, telling us that we were free? Every day from morning till night we undergo the most hideous slavery . . . and then "freedom!" The fact that the idea so totally at odds with our daily experience appears both wise and intellectually fertile only makes it worse.

But can a philosophy based on consciousness have much in common with existence? Consciousness in itself is neutral toward life. Life knows only pleasure and pain. The world exists for us only as a possibility of rapture or of grief. The consciousness of anything other than pain or pleasure is of no consequence. I am conscious of the existence of that tree—and what of it? It leaves me cold. The existence I am conscious of had no existence at all, till I felt it. It is not being conscious of a thing that is important, but the ability to feel it. The consciousness has to be a consciousness of feeling, and not simply a consciousness of existence.

But there is a fundamental contradiction between pain (or pleasure) and the concept of freedom. To say that we have potentially some freedom in relation to suffering is to deny the sense of the word "suffering" (even if it were only the freedom in a given situation). Suffering is something I don't want, something I have to suffer; the essential element of it is compulsion and the absence of freedom. In fact, I can't imagine a more violent contradiction than that between suffering and freedom.

So by assuming that existentialism could start only from sensibility I ruled out the possibility of any existential philosophy, a philosophy of freedom.

I am really writing about Sartre to get away from Berlin. Of course, I must not write about Berlin, or about Paris. I must always write about myself and never allow my writing to digress from its subject. But it is becoming more and more difficult to concentrate on myself since I left Buenos Aires for the wide world. I had become an Argentinian, corrupted by the South, soaked in that sun and that air. I had abandoned and forgotten the shape and the light of this other sky which now was above me. . . . In Berlin I tried to get inside the moss, to penetrate the shrubs. They excited me; I felt like a dog on the scent . . . the sharp northern skies covered space and time with speeding clouds. The clouds above me are a rushing eternity. I wrote once that on arriving in the Argentine I had begun another youth, but the second youth somehow killed my first, Polish one. . . . Bodzechów, Małoszyce, the school years in Warsaw, the literary beginnings, the literary cafés—all of it died and fell away from me. But what now? Must I recover not only the immensity of the skies in myself, but all of that deserted immensity, must I soak myself, drown myself in it?

In the meantime Berlin was presenting itself to me as a somewhat difficult city. . . .

I had no illusions about my German—but had not expected that it would be quite so bad! I found how bad when a local worthy invited me to dinner. The other guests spoke only German or English, while my good languages are Spanish and French. They all addressed me politely from time to time, but it all ended in gestures. Then one of the guests took the German translation of *Ferdydurke* from a shelf and started reading aloud.

It was, of course, extremely courteous on his part. I heard myself speak; they were my words . . . I could not understand . . . I heard myself speaking, and the others understood me, but I could not understand myself. I felt a most extraordinary rupture; As if I were only the bodily appendix to the other, written, Gombrowicz. . . . I understood there and then that my existence in Berlin must necessarily be incomplete and confined to the physical side of things. It frightened me. But that wasn't the point. . . . Should I go to Poland? The question had been with me since I left America. In Paris they had tried to persuade me to go . . . they said, Why not? You would see how many friends you have. And it was enough to go to the window for the northern dark sky to assault me. . . . My pre-history was laying siege: there were the colors, the way they all walked, the way they boarded a bus, their hats, their German smile, a neighbor of the Polish smile. Should I go? Or shouldn't I? I wouldn't be going to Poland but back to myself as I used to be. . . . I felt alarmed at that. It didn't matter that everything there was upside down and unrecognizable—I would still find myself. And I couldn't quite face that. Since the boat left Buenos Aires I had felt myself losing my grip on the whole Argentinian period, I felt too lost to undergo another upheaval. . . . Now this is a splendid moment for the usual hacks to intone "Such is the lot of an émigré and an egoist." Nonsense! It is the lot of every man of a certain age, whose life has broken into two. To go and look into the mouldy well to see myself at ten years old, and then sixteen, and twenty? To go to the cemetery and to open my own tomb? And at the same time to meet my family and friends, exchange views, take part in the social round?

I started life in Berlin with those fears on my mind (I have been pursued by fear since I left the Argentine), and accompanied by the death I had met in the Tiergarten. After a fortnight at the Akademie der Künste I was transferred to a comfortable flat in Hohenzollerndamm. I unpacked and made myself at home. I met most of the important writers and editors (the top German writers all seemed to live in Berlin at that time) but, unfortunately, conversation was not often possible. My fellow writers, Günther Grass, Peter Weiss, Uwe Johnson, all spoke French badly. On the whole, after a quarter of a century Europe seemed to me to resemble the Tower of Babel. Sometimes, at a dinner for ten, six languages were spoken. The planes hurried people along, I knew some who had one flat in Rome, another in Berlin and a third in Zürich, each for ten days in the month. This new modern Europe rushed along so fast that I couldn't catch it. And when I did, I held it uncertainly in my hands, like a bomb ready to explode. But all this is unimportant. . . .

West Berlin, on this side of the wall, has no more than two million inhabitants, but it spreads over an enormous area full of parks, lakes, and woods. Parts of the city are so well planted among the trees that it is difficult to know whether it is a town or a forest. It is a town—resort, the most comfortable of towns, where cars move smoothly without jams, where people walk without hurry, and where the swarming crowds and stuffiness of other capitals are hardly known. An IDYLL: Elderly gentlemen walk their well-cared-for dogs, tidy women water flowers in the window boxes, the cars stop politely at the traffic lights, smiling workmen unload cases, someone is enjoying a pastry on a café terrace, a well-brought-up young woman examines a shop window. . . . POLITENESS: People going up in a lift exchange polite bows and polite words. When you ask the way, they take you there. The tone of their conversation fills you with confidence; lies, irony, and malice have been exiled from here. There is infinite CORRECTNESS in their collars, ties, fingers, nails, shoes, in the way the taxis pick up their passengers, the salesmen deal with their customers, in the gesture of the man at the post office choosing the right stamp to put on your letter. Their eyes are full of HIGH MORAL PRINCIPLE, but so also are their whole bodies, from head to toe. BENEVOLENCE, CALM, KINDNESS pervade the city (where the standard of living appears to be higher than in the States). Quite often one meets BEAUTY: northern, reserved, and strong. In this city, the neuralgic center of the world, on this island surrounded by a wall, you hardly see any police. In this green resort, this idyllic Berlin, you walk for miles without meeting a uniform. But that again is not important. . . .

I often had dinner in the garden of a restaurant in Fehrebellinerplatz: calm, trees, and umbrellas. The sparrows, unafraid of the kind Germans, used to sit on the table and peck at the food on my plate. There were two illuminated fountains, colorful as peacocks or as two ever-changing bouquets of flowers, set among the chattering guests and busy waiters. From time to time the color changed to red and inevitably, in that innocent Berlin, I thought of blood. I saw blood, spurting from the stony ground. But that too is not important. . . .

No, Berlin is not easy. . . . It might have been easier if (shades of Hamlet!) I did not suffer from nightmares. Six months later, when I lived in Bartingallee, I was having breakfast in a restaurant in Hansaplatz and this is what happened: An elderly German with trembling hands, touchingly sociable, used to sit a few tables away from me. He was probably living on a pension, was slightly mentally deranged, and sat there with his mug of beer, greeting the waiters, me, and other guests with great cordiality, seizing the slightest opportunity to talk or to make an inviting gesture. His solitude must have been very great (and where did it come from? Perhaps from *there?*) He particularly liked talking to me: "Isn't it a beautiful day? (Silence) . . . beautiful snow!" (An interval of fifteen minutes) . . . "What about a cigar?" One day, on a Sunday, we left together: "Do you know that on Sundays the excursion buses leave from here? Should we go?" I refused politely. He looked at me and was silent for a minute, his hands trembling. Then he said something in German and I caught only shreds of meaning "to go, not to go, not to get there . . . various things could happen . . . you can't, there is nothing, nothing, what do you want? (*was wollen Sie?*) . . . *ganz unmöglich*, impossible, of course not (*das kann nicht sein*) . . . pity, pity (*Schade*), nothing (*nichts*) . . . (*Nein*) . . . *aber sehen Sie, mein Herr, das ist vielleicht trotzdem, und gegenüber*" . . . and he ended emphatically: "*nichts*." He stood there, somehow negative, stubborn, resisting, elusive and firm, decisive, resigned and desperate, shaky, soft and hard, dramatic, a kind soul and a man with something to say, a man with a complaint, protesting, denying, or perhaps a man with nothing but emptiness. I couldn't catch his meaning, I could neither understand nor guess, and I stood brooding over his words as a child over a heap of scattered bricks. Or was I standing over a gaping hole breathing negation. And still, even that was not the point! What was then? Since I had left the Argentine I lost the thread, and here in Berlin there were too many threads crossing each other. So here I was, standing among the trees, the houses, and the asphalt, while he talked. Then my death touched me again. Mine, or theirs? I had to return home, to smile and bow. . . .

Lady Macbeth. They keep on washing and washing their hands . . . (to start with).

Taps. Bathrooms. Washing is cleanliness . . . after all.

Their legs are long and their eyes and their necks are faded . . . the color of their skin . . . perhaps denotes selfishness (what about Sweden? Norway? Holland?).

The waiters. Ballet. Like a rock! Never tired. Immaculate. Politeness. (The German as an actor.)

Do they like masks and games? (One could start from here. Alas, one can start from anywhere; it doesn't matter.)

Isolation. They cooperate, that is, they communicate, only partly, through their function. The solitude, given up to transforming the world and to satisfying their own needs. They marry early. To make use of the woman, to make her work. . . .

The North. . . . How much are they themselves and how much of it is simply being a northern people? (The English? The Swedes? The Danes?) The answer: the northern characteristics are intensified and transformed in this tightly knit community. Finally they are transformed into wings! Entrancing! (One could do it this way . . . all methods are admissible when one man is contemplating sixty odd millions. . . .)

A German is doomed to live with Germans.

This means, in the simplest terms, that he has to trust a German technician, a German general or philosopher. Whom else? German workmanship has always been more reliable. Germany is a country where workers trust the élite and the élite relies on the workers. Although they lost two great wars, they had held the world in their hands and until their destruction, their generals led them from victory to victory. Despite the final defeat they are used to victories: in industry, in war, in solving problems. . . Hitler was also, above all, a matter of trust.

Because they were unable to believe that he could be as primitive as he appeared, they had to assume that he was a genius.

A parallel: Poles formed by disasters, Germans formed by victories.

They aren't more gifted, but they abhor any botched work; they don't understand it . . . (the face of the electrician repairing the lift cable: concentrated, tense, almost the face of a martyr).

Etc., etc. Or one could follow a line of arbitrary, or even fortuitous comparisons, and see the result . . . e.g. eyes—eyeholes, work as a variant of the apparatus, reduce the problem to food, the relationship between rest and movement, or what is always *behind* them when they move? . . . (One could think of a lot of answers and one definite gain for myself would be that it would save me from the dreary sameness of accepted ideas in which the Germans remain as if in a cage).

I must not inform myself better.

I must not read either books or newspapers.

I must not look at the Wall.

I must not get too interested in anything.

I must sit in a café and stare at the street. . . .

(These notes were made in a café on the Kurfürstendamm when I was waiting for Susannah Fels).

No. I am not writing about Berlin, I am writing about myself (this time it is about myself in Berlin), I have no right to write about anything else. Keep to the point!

I met several people, invited here like myself by the Ford Foundation. I ordered several good suits. I was polishing up those parts of the *Diary* dealing with the passage from the Argentine and my stay in Paris. I had masses of invitations to concerts, exhibitions, and talks.

The happenings of a quarter of a century before kept me awake at night (me, the a-historical tourist from beyond the ocean), and yet they made me dream. The Idyll was linked with an enormity. It was uncertain whether the enormity belonged to the present or to the past—does not the present always derive from the past? Today the dogs in Berlin are extremely "correct," but I did see some monstrous animals from the past hovering in the background. Occasionally someone would drop a monstrosity in conversation, again half in the past and half in the present. Perhaps I only dreamed it (the confusion of time makes one dream): Somebody said that there was a hospital nearby where they kept people too badly maimed to be shown even to their own families. The families had been told that they were dead. Somebody mentioned that Hitler's bunker was on the other side of the Wall (was? or is? Surely it still is, even if only as an ex-bunker!). I was told that the war years were terrible. I was told: "I have been alone since the war. My husband and my son were killed." I was taken to see a prison and I was shown an ordinary light room, with metal hooks in the ceiling. They had been used to hang the plotters against Hitler. Or perhaps not to hang, but to strangle (I was no longer sure that I understood or even heard properly—it was the feeling one has in the mountains or on a great river, where nature transforms itself into a myth). And again: that "was" or "still is" (but the "is" is no longer complete—time is eating it away). I must have met in the streets of this highly proper and decent town not only deformed dogs but also human monsters. Who could be sure that the right foot of that middle-aged gentleman had not once pressed somebody's throat to the very end? They display such remarkable talent in getting over the past that often it is difficult to believe that it had happened. In Berlin, the macabre howling of mad dogs goes hand in hand with an impressive will to achieve normality.

Is it a place of virtue or of crime? It seemed to me—(the a-historical Argentinian!) that Berlin, like Lady Macbeth, was constantly washing its hands. That is why it was especially important to get to know the young, the new wave, cleansing and renewing life, starting almost from the beginning and drowning the past. But I had great linguistic difficulties with the German young and we were unlikely to establish a genuine communication with my German and their limited French. Of all our meetings, I best remember New Year's Eve in the studio of a young painter. I was taken there by a Greek friend of mine, Cristos Joachimides. As soon as I came in I faced the northern young, sprawling on the divans, or standing in the corners of the darkened room, and I realized that the most significant thing about them was their hands. Their hands filled the room, crowding together or falling apart, omnipresent hands, large, strong, and clean, with well-cut nails, civilized hands. The heads followed the hands as clouds follow the earth. I had noticed a similar thing once before, in the Argentine. It was Roby Santucho, who had seemed to be all hands.

Were they criminal hands? Not at all, they were new and innocent. New, not the same and yet identical. . . . What was the difference? Were their eyes, their hair and mouths and their laughter not identical? Golden and blue, a fair and friendly young man handed me a glass of whisky. But his hands came from *there* and his eyes looked at me from *there*. Someone put a brotherly hand on my shoulder. It meant friendship, but even friendship came from *there* and was death, I was sure, whether kindly or hostile. . . . At the same moment a charming girl shrugged her shoulders, rather amusingly—they were talking about love—But *that* too was love, that forest of conquering hands thrown up in a victorious gesture. . . . *Heil!* Loving, creative hands! Nonsense! Be off, ghosts! Those were Europeans (more European than the Parisians), they were calm and at ease, with no trace of chauvinism or nationalism, they saw the world in perspective. Yes, they were the most modern young people I had ever met. They were not even denying the past, but I could see in the half light that *That* was really not their affair. They were something new and different. They had torn themselves away. They were a parentless generation, foundlings, without a past, unattached; they lived in a void. They still had the same hands, but no longer for killing. . . . Instead they were busy with diagrams and accounts, with manufacture and production. Also, these young men were rich, with their exotic jackets and rare watches, and their cars waiting outside.

It was the luxury of civilized young people, living in the heart of Europe. . . but death was still in my mind, killing followed killing—I couldn't free myself from these thoughts. To cover a gap in my German I quoted Goethe's "Hier ist der Hund begraben" and my thoughts turned to burial, but not of a dog, only of an imaginary contemporary of mine, someone who might have been buried quite near. Perhaps by the canal, or by these houses, where many must have died in the last battle. His skeleton was still rattling. I looked at the wall and I saw a hook near the ceiling, a solitary tragic hook on the bare wall. Could these sophisticated young Europeans guess what was in my mind? I knew that they did not wish to appear "German" to me, and I had no desire to be "a Pole" to them. Perhaps they did not wish to be Germans at all, in their desire for a new beginning and unlimited opportunities. But the hook was still in the wall. Whisky, wine, sandwiches, cakes, fruit. Conversation, flirtation. And all the time we talked about *something else*, about Brecht, Grass, reading, travel, Lessing. As midnight approached my curiosity grew. . . What would they do about Time? What would they do about the New Year? What would they do with that moment in time when you can't get away from the past and the future? When the moment came, they opened champagne and glossed over the dangerous instant with smiles, embraces, and good wishes. "Are you going to Greece?" "Have you seen the Benrath exhibition?" "You'll see, I'll be married by this time next year." The New Year appeared calm and middle-class, divorced from Time and History.

They were private individuals. I (who had always tried to remain a private person), could only applaud. The citizens of the world. Europeans. If only it were not for that hook in the wall. . . and that skeleton, and death so close. . . and the elusive power of hands. . . I quickly drank another whisky. . . *Then*, at those death-loving parades, they had followed the advancing forest of outstretched hands . . . Here and now the hands were calm, unoccupied, private, but in my mind I saw those young chained to their hands, and led by them.

* * *

Surreptitiously, I had been watching their hands for some time . . . they were alarming, so much more efficient and serious than other hands; their work carried more weight. But at that party I realized how empty and dead those hands were, the hands of the orphaned young living in a reconstructed city on a temporary island. They had nothing to cling to. The great tradition of Goethe's Germany has been compromised by what had happened since. The slogans of the new Europe were not sufficiently vital. Besides, they feared slogans, programs, and ideologies; even morality, the scrupulous German morality that had led them into evil excess. The only thing left was work. I knew that each of them had something pressing to do: examinations, office, workshop, painting perhaps, or literature, production, construction, technology . . . They produced and transformed and that was enough for the time being. Their work determined their function; it dictated the part they played in this improbable city. . . the emptiness. . . the calm of the hands. I saw that the young Germans were hammering at the world outside to find their own identity; they were transforming the external world to establish for themselves who they were. How often, in the past, the Germans had challenged the world in order to solve this mystery. I repeat, what depresses one in meeting them is the certainty that they are serious. They are not playing games. They are not a nation of imitators, but one moving forward, blindfolded, in the forefront of humanity. A nation of creators, of pioneers in virgin lands. They do not know themselves what they will be, they don't even know what they are capable or incapable of being; they are at their most exotic and impenetrable when communicating with outsiders. Their inner life is shrouded in mystery, their discipline close to insanity. Their humanity is the beginning of another unknown humanity and their "functionalism" makes five Germans into an inscrutable entity. . . it's not simple at all . . . Enough! Stop! It's just a bad dream. The hands of those young people were calm and private. And what did they expect from life? A wife and children, a promotion. . . that's what they worked for . . . they wanted a decent life, that's all. The hook? The rattling of a skeleton? The forest of hands? What a very personal interpretation!

In the end it was difficult to know what to think: here they were, the young humanitarians, the universalists, the democrats, the innocents full of integrity. But their hands!

* * *

They are strangely beautiful, those calm heads, those thoughtful eyes, the punctuality, the order, and the good humor . . . and yet they are rushing forward, galloping into the future. Any German is a slave of Germans, each dominated by the others. He is intensified, increased, propelled, and carried forward; he is inspired by other Germans. And it happens as a matter of course. I was able to observe from the shadows their behavior toward one another, and I came to the conclusion that among themselves they were in fact merciless. . . or powerless, perhaps?

Production. Technology. Science. Hitler was the curse of the other generation, but the young may yet be defeated by science. Science unites them in an abstraction and holds them under a spell.

How could these young men discover and understand their own dreams? It wasn't in their time-table!

* * *

Let's imagine that I asked one of them if he liked jam. He would answer in the affirmative. But a negative answer wouldn't have made any difference. His needs, his tastes, his preferences are all governed by his dependence on other Germans; they are determined by the common image they project at a given time. The individual personality is formed through interaction.

When I left at dawn, the night was fading in the frosty streets, and some people, still in high spirits, were going home. Calm and sleep were descending on the city full of wallets, watches, rings, and cashmere sweaters.

One knew, of course, that the following day the city would work a little harder than the day before; each day the pace increased. The work would be reliable and normal, as always, and its results would be better and better. . . Sound work. . . pleasant tree-lined streets. . . solid, comfortable, quiet houses. . . Berlin was like a man walking firmly straight ahead to an unknown destination. What will they do with themselves? What will they make of the situation? I wondered. . . Was I too rash in my judgment, for someone so newly arrived? Since my landing in Cannes all Europe seemed to me blinded by work. . . I never met anyone who wasn't a function, a cog in a machine; all lives were interdependent. And conquering, frenzied genius deserted individuals to become an inexplicable vibration of the human masses, forging ahead. Goethe? Instead of Goethe there were the giant factories (no less creative). Berlin went on in the same general direction as the rest, but just a step farther; existing alone, it arrived at its own kind of vibration.

During all my stay in Berlin I didn't meet a Goethe, a Hegel, or a Beethoven, or anyone resembling them in the least. Technical talents there were in plenty, but genius—the spirit—has left men for machines, for the buzz of transmission belts . . . and it dwells now outside humanity.

Their health! Their poise! Their wealth! It was almost like a trick of fate that here, in the center of disaster, people lived in greater comfort than elsewhere. Isn't it funny that they emerged from under the bombs healthy and wealthy, together with their dressing cases and their bathrooms? Shocking! Where is justice? Where is ordinary decency?

It would be a good idea to try and understand, and remember, that this ascetic and religious nation (religious even without God) has two realities, two meanings. They are pampered and flattered by their pig-skin wallets, their dressing cases, and their electric gadgets, it's true; but they are also exalted and transported by them.

Where? In what direction? Whatever the answer to this difficult question, it's worth remembering that for them luxury often represents a sacrifice, and bourgeois tranquility a state of acute tension. When they stop in front of their shop windows on a snowy sunny afternoon wondering what else to buy, at that very moment a new pressure is born at the summit of their private mountain, in their own desert, an avalanche of toil which roaring, crushing, whirling, thrusts them further toward the new unknown.

* * *

I wish to keep my writing as far as possible from politics.

It may not be wise, because the rapid economic renaissance of the Federal Republic has had a tremendous impact on the whole of Western Europe etc., etc., etc., as is generally known. It's snowing now, the swaddling white I have almost forgotten . . . the white silence, white softness spinning a web of dreams, falling steadily, blurring all . . . sleep. Instead of an alert observer, I prefer to be a chronicler of dreams. I'm sleepy even when awake; my wakefulness, too, is a kind of dream. Sometimes I feel I'm really waking up, then the snow starts falling again, one flake, two, three, lulling me to sleep. . . . I fell asleep on leaving the Argentine and I still haven't awakened. Snow and sleep. In the end, if these notes are to represent my observations, I would like them also to be drowsy and relaxed.

* * *

Sitting in Zuntz's, with Max Hölzer the poet. Behind the window Kurfürstendamm, crisply white and full of neon lights. Hölzer complains about the absence of genius: "Where on earth has it gone? We had so many men of genius in philosophy, in the arts—men who were concerned only with fundamentals. Where are they now, those *grands seigneurs?* Our literature is still digesting the war, Hitler, and politics, genius has degenerated into an argument between democracy and dictatorship. . . ."

Cars in the twilight, cars in the white snow. Hölzer is an embittered descendant of Goethe: "Hitler, Hitler, Hitler still obscures the view. Hitler is our limitation, our restriction. Hitler is the red rag for the German bull." I agree with Hölzer: Today, genius in Germany belongs to the dead and annoys the living. It is still present in the supreme achievements of those *grands seigneurs* full of incomparable *élan*—and it is now confined to their monuments. Today greatness tortures, humiliates, and galls. *Göttliche Funke*, but how can one be a genius among the telephones, radios, and newspapers? . . . one is caught in the web of daily activity. They are victims of a continuous encircling action . . . in a Berlin bombed, destroyed, hurriedly rebuilt, a temporary town with a battered past, in this island within a wall, in this former capital. . . . It needs revival on a scale that would equal German music and German idealism of the past, and it gets instead telephones, activity, cars, offices, work, a growing spider's web embracing all. Occasionally I was awakened at seven in the morning by shooting and I could see from my fifteenth floor the anti-aircraft fire from the Red side, I saw the Wall, American helicopters, and British soldiers. Tension. Another desperate attempt had come to an end: they had shot a man running through the desert between the Wall and the Western guards. So was it History after all? It wasn't. In Berlin it's the quiet daily routine that is ominous and menacing, it is the ordinary and the insignificant that count.

But what about genius? I enquired about Heidegger.

Hölzer told me that his influence was on the wane and that it was confined to university people. He has not been forgiven for his pre-war Nazi connections.

Politics again!

The restaurant was humming with movement and activity, as all eating places, but they were German movement and activity, and they were made of steel. Someone was eating ham. There were waitresses, a few men came in, the rush increased, some tables were pushed together.

"Those people? Who are they?"

"Experts."

"Experts on what?"

"I don't know."

"What about the young corpse, the skeleton, with them?"

"Corpse?"

"Yes, the one who has just ordered another gin."

Hölzer wasn't sure, he asked "what corpse?" to save face, but in fact he almost agreed with me. He elaborated: "Even if they had a corpse with them, bear in mind that they themselves, being experts, are not wholly present here; one might even argue that they are absent: an expert exists properly only within his own field. Their partial absence mitigates the presence of the corpse. He is with them, yet he isn't." Hölzer spoke slowly, with hesitation and some reserve, while I looked round the room. To be honest, one had to admit that all of them both were there and weren't. Sipping their coffee, they were, in fact, firmly fixed elsewhere, in their offices, in their own expertise. The incompleteness of existence that I had seen so often in Poland and in the Argentine, the incompleteness inviting illusions, visions, perversion, and abuse, seemed to me totally different in Berlin, where it carried with it the seriousness of German technology and German workmanship. But all this was imagination. . . .

Perhaps the Germans were not as real as all that, but they were certainly making the world around them real. Could they be real in the way they influenced others and yet unreal in themselves, in their own existence? I wasn't sure, and perhaps it didn't matter?

"Look," said Hölzer, "there is Höllerer looking for us. . . ."

"Are you sure," I asked, "that he really came in, is here, and is looking for us?"

"Of course he is," said Hölzer, a little annoyed, "you can see him yourself and you know very well that he has come to take us to a *Lesung* at the University."

* * *

Indeed Höllerer was there. Höllerer the professor, the expert, the theoretician of art, the organizer of cultural events, editor of that important quarterly *Akzente* and of another even more specialized publication devoted, as far as I knew, to highly esoteric research on the mechanism of subconscious expression. It is, of course, highly improper on my part to introduce real people into a literary work, however laudatory the context. With a text only half-realistic like this one, the author is God, he can do what he likes with people, once he gets them in. They become his creatures without the right to appeal. I hope, however, that my Berlin friends, Hölzer, Höllerer, and others, will kindly forgive my abuse of their hospitality, the hospitality of their city and of the Ford Foundation, on the simple grounds that provided one knows one shouldn't eat peas with a knife, one may sometimes be allowed to do so. After a drink, Höllerer put us in his car and took us to the *Lesung* in a quarter of Berlin quite new to me. Again there were buildings in a park, all very luxurious, with students' cars parked in the middle. We went into a large room and sat on a platform, Höllerer as chairman, then Hölzer, Berlevi, Miss Ingrid Weikert, Klaus Völker; in front of us were rows of chairs filled with students, their faces calm and concentrated. There was some applause. I asked what it was all about? (I didn't know the word *Lesung*)

"It's simple enough. You are going to read in German a few fragments from your work."

"But my accent. . . ."

"It doesn't matter."

"But I won't understand . . . nor will they. . . ."

"It doesn't matter in the least. You are a foreign writer staying in Berlin; it's simply the polite thing to do. Also, it will improve the cultural exchanges between our countries, not to mention the brightening up of the curriculum. When you have finished, Hölzer will read his poems, and we will have a discussion."

* * *

I was trying to grasp the situation in which Höllerer and I found ourselves. Höllerer inspired confidence, and I had no doubt that he was a distinguished lecturer and an equally distinguished organizer. His eyes, his step, his words exuded German ability . . . I knew that I was in deft, experienced, competent hands. He also had another characteristic: by nature, he was an eternal student, still retaining the happy temper of a schoolboy. When Höllerer was at a party anyone approaching the house of his host knew it; one could hear his young laughter from a distance. I was hoping for that laughter to deliver me now—obviously, he could not take my situation seriously any more than I did—he must have grasped the nature of this non-event with the students and their *Lesung*. But, because he had been cast in the role of a German professor confronted by students, he let the student in himself disappear, and became, as his function required, a typical professor sitting on a platform, preparing to open a meeting. Try to understand my own position: I was coming to the end . . . not so much of my strength, as of reality . . . Since I had left the Argentine, I was being sucked in by Europe as though by a vacuum. I felt lost among countries, cities, and crowds—a wanderer engulfed in the vastness of the mountains. Then, having reached the city-island, the city-sphinx, I met my death among the Polish scents of the Tiergarten. Weakened by inward death I yet had to stand up to the secret agony of the city, which had both inflicted death and received it. I found my life here extremely difficult, whether I was trying to say something that mattered at Zuntz's, or when I went to the international and multilingual dinner and cocktail parties, attempting to find the way in a strange landscape, shrouded in fog and mist like a cloud-capped mountain, unknown, undiscovered, undeciphered. And at the same time, and in spite of it—so real! The reality of Berlin seemed to increase daily—solid and reliable. They were capable of conjuring up reality out of nothingness. Take, for example, the event in which we were taking part: I had no doubt that the *Lesung* would take place—good, solid, and thorough. The workmanship was sound, from the door handles and the windows to the calm faces of the students, serious and attentive, their bodies hale and hearty, their notebooks ready and Höllerer on the platform waiting to conduct the performance! My only hope was in his laughter—I, the poor Ferdydurke,[2] at my journey's end, was entirely dependent on that young, easy-going laughter and its demolishing power. But no! The parts had been cast. This was an organized event; there were parts for the students and a part for the professor. Höllerer, very serious, opened the meeting, and introduced me. The students clapped, I bowed, Höllerer gave me a marked page of my *Ferdydurke* to read and I refused

I refused

I refused

a little confusion, a short-lived muddle, and then Klaus Völker, asked by Höllerer, took over the reading.

I listened and I didn't

I sat and I was and I wasn't

the reading

everything functioning as expected

was I there?

were they?

I was listening, sort of,

and up there the hook in the wall, high up, but not in this wall; in another one . . . the hook well hammered in, but not here, it was elsewhere, but it was so difficult to be sure among mountains, mists, clouds, and fog. Down on the plain everything functioned so efficiently, with such faith in the reality of what was being done, that I felt I was dying.

2 The title of Gombrowicz's first novel. [Translator's note]

the end, the applause, I smiled, and the unreality of my smile transformed me into nothing.

then Hölzer read his poems, the end, the applause, he smiled and sat down

Höllerer, Berlevi, Hölzer, Klaus Völker began the discussion, they discussed

they discussed

Höllerer spoke as a professor and only as a professor, within his Function. Berlevi spoke as a Pole and as a pre-war Warsaw Futurist and as a painter preparing an exhibition, and also as a guest of Höllerer's. Hölzer spoke as a poet and as a participant . . . Völker spoke as a young writer.

I wouldn't say that the sight of six or seven German builders with eight machines distresses me unduly. It is just a little off-putting, that passion to realize something, the quiet, gentle, and persistent passion . . . but it is infinitely more terrifying to see them realizing themselves through this other, more esoteric medium—culture. . . . I knew how well the spiritual and intellectual life of Berlin was organized with conferences, sessions, seminars, exhibitions, lectures, etc., etc.,—all so functional, and so well done that no one could possibly doubt its reality. I could go on and on telling what I have seen . . . above all, that incredible loyalty of any German concerned with cultural activities . . . incredible, because it went hand in hand with the most devastating scepticism . . . Take Höllerer . . . of course he knew just as well as I did that this was only a non-event . . . and yet he never hesitated, he functioned on the same principle as an actor whose thrust of the sword is real for him, but unreal in its effect, and therefore a half-action, an incomplete realization. I still hoped that an outburst of Höllerer's boyish laughter would destroy, squash, and smash to smithereens the whole affair, but for some reason, comprehensible only to a German, he remained serious to the end.

I felt my existence was being threatened, but I did not want to die, so somehow, I had to defend myself. I wanted to send out a signal that I was still alive but I didn't quite know how to do it, the discussion was still going on . . . and then, just like that, in my gibberish German, I asked to speak and interrupted the discussion—in fact, I made a speech.

I spoke and the whole room listened. The outrageous absurdity of my mumble overpowered me from the start and I lost my train of thought, spluttered words as they happened to come, for the sake of going on, to get somehow to the end; the words took over, they pushed and jostled, this way and that. Reeling, shaking, clutching at the words, I—the drunkard, the madman, the fool, completely unintelligible to the audience and myself—went on talking and gesticulating with less and less sense, but with growing emotion. I looked round and saw to my horror that the audience, presided over by the unperturbed Höllerer, were still listening. The students, calm, attentive, and unmoved, listened so intently that my anarchy sank into their will, which had before strained after sense, order, and method. My nonsense was being accepted as sense! My madness was instantly transformed into something within a norm, something *normal*. Were they perhaps prepared to take in all the madness of the world and to transform it in that fashion among themselves? Or were they so self-sufficient that no excess could upset them?

What about Berlevi?

I felt I couldn't continue to address the German rock drunkenly. But Berlevi, my countryman from Warsaw, the pre-war Futurist from Ziemiańska and Lourse[3] sat only a few chairs away . . . he stood out as a little crack in the solid mass, a door left ajar, a relief . . . could I escape through that crack?

So I addressed him directly with passionate accusations, I attacked him sharply, started a mighty argument beyond the bounds of sense and reeled into the absurd. He might have been a pillow, my twaddle sank into him and slowly, slowly, both our heads dropped off to sleep. Berlevi went first and I followed like a drunk in a bar after too many vodkas, when one talks and talks and talks, never mind let's have another, what's the time?, it doesn't matter, just one more . . . and one more, surrealism, realism, neo-realism . . . sociology, psychology, analysis. Three o'clock, five o'clock, stop.

Alas! Both Berlevi and I were dead drunk.

By then the students were applauding and getting up from their seats. Höllerer made a short speech to thank Hölzer and myself; the *Lesung* was over. I also got up, thanked them all with a bow and prepared to leave, but I took a long time about it. I was leaving and I couldn't leave, I felt like screaming and I couldn't scream, I decided to complain to someone that I couldn't get out, try as I may, but there was no one to complain to. What an odd

3 Warsaw literary cafés. [Translator's note]

place, where functions stretch as if made of rubber to become traps for the unwary. . . . Then I saw Höllerer standing against a wall, holding his own laughter under his arm like a briefcase . . . he was changed. I looked again . . . he was heavier, heavier than anything imaginable, made of the same stuff as the dead planets, asteroids suspended in the dark corners of the universe. Why was he like that? What had happened to him? He stood weighed down by his own gravity . . . further on I saw Senator Arndt, who had been so kind to me . . . but it was a mutation of Senator Arndt rather than the Senator himself, he and yet not he. They really had an amazing gift for getting away from themselves, I thought—and I felt the ground move away from under my feet; a frenzied flight of pride and power transferred me in an instant into the center of the solar system, I saw fiery bodies fly past and disappear and I heard cries and the sobbing of despair. Was it possible? So one had to be even more careful? Obviously they were not really a human race, the earth was not enough for them, they reached out beyond humanity . . . Sobbing. Despair. Regret. Just then I saw the charming young Frau Kurpiers watching me through a telescope (I also saw her through a telescope). Infinitely far removed, she looked at me and she cried out through her instrument "try to understand our pain and our agony, we have to move farther and farther away into another sphere, no longer of this world but of beyond . . . we have to move away from ourselves, to leave ourselves behind."

Enough of this. I won't continue these metaphors, visions, etc., enough . . . it's getting boring. In the end I managed to get out and return to my beautiful apartment in the Bartningallee, opposite the Akademie der Künste. I threw myself onto my bed fully dressed and slept.

* * *

N. is one of the many people who told me stories about the Americanization of Berlin.

"We needed America after the catastrophe, even more for her spirit than for her dollars and her military power. America rolled over us, leveling, simplifying, democratizing. We got rid of the remnants of our towers, with their flags flying high, of our metaphysics and our romanticism, of the fog and the haze. Our feet touched the ground, we grasped the sense of ordinary life and of day-to-day existence."

I didn't mention to N. my other adventures, like the one I have just described . . . but they all served to bring home to me the fact that the Berlin reality was neither clear nor settled. . . . It was all very convincing on the surface, very solid . . . but the cellars were there too, where they worked on reality as on a guinea pig, as on a piece of rubber that can be moulded at will into a product. . . .

* * *

Eva Bechmann said to me:

"Nothing calms one better after Paris than the sight of a Berliner sipping coffee on the terrace of a café on a summer morning. He and his coffee together are a kind of Absolute."

True. Only . . . are they really human? Well, they are—and very much so—but their humanity knows no limits, and that makes them something else again: beings to whom the human form is only incidental, a temporary disguise. I didn't trust the Americanization of Berlin. The absence in this present generation of the *grands seigneurs,* who used to dive headlong into the Abyss of Existence at the slightest provocation, does not in the least assuage my doubts. On the contrary. The fact that Hegel lies asleep in a quiet grave in East Berlin is no guarantee of the Absolute insofar as coffee, cakes, or men's and women's fashions are concerned. If I were coffee or a cake, I would not feel too safe in Berlin.

* * *

Their metaphysical anxiety can no longer find an outlet in the mind of the individual genius, and it wanders at large, an exiled spirit looking for a means of expression through collective forms of social organization. Could this be the most important development for the future of the new Europe?

The vast increase of humanity may throw open the door for the arrival of new deities.

* * *

Politics. Economics. One hears of nothing else. Hard-headedness. Matter of factness. I ask, What would happen if, in fact, they were concerned with something altogether different? . . .

They work. Of course they work. But while a Frenchman works to make something, they work for the sake of working.

I am even inclined to think that their impressive material achievement owes much to the fact that they did not take too much interest in it.

How much of my reasoning is the result of my sickness and how much of the sickness of Berlin itself? In some respects, this city is so much like myself that I am not sure where I end and Berlin begins.

* * *

I missed in Berlin the literary cafés of other capitals: something like Ziemiańska and Zodiak in Warsaw before the war. J., an editor, rather liked the idea, and we made it known that we would be holding sessions in the café Zuntz on Tuesdays and Thursdays. At first a lot of friends and acquaintances came, and we rather hoped that the tradition of the old celebrated Berlin cafés was reviving. The foreign artists invited to Berlin by the Ford Foundation came, and from among the Germans Günther Grass, Uwe Johnson, sometimes Peter Weiss . . . but it did not last. After a few months only my table survived, and it also folded up shortly afterward. I suspect that if the initiative had been less international and more their own, it would have lasted a little longer, but not much. I don't think they really like to communicate, or exchange ideas. Everyone knows as much as he needs to know and expresses what he knows through things: articles, paintings, books, or other forms of activity. They generally tend to remain extremely sceptical about any direct contact, other than with a definite purpose. Their eyes met sometimes when watching the same object, but never did one pair of eyes simply immerse itself in another.

* * *

Professor Hasenclaver invited me to address his students—the students of the *Literarische Colloquium.* They are being taught the odd discipline of how to write, how to become a writer. The young people conscious of a vocation study the techniques of composition, of artistic expression, of description, of action, goodness knows what else, perhaps even the technique of inspiration. A beautiful villa on the Wansee and an impressive building in the center of the city form the setting for the experiment. Veni, vidi . . . and I said, first, that if they wanted to become writers they should get away as soon as possible, and secondly, that they should beware of seduction by Michel Butor, who would try to turn their heads with the miracle of the *nouveau roman français* and his other theories. As far as I could judge, the students and Professor Hasenclaver himself accepted my advice with considerable pleasure. It really is odd: they are up to their ears in theory, scientism invades even those fields that until recently were preserves of human freedom, and yet every now and then I would hear their easy-going laughter and I felt that somewhere, somehow, we were allies.

* * *

Butor has been extremely good to me. He came to see me when I was recovering from the flu—and I repaid him by attacking his artistic credo. Not very handsome? Indeed not, but I maintain that because artists by nature must be dramatic, they cannot possibly meet without producing tension and heat. A curse on the children of Joyce! Cursed be all those who, slow and unmoved, like him, cultivate literature for literature's sake, an esoteric lofty creation for the initiated—boring, shriveled, and weary.

Not only Butor and not only Berlin . . . the whole of Europe is like a horse ready to be harnessed. Obedient, tame, full of good will toward any theory, constructive, positive, methodical, cerebral . . . the desert.

Translated by Krystyna Griffith-Jones

Alicja Iwańska

Fragment

Mbayo, July, 1963

L*os Señores* came to visit me in my cottage—married men with responsible positions, from Mbayo. They came on a cool morning, in brown *gavanas:* wool blankets with geometrical patterns. The designs were mostly motifs from their ancient, distant, and generally unknown ruins. "Gentlemen from Mbayo, knights out of the Middle Ages. . . ." I thought, as usual, moved by their remoteness, of which they had no awareness themselves . . . yet at the same time I was conscious of thus falsifying their unique existence. For why am I thinking again in terms of "knights" and "the Middle Ages"? Isn't such a translation of their strangeness into my language a paper idiocy—unforgivable? But they didn't want to leave me alone, these medieval knights in geometrical *gavanas;* and they were not really knights at all, but Indian peasants, not medieval, but contemporary! I immediately forgave myself this falsification, however, for what is so odd about it being difficult for me to bear the remoteness of these people already so close to me? "One somehow has to cope with strangeness—if not sincerely, then falsely," I thought.

The gentlemen from Mbayo know how to sit on chairs, because in almost every Indian hut there is at least one guest chair, and when there is no guest, then grandfather, father, or eldest son sits on the chair, while women, children, and younger men sit cross-legged on the clay floor. But there is furniture in my hut. It is the only hut with furniture in the whole village. I have a large wooden bed, two chairs, and a huge table. Four gentlemen on the two chairs, six on the bed, and I myself on a suitcase. I offer cigarettes. They smoke, choking a bit and asking, as usual, about my family and "my land." One of them again forgot what this land is called—"Polonia?" he repeats with amazement—"that's just like my wife, Apolonia. . . ." And then all begin to ask at once about the harvest in "my land beyond the sea."

Because we—suddenly one of the gentlemen begins speaking in a quiet monotone—just lost our harvest.

But this is spoken about for only a moment, about the flood that drowned their corn *milpas,* that the engineers are doing what they can to control the river "but what do they know". . . and again someone repeats in the same lowered voice, "Yes, we lost a harvest, all the corn is under water . . ."—and that is all that's said about it. They don't like to talk about the too frequently occurring catastrophes. It is a fact, there will be famine just like three years ago. One will have to starve awhile . . . and things will turn out all right.

These are no longer "medieval knights" in dark *gavanas*—it is we in uniforms captured from the Germans, we ourselves a few weeks after the Uprising, when hope had already faded or died away completely. We knew . . . in a moment bombs again and new fires tomorrow, just like in 1939—but bigger and louder. And after that? Those who will survive will live and . . . things will turn out all right.

After that we only spoke about the fiesta, about how the church will be decorated and what a great firework castle is being prepared this year. The fireworkers from San Martín this time demanded 500 pesos more than before. Hopefully it won't rain on the eve of the fiesta, because all the fireworks will get wet and there will be no castle.

And when they left and only Don Edmundo remained with me, we immediately drank a cup of coffee, for how do you serve coffee in six cups to ten gentlemen from Mbayo? "How fortunate that I could at least offer them cigarettes," I said, but Don Edmundo didn't hear.

"If it rains on the eve of the fiesta," he said, "we will light up the palace on August first, and if it rains on August first, then on the following day, but it would be better if it didn't rain. In a few days, who knows, maybe it will calm down," he said again, "but now, Doña Marylita, look, the WATER is coming again."

We looked out the door and the water was actually closing in

. . . heavy clouds lowered themselves onto the light-green hills, and on the other side of the valley above the river where the San Lorenzo ranch stood, the sky and earth came together with dark streaks. "Too bad," said Don Edmundo. "It's raining and it must rain, because the moon grows from the rain, but the full moon is near, so maybe it'll cease."

"What do you do after such a lost harvest?" I asked without introductions. "What do you live on when there's no corn?"

Don Edmundo was silent for a moment. I already know so well their unembarrassed silence. And then in another, quieter, and more monotonous voice, not the same one in which he spoke about the fiesta, he said, "Everybody has to look for work in the capital then; there's no other way out. Whether they want to or not, everybody goes after work in Mexico."

Mexico is hell for the Mazahua Indians, the Mazahuans of this generation, for *Los Señores*, gentlemen accustomed to the uncertainty of tomorrow, but also to the respect of their neighbors, to an everyday portion of appreciation, cordiality, hope. But when there is no corn, when there are only three tortillas for breakfast, then work must be sought in the capital, without cordiality, without respect, without hope . . .

There is no cordiality in purgatory either, because why should there be, and there is no respect . . . but one thing is certain, that there is hope! In Mexico? Maybe for the sons and grandsons, but not for this generation! There is no hope in the capital of Mexico for *Los Señores* from Mbayo. Cheated, humiliated, and hungry, they save every centavo for tortillas for their children. The only solution for them is the fastest possible return to Mbayo. In Mexico Don Edmundo carries a long sharp nail with him to defend himself against bad people when they attack. In Mbayo there are no bad people and one can walk peacefully at night. The only danger is devils, but neither knife nor nail can protect one from devils. The only thing that can help is prayer, and when it is necessary to walk at night near the bridge by the roadside to the hacienda, it is better to have a crucifix along because the devil from beneath the bridge is worse than others!

"During the war we used to carry pepper in our pockets, because pepper blinds, so maybe you should use pepper in Mexico instead of a nail?"

"Rather not . . . because you won't always hit the eyes with the pepper, but with a nail, especially a long and sharp one, you can always hit someplace. So the nail is better!"

When it was all over and after two days the evacuation of Warsaw began, we went out into a greater unknown than the Mazahuans migrating to Mexico for work. Before us were prison camps, concentration camps, and prisons, and there was no Warsaw to which one could return. While they—the fortunate—could always return to Mbayo, even if on foot and begging.

But I could not explain this even to Don Edmundo, so we remained silent again and the rain swished above us and from time to time playfully trickled through the ceiling in little droplets.

"Auden, an English poet living in the United States," I suddenly let go, "said that the greatest pleasure he ever had was eavesdropping on a prostitute, who recited a poem of his while taking a shower. She recited something of this sort: 'Hundreds of people live without love, but no one can live without water!' Good, is it not?"

Don Edmundo smiled and asked: "Are poets people who know more than others?"

To really translate Mbayo into Poland it would first be necessary to create a United States of Europe and then to imagine the bureaucracy and impersonality that would result. Naturally, Poland would belong to these United States, and after a "lost harvest" (because every country would have an autonomy allowing for such local losses) the Poles would go to the centers—Paris, Brussels or Geneva—for work, for bread, for better opportunities. Of course they would consider themselves citizens of these new United States of Europe, but probably not completely, because such loyalties do not arise instantly. At any rate, legally, intellectually, and so on, they would no doubt consider themselves to be such. In spite of that they would be called "Slavs" in the West (not "Poles" but "Slavs"), just like the Indians from Mbayo are called "Indians" in Mexico, and not Mazahuans as they call themselves.

And actually what are they if not Mazahuans, and if not Mazahuans then Mexicans . . . and if not Poles then Europeans!

But "Slavs" with "Slavic souls" . . . but "sly and lazy" Indians . . . But there are no such generalized Slavs, and there are no such generalized Indians!

"No, poets are not always those who know more . . . sometimes they know less than others, but they can express it better," I say, "but to express is not necessarily to know. Sometimes those who cannot express know more . . ."

Again a poem. First I recite in Polish:

> In words we only see desire,
> Might in action.
> It's harder to live a day through well,
> Than to write a book.

Then I translate. But Don Edmundo smiles sceptically when I say that this poem was written by a very famous poet from "my land." Now he knows that poets don't always say the truth, because clearly it is not easy to write a book when writing and even signing one's name is so difficult. And this "living a day through well" probably means nothing to him, because they do not think in those terms here. They do not think about experiences nor about such an individualized good and bad.

"That about the water is truer," he says, "because indeed one cannot do anything without water, and though the water destroyed the harvest and will destroy it many times yet, nothing will grow without water; there wouldn't even be anything to destroy."

Where there was corn *milpa* last year, a young oat crop is growing this year. Through the soggy earth, covered with light-green oats, beneath the same cloudy sky, with the same wide valley all around, I walk for dinner from my hut to Ngeme, the large house belonging to Doña Elena and Don Pancho. Over stone fences, along a stony path, past turbulent, yellow streams of muddy rain water, then over slippery bumps, up to the terrace of Ngeme. It is a true terrace. Spacious, cement, several times larger than the Big House, which is simply a two-room hut. On the terrace brown and shiny Doña Elena, the beloved daughter Veronica, young and wide-spanned, her husband Jorge, slim, bright-faced, and as usual a bunch of kids, some piglets, turkeys, and two guest chairs. Only Doña Genevieve is missing, having been buried two weeks ago at Calvary. But what a moving combination . . . there's eighteen-year-old Ernestina with Doña Genevieve's profile, cleaning wheat grain with her hands. . . .

Don Edmundo and I occupy the two chairs, while Jorge squats

down on the cement wall girdling the Ngeme terrace. From underneath the roof, thick smoke comes flowing out. Doña Elena and Veronica have already begun cooking in the good smoky kitchen. Meanwhile we want to talk over the matter of the publication of *El Libro de Mbayo*, the Mbayo Book. If, how, and what should be added, changed? Jorge calls Aurelia. Let her bring us each a glass of *pulque*—agava juice.

"The pulque is watered down by the downpour," says Aurelia, "yesterday we drained some honey water out of the agava plants, but it's so watery it doesn't even want to ferment. . . ."

So the Mbayo book without pulque . . . "We'll have to add how they killed the Gringo, the American in Los Piños," says Jorge, "because, after all, those cows he murdered in the vicinity and that injustice, everything that happened there afterward . . . When my Ignacio grows up, I want him to know about this. After all, we've written *El Libro de Mbayo* so that our sons will know . . ."

That's the tying-in to the previous strands. Jorge has been demanding this chapter "about the murdered cows and the killed Gringo" since last year, and I am on his side, naturally. After all, that's the everyday subject of talk in Mbayo, and hence certainly an important event in the village. At least as important as the Great Famine of 1910, or the earthquake of 1912, or the influenza epidemic of 1918, only it's closer, because the American was killed in 1948, when Jorge was a small boy.

But, as before, Don Edmundo doesn't want this chapter. "It's sufficient to write that in 1948 hoof and mouth disease spread in the area. That's all," he says slowly, "Our sons, grandsons, and great-grandsons shouldn't know more . . ."

So that's it . . . Censorship . . . and Don Edmundo, one of the most important men in Mbayo as the censor! And what for? But how to explain it to him? How does one translate the idea of censorship into the reality of Indians from Mbayo. And Jorge is the nephew of Don Edmundo, and besides this Jorge is younger and is already silent, and it is already obvious that he won't help me . . .

"I shouldn't interfere anyhow," I repeat to myself in my mind; "I shouldn't butt into anything." But that's so difficult, because for the Mbayans the killing of the Gringo and what came after was like the war for us, so how could one forget! They can't and don't want to forget. I can't and I won't! How can I be objective, indifferent, scientific? How can I allow this Great Silence, just like that, without protest?

I almost, almost said in spite of myself, that obviously, without me, nothing would have come of the Mbayo book, without my tape-recorder, without my typewriter, even without my best Spanish grammar, and naturally, without my introduction about the pre-colonial past of the Mazahuans it would also have been difficult to think of publication . . . But I restrained myself at the last moment.

"Don Edmundo, consider a moment," I said calmly.

Actually there's no reason to fear that one of the government's, American or Mexican, would now, in 1963, seek revenge on Mbayo for that Gringo murdered in Los Piños back in 1948; and what happened afterward will never repeat itself again. Nobody outside of Mbayo recalls it, and if that chapter won't be included, your progeny will forget . . .

Jorge didn't say a word, Ernestine listened carefully, never once ceasing the wheat-grain cleaning, and the white and gray female turkeys kept walking about on their pink legs. We waited for Don Edmundo's words, and Don Edmundo, as usual, said something unexpected:

"It is not a matter of danger here," he said. "The whole thing rests on the fact that it was an unclear matter. Because the people from Los Piños were right in killing the Gringo, and he, the Gringo, was right in killing the cows . . . So it shouldn't be mentioned because how do you explain that both they and he were right at the same time . . .

So that was it! It wasn't a question of fear of revenge, it was a matter of not being able to express something in the simple language of the people from Mbayo. It was a question of things hard to express even in the complicated language of the highest civilizations. It was, after all, a matter of unlabeled justice. So that's why the censorship! So that's why the Great Silence! Yes!

Translated by Albert Juszczak

Wacław Iwaniuk

I Fear Continually that the Premature Night

I fear continually that the premature night
Will hunt me down darkly one noon,
That time will betray me and I'll fall
And with lips attuned to earth
I shall drink as though I had never known
The pit of isolation.
Surrounded by the unremembered calm
Of gentle hills and patient vegetation
I shall forget the horror of the earth.
Softly the whisper of abundant rose
Blooming like starfish
Will mingle with my flesh.
The melancholy pines
Coerce the landscape. The heat-distorted trees—
Flat and dark physiognomy—
Are wrapped in the quiet of oxygenized hills.

And all around the summer column burns
While the night collapses, expiating.

Who does not love this architecture
Who has not loved to climb the airy stairs
Refreshed by daily tidal foam?
Is it not better to hide within the calm
And to take cover under stone, to cry with marble's cry,
To see the moths like angels raging in the ruins
And like the saints to despair with blinded hands?
To disbelieve the heaven's iron fires
Although it tempts with flowers, and underpinned with fog,
Sweats with dew.

Poets like pilgrims flock, although they know
They've been betrayed again. Virtue is feared.

Thin air breaks under the word
Stony waves scatter the sand
The vineyard rushes down into the bay
Nothing remains after a burned-out day
Except the ruins spoken of in song
Which the poets have renamed: defeat
The poem like a supplicant kneels down
Does not reveal, though it will try to soothe
And even if like a hermit it believes
It will be here forever out of place.

Translated by Gustaw Linke

Wacław Iwaniuk

Après le Déluge

In our world even the innocent birds
Are swept from their nests by the raging storm;
Turning towards the sky a harmless dove
Will soon become a ruse of propaganda.
The artist sells his soul for any slogan
And art is measured by the empty word.
Time drops towards darkness
The moon escapes earth's apparition
Dreaming of Ararat
We wait for the dove to bring to us
Swiftly the laurel leaf.

What is salvation if those who survive
Hurry to be devoured again by night.
Bathed in the rising dawn, impatiently
We wait for the approaching night.
Our garden lies untended,
The canary sleeps
And our lips cannot utter a word.
With a sack on our backs, and not salvation,
We carry with us our cemeteries.
Preferring chaos, though order is better
Preferring hell, though heaven is nearer
We measure God again with silver pieces
And Christianity with cybernetics.
Temple in our time does not mean temple,
Nor Bible—Bible.

Translated by Gustaw Linke

Wacław Iwaniuk

Who Calls What a Poem

Yes, the poet does
what he can—
collects strips of
words, chips of sighs
links them together
with an invisible thread
like a spider
moistening sore
nerves and gathering
in striae his
own darkness, and at
every turn erects
signs made of
his private passions
similar to Homer's
marble voices;
Others wonder
see there perhaps
Chagall's flying scene
where the black
dense beard hunts
the heavy barricades
of clouds; where the white
goat in pink woolens
grazes in green
air; They regard him
as a charlatan; not even
an alchemist deforms
words, extracts them
from the gum of rules and codes,

violating the sanctity of grammar,
to emerge at last like a hoodlum
riding on something
so painfully mutilated
which he then calls
a p o e m.

Translated by the Author

Andrzej Bobkowski

From the Diary of a Model Airplane Maker

June 2, '54

I PLAN to take part in the world model airplane championship matches scheduled for the 24th and 25th of July on an American air base on Long Island, near New York City.

A lot of work. I drew up the plans for my model, completely forgoing universally accepted forms in this very special category and opting instead for the shape of a modern jet for my rubber-propelled model. Further development of the sketches and construction, which aroused so much interest in last year's matches in England. Then I was represented by a proxy; this time, however, I want to take part personally in the competition because it's not too far from here to New York—less than four thousand kilometers. Besides, I plan to open a larger shop in partnership with one of my friends here. My personal participation in such important matches would be good publicity for this new enterprise, to say nothing of the pleasure I myself would get out of it. We foresee a large shop and the first so-called "hobby-shop" in town.

After six years of dreadful work, beginning with nothing, renouncing everything, I reached the point where I must again "enlarge" myself. If I don't do it, then others will do it for me. They'll pluck the fruit from the tree I planted and nursed anxiously, with clenched teeth, from the very moment I settled here. My capital, created by means of obstinacy, frugality, and such sacrifices that it all seems to me improbable when I look back on it, is too small at present. It's true, though, that for a year now I've been able to stand on my own two feet and stopped being a poor white exploited by the colored (*figurez-vous, mon cher . . .*). I live just from my models, but I've got to leap forward again.

I can almost feel the approaching danger in my fingertips. If I'm not the first now, any shopkeeper with a little capital who knows nothing about model building will bring in a lot of merchandise, offer a greater choice than I do, and push me out of the market with all my know-how, experience, and pioneer past in this field. The merciless law of the capitalist economics in a free competitive market. Bless it! If not for it, I'd die of inactivity, sunk in the same old routine. Everything would go to hell, and I'd take it out on my wife and on Free Europe for not helping an intellectual. No—*primum vivere*.

The local shopkeepers and wealthy people (ricos) are a special caste. They are lazy and without any initiative or ingenuity. They are passive, but also have a colorful cunning and craftiness, combined with an absolutely perfect talent for imitation. Now they're buzzing all around me, even stopping to say hello to me on the street. There's a furtive look about them and in their smiles, in their effusive greetings; you can detect the envy lurking. They see suddenly that "it's all over." But they perceive the result and only the result. They are incapable, however, of grasping the chain of equations making up the inhuman effort that brought me to this modest result. I'm just another of these white *extranjeros* who cheated them. Cheated them by industriousness and drive, the way the Germans once upon a time cheated us and later the Jews. When I sat around in one of their shops for a miserable hundred dollars a month and was a good worker, when I let myself be exploited, then everything was all right. I was harmless and useful. But now it's a different story entirely.

I understand them and I'm not surprised at them. An ever-present inferiority complex, laziness, lack of initiative and enterprise give rise to envy and hatred, and eventually foment a blind nationalism. An old story. At this moment the Communists are reaping the profits. Not only in Guatemala. I am now experiencing here personally on a small scale what the Americans are exposed to on the world scale. The industrious are "cheaters" and "exploiters."

June 3, '54

Like behind the Iron Curtain. I'm curious what it will finally lead to here. The radio station of Castillo Armas, whose forces are concentrated in Honduras, broadcasts very militant programs, but I still have a hard time believing that he's been able to accomplish anything. There are a lot of rumors circulating. There's serious talk, for example, about liberating Guatemala. In that case, there's going to be a small war; it'll be much worse than the usual sort of revolution they have here.

The atmosphere is heavy and potentially dangerous. Revolver ammunition can now be bought only on the black market. An acquaintance of mine today offered me a genuine Polish "Visa" for seventy dollars. My heart ached that I didn't have money enough to buy the trinket. In perfect condition, just like new. Doubtless brought here by some former German officer. Or perhaps it was among the new supplies of armaments brought in in May from Szczecin?

I don't consider it won. I'm making further efforts in connection with my intended trip. I was at the American consulate today to file an application for a visa. It's pouring cats and dogs. A tropical downpour. It's coming down so hard on the roof I had to turn up the volume on the radio as far as it would go just in order to be able to hear it. You have to talk with raised voice. All the cats are sitting on the railing of the veranda absorbing the coolness. I'd like to be a cat in my house. They're making out quite well. . . . Banana palms alongside the kitchen grow almost in front of your very eyes. Rolls of gigantic leaves stretch out one after the other, succulent and wet. From the leftovers of tomato salads, of kernels mixed with vinegar poured from a window onto the yard, a whole plantation of tomatoes has grown up. I'm now waiting for the day when coffee will start sprouting up from the grounds we've tossed out. The tropics are surpassing Michurin.

June 5, '54

There's no reason to go to a movie. Just like in some satellite country. In one movie house there's a Soviet film based on the life of Rimsky-Korsakov, in a second the Soviet capture of Berlin, in a third some other Soviet crap with the inescapable wheat fields in the sun and farmers on tractors. In others nothing but Mexican, Argentinian, or European junk. For four months the supply of American films has been cut off. And now one is sentenced, at the very best, to the bare shoulders of Martine Carol, to that would-be *esprit* always revolving around the same thing (*coucheries et decoucheries*), to the shallow nonsense of a *La Ronde*, *Caroline Cherie*, *Adorables Créatures*, and other *Belles de Nuit;* or to the uncleansable dirty-black-white sexualism and Socialist Realism *à rebours* of the Italians. As to the rest, I've become a clod. I like Technicolor and Cinemascope.

Today I'm off to *Salaire de la Peur*. A masterpiece. Romain Gary gave me an enthusiastic report on it. A superb example of the kind of exquisite depravity the intellect can lead to. The whole film, the whole plot emerge from a completely dry skull and are presented deftly and with considerable subtlety.

I read raves about it. Grand Prix Cannes. The idiocy of the film exceeds all bounds, but the devotion of the present to a nothingness, in which only an obtuse, intellectual anti-Americanism is graspable, borders on madness. Where in Central America can you find a place in the jungle from which the nearest location in the civilized world can be reached by plane for a hundred dollars? A plane ticket from Guatemala to New York costs a hundred and forty. What American concern, in this case petroleum, would open up oil shafts without first building a road or a railway line? One bit of nonsense after another.

Why don't these gentlemen, these intellectual cavemen have a look and try it themselves? The degree of dishonesty and ignorance, exaggeration and falsification we've come to on this side, the free side, is striking. Americans. I'm afraid I have to look at them differently from what is indicated by European fashion and the fashion, in general, of "enlightened circles." I can't manage to smile in a superior way and toss around intellectual slogans. To say nothing of the fact that after six years of a magnificent struggle for existence I can no longer have anything in common with this stupefying socially onanistic *Weltschmerz*, with these "Christians" without any religion and faith parading their "sense of guilt" through coffee-houses, books, films, and the theater. A sense of guilt is always unilateral: from the Elbe westward.

Where does one receive a proper and pitiful recompense for fear? Why don't a Clouzot and the dozens of socio-economic weepers with him try to extend their gray imaginations beyond certain borders? Because the taking of mud on this side of the

Curtain and making it into dung, the manufacture of films and works of literature in accordance with the principles of Socialist Realism *à rebours* is serious, profound, philosophical; on the other hand, helping one's self to dung from the other side—there is no lack, really, of accurate accounts—and making of it even mere mud, would be American anti-Communist propaganda. At each of these three last words individually tremble the orchids cultivated in the hot-house "caves" of Paris, Rome, London, or Manhattan, and in the naphthaline vapors of the leftist darkness. Salivating, lowering the corners of the mouth, splashing through imaginary situations, feeding on human misery from the height of a bird in flight, not only not proposing any solutions but not even reaching any conclusions—that's wise, profound, interesting. Everything else is nonsense, American boorishness, lack of finesse, complete incomprehension of the problem.

An American film, a refrigerator (it's really high time we finished with this refrigerator-freezing European judgment) or a television set—that's the fall of culture, the triumph of materializing capitalism over man. But a Soviet refrigerator or some sort of miserable Soviet car—ah, that's something different. That's the construction of a new civilization, a jewel which when viewed in a photograph (doubtless for that reason) arouses the emotions. That's the music of the spheres. For the great initiated, however, the one and the other are the same. But to such heights I do not aspire. They drown in the star dust in which, in fact, they spend their entire lives.

Ignorance, refined intellectual ignorance. Irony and contempt, and at the same time unyielding slogans. Faithlessness and superiority. But hop over THERE. Ah, THERE, in Europe, it's something quite different. There the idiot Helvetius is still, as ever, a sage. There you can arbitrarily make a Licurgus or a Newton out of some Alpine or Turkestanian herdsman. Because there is *culture* there. What culture? Like a Robespierre extending his sham infallibility to the entire populace (he managed to convince the French), so they extend to entire nations their élite little culture of hot-house plants. Which culture? Where? Warming over in different sauces something that's enough to make you faint. Sad, with a technical sense of guilt, heartless, boring, eternally unhappy. But let anyone of them buy a watch for a few dollars and he'll be constantly happy, each single minute that it keeps on going.

June 7, '54

It seems that nothing will come of my trip to the USA. They're getting ready here for a little Korea. Castillo Armas is making serious preparations to overthrow the present regime, which still continues to be characterized as democratic not only in Europe but even in certain American circles. No doubt because the censorship is running away with itself, people are perishing, the jails are filled to overflowing with anti-Communists, and because from the concentration camp opened for the first time in the history of Guatemala by this same "democratic" regime stories are emerging about methodical cruelties which generally have been unheard of in the Americas. Methodical cruelty has not been resorted to here since the days of the Spanish *conquistadores*. The streets are full of Soviet publications, the movie houses advertise Polish, Czech, and Hungarian films. Czech goods are everywhere in sight, and the newspapers are full of huge expensive ads for Czech aviettes and gliders. For whom? Typical.

A decree is being prepared concerning the expropriation of real estate within the area of the capital city and the nationalization of the meat and similar trades. Granted agricultural reform, the Indians have sold the harvest of coffee from parcels of plantations in which they have shares and, in most cases, have either spent the money on drink or on taxi trips from outlying towns and villages to the capital for shopping expeditions for electric phonographs, irons, beaters, juice squeezers, and the like, although there is no electricity in the villages. Now they're digging up coffee plantations and sowing maize and beans. Progress. Democracy, too, because now the "barefoot Indians are riding cabs" as I was told enthusiastically by one of these slavered "democrats." And now he's bubbling with enthusiasm over Mascolo's *Le Communisme* which I lent him and which I annotated with "deviationary" comments. That the entire work itself is a deviation from common sense, the monstrous aberration of a rotten intellect, doesn't enter his mind. We cease or already have ceased seeing reality; we are perishing by abstraction, we are anaesthetized by abstraction, the way we are by ether.

Neither Moscolo nor those like him see reality; it is rather the abbé Pierre who sees it and—acts. And because he acts he is already almost a saint. Now, certainly, the orchid pleiad will make a film about him and write novels about his life in dozens of variations. I also have a desire to write a story about this abbé Pierre with an unexpected variation: at the end of the story, after all the madness of enthusiasms and hysterias, it turns out that the humble priest is—a disguised American. Can you imagine the scandal? How he deceived us. The whole thing was just some vulgar "business" in which some prefabricated house manufacturer was doubtless mixed up.

If it now appeared that Simone Weil had converted to Catholicism before her death, how low she'd fall in the eyes of many of those who've been smacking their lips from excitement down to the very present. For if you're intellectually esteemed, then you're not permitted to believe, you're not permitted to act practically, you're permitted to have only a "sense of guilt" tucked into the buttonhole of an elegantly rumpled jacket and to strike poses from the window of your "studio."

An excellent novel. At last, a good, solid novel. I ran through 800 pages of *From Here to Eternity* and am quite enthusiastic about it. It's like a plank of wood turned out by a buzz saw in a forest sawmill. Big, rugged, but still smelling of its sap knots. The novel deals with one of the best epics of the army, that distasteful but necessary institution. I'm afraid, however, that it will not win the approval of our military men (if they've read it) and doubtless even the American "brass" took umbrage to it. The love affair between the sergeant and the captain's wife—ma'am, ma'am. What's more, the professional sergeant is more intelligent than the captain, a typical hick from Kentucky who wants to be an individualist. Good for him. Tiresome dialogues, but well done; seemingly unpolished, but subtle indeed in the execution.

Spent the evening at my American friends'. He's a sergeant mechanic in the air mission in Guatemala. His wife, Virginia, was alone and was reading *Time*. With unconcealed indignation she showed me that an entire article on Guatemala in the magazine's "Hemisphere" section was ripped out before copies of the magazine were put out for sale in kiosks. I explained to her the secrets of "democratic" censorship. We spoke about the political situation. Virginia was reading Koestler and Orwell, so we had no trouble communicating.

I was sitting in the sergeant's apartment, thinking about the novel I had just finished reading and looking from time to time with a longing eye at the bookshelf containing the complete set of the *Encyclopedia Britannica*, including the last supplement. "Good for working out crossword puzzles," I told myself, making a wry face. In a little while in came Sergeant Fred and Captain Mike, both dressed in civvies, in loose shirts. Fred made drinks for everybody and we talked about the excellent British film, *Breaking the Sound Barrier*. Then we carried on a discussion about the rules for model plane matches, which I want to set up here. Since the decision has to be based on the number of points awarded to each participant, I have to have the Americans as judges. Only their word would be accepted without opposition and suspicion. The local judges would certainly be beaten up and shot for giving more points to this fellow instead of that one just because they happen to like him more, and so forth. Mike and Fred are very enthusiastic about their role as judges.

We take our drinks and head for Fred's workshop above the garage. I draw a sketch of my model. An entire discussion about the aerodynamic peculiarities of various rib profiles, about Reynold's numbers, about the pressure points on a concave wing surface. And that's what they call "fooling around with little tiny airplanes." There's only one complication with my model: a political one. In silhouette it looks like a Russian MIG–15. "If you come with a model like that, and besides from Guatemala, they'll certainly call you up before the McCarthy Committee," Mike said with a smile.

June 9, '54

Trouble with the passport. It seems that everywhere I have down as my place of birth Wiener Neustadt—Polonia. All of a sudden, some pedant in the Ministry of Foreign Affairs discovered that Wiener Neustadt never belonged to Poland. There followed a discussion with the head of the passport section of the Ministry whom I tried to convince dialectically that this was not entirely accurate because if a small piece of Poland belonged to Austria and—let's say—Cracow was considered an Austrian city, then Wiener Neustadt likewise should—to a certain extent—be considered a Polish city, and so on. Everything depends on the time involved. Take, for example, the case of Belice, which belongs to British Honduras as far as every Englishman is concerned, but which for a Guatemalan will always be part of his own country. Besides, I was quick to point out, the trip was an important one for me—I was going to represent Guatemala in the most important matches in the model plane field. My model is of a unique construction similar of a MIG–15...

"Ah, similar to a MIG–15? What you're saying is very interesting."

Just mention something Russian, and right away they soften up, they melt, their eyes get misty. And now he starts asking me about the MIG.

"You know about such things, eh? Is it true that it's faster? And also more maneuverable? I heard that it flies higher than an American Sabre-jet, right?"

All true, I tell him, but in Korea "los gringos hicieron polvo de los MIGs," in other words, they made mincemeat of them.

"Maybe, but don't forget it was the Chinese who were flying them there. If the pilots were Russian . . . ," and he began laughing knowingly. "I'm sure we can straighten out the matter of your passport," he said, "but I doubt whether or not the Americans will give you a visa." A Pole, he went on, raising one finger; from Guatemala, raising a second finger, and at the present time, raising a third finger. A wink of understanding.

I enter the sun-drenched square and stop in the shade of a cathedral; I'm in the Americas and I'm suffocating. I'm suffocating of impotent anger and I envy Leszek. A lieutenant in Bierut's army (with no degree, but sincere desire), Leszek fled Poland in 1948, reached Guatemala, married a local schoolteacher, had two children by her, and now manages a piece of land he got as part of her dowry. Yesterday he came to the shop to say goodbye to me. "Where are you off to?" I asked him. "To Castillo Armas to fight those bastards. If you lived in the country the way we do then you'd really know what's going on here." Thanks to a lot of hard work he earned enough to buy a small tractor. Now they want to take it away from him and set up communal tractor stations. This time it looks like a well organized undertaking. Leszek got hold of a map with points of passage indicated, and with precise information on routes and contacts. There are a large number of people inside the country active in the Castillo Armas expedition. Women and young people working, poor people and rich people. Later on, everything would be called "American intervention."

I've become attached to them and to their country. I don't feel myself alien, or that I'm something different from "them." They are specimens of free people in this stupefied world. When once, a long time ago, in something like a line in front of a movie house I pointed out to some *caballero* that he ought to stand at the rear of the line and not shove himself up front where he didn't belong, he looked at me with indescribable contempt and said, as if spitting with each word: "Señor, no tengo ganas, ¿comprende usted?"

He had no wish to, if *ganas* is in general translatable. I was upset, but a moment later I had *ganas* to drink a toast in his honor. He's right. Standing in line is repulsive, but the docile, submissive standing in line is a contemptible sign of a fall, of slavery, of the surrender of everything dearest to a person. Latin America refuses to stand in line. It does not wish to be docile and has no *ganas* to be disciplined. It changes its regimes and its politicians the way regimes and politicians the world over deserve to be changed: in a manly fashion, with a pistol in hand. Politics here is a risky business, a game in which life is at stake almost always. The fruitful bacteria of anarchism, individualism, the exalted *no tengo ganas* have endured here and have not yet been completely vanquished. They should be preserved, because perhaps only that way can many people in this world of ours save themselves. When I talk to them I always tell them, Be yourselves, try to get rid of that damned inferiority complex, don't be concerned in the least when people make fun of your revolutions. Just remember that today there are millions of people throughout the world who envy you, that it's becoming ever harder to give expression to the feeling that you've had enough of something, because millions of people nowadays can't even curse out loud. Be the inspiration of revolt.

The pressure is building up in all of Guatemala. A joyous expectation, difficult to conceal, is abroad on the land. Something is bound to happen. This is something serious, without a doubt.

June 11, '54

One of my customers came to the shop today and told me, with a furtive look, that he has a chance for *ganga*. "Cheap and fresh," he said, winking at me. I follow him behind a partition. He pulls out five hand grenades. Five dollars apiece or a motor for his model plane for eighteen dollars. He went too far. You can get them for three dollars apiece—so we conclude no *trato* or transaction.

Somebody buys a radio and the salesgirl tries it out, tuning in one of the government stations. Suddenly a gnashing noise and after a moment a loud voice: "This is the station of Free Guatemala. God, Country, Freedom". A pungent, refreshing speech. Then the government station cuts in again. Joy. The salesgirl's eyes are radiant. She too belongs to the organization and is absolutely convinced that this time they'll make it. It reminds me of the days just before the liberation of Paris.

It appears that even model plane making can also be a threat to a state. In a very nicely done publication about other international model plane matches (only satellite, of course), which took place in Poland in September 1951, the preface includes the following statement: "How different are the goals of model plane making in the capitalist countries from the goals that motivate enthusiasts in the Soviet Union and the peoples' democracies. How different is the atmosphere in which model plane matches take place among them and among us. Among them, the capitalists, people amuse themselves with the automated dropping of bombs from a jet model onto the plastic model of an open city, while we encourage the planned acquisition of the fundamentals of aeronautical knowledge, the sport of future pilots and builders of an aeroplane industry dedicated to the cause of peace." Apparently local politicians here share the same conviction.

Around twelve, the wife of Captain C. came to see me, unnerved and in obvious fear. C. can't return home and has to go into hiding. Fortunately, when the authorities came he wasn't at home. What's the matter? C. constructed a huge model, piloted by radio. I helped him, because the model was quite large, a complicated setup with a wing span of nine feet. This morning the police came, smashed the model to smithereens, and destroyed the receiving apparatus because they had information that C. had constructed the model in order to place a ten pound bomb in it and kill Arbenz. I couldn't bring myself to laugh in the presence of the serious, emotionally distraught woman. I left the shop, had myself a laugh, then came back and the two of us seriously discussed what C. should do now. The best thing would be for him to seek asylum in some embassy or other. And they say that model planes are just toys!

June 14, '54

It's begun. I went to the prefecture of police in order to get a statement *de buena conducta* which I need for my passport. Everything's closed. The building is surrounded by police armed with submachine guns. They don't let anyone pass. I go back to the shop. Everybody's got an ear to the radio. At seven in the morning unidentified planes bombed and ignited the oil reserves at Puerto San Jose and Rethaluleu. A state of siege. Gas rationing is now obligatory throughout the entire country. Communiqués, then a Prokofiev march, more communiqués in the style of "strong, courageous, prepared" and a Prokofiev march, this time for a change the oranges. For the past two years the official government radio plays almost nothing but Russian music. Tchaikovsky, Rimsky-Korsakov, Borodin, Mussorgsky, Prokofiev, Kachaturian, and Shostakovich. Enough to make a person faint. I've had enough Russian music to last me the rest of my life.

War. Have they entered the country or not? We don't know. Excitement. Nobody feels like working. I go out into the street. A holiday atmosphere prevails. I go to buy some extra provisions in case I can't get out of the house for the next few days. A lot of people in the grocery, everybody loading up with supplies, like before Christmas. All sorts of remarks, jokes. I go back to the shop. A group of my "boys" there. In seventh heaven. They sent them home from school; vacations. It's enough to make one envious. But it's good for business. They're also loading up with extras. Julio is to travel with me to the USA to take part in the matches in the motor model category. I quickly draw him a scale model, we select the wood, I give him a motor, and explain how he has to handle it. Hubbub, confusion.

They tell me that Benjamin, whom I met a few years ago when he was a thirteen-year-old boy, left four days ago to join Castillo Armas. Ricardo, a young photographer, and still nine-tenths Indian, smiles maliciously and is convinced that the regime will come out all right this time too. "When things really get started, you'd be better off not going out into the street at all," he said with a venomous smile. "Why?" I asked. "Because they'll be shooting at every blond they see," he said laughing. He makes believe he's joking, but beneath the smiles a poorly concealed friendliness is hidden and the fear that perhaps I was in danger because of the color of my hair.

In countries in which the color of the skin is not white or is mixed with white, as here, communism has begun playing on racial hatred and thrusting it skillfully into its classical repertoire. It's giving it the maximum play. Hatred for the white man is disseminated in a barely perceptible but methodical way. Under the cover of the official tactics of the Communists one senses quite unequivocally the premeditated strategy of colored racism. The Communists have in it an ally which in these countries is perhaps stronger than all socio-economic arguments. They make use of it every step of the way, liberating millions of people from the fetters of a complex of "non-whiteness." A chocolate-skinned indigene (especially a literate one) until the present pridefully searching out admixtures of white blood from the time of the Spanish conquerors and at the same time chained by the constant fear that some white person or—worse yet—somebody a shade lighter than himself, will suddenly hurl in his face the insulting *tu Indio desgraciado*, all of a sudden feels himself liberated. Not only liberated; now he feels even prouder that his complexion is darker. This pride the Communists teach him at every turn.

These are the tactics of a thoroughly premeditated provocation toward the white man, toward the builder of all white civilization. Moscow knows perfectly that in the present situation it could tear down this civilization in almost the twinkling of an eye if it were successful in shifting the emphasis away from the ideological conflict and unleashing a race war. By arousing racism and colored nationalism it attempts to stir a racist reaction or backlash on our part. If we don't last out this war of nerves, we can easily perish.

Toynbee is right. It's about the only observation he doesn't fall flat on his face with in the whole collection of essays *Civilization on Trial*, which is about as powerful as lemonade. Speaking once about Voltaire's *Candide*, the Goncourt brothers characterized the work as a "denatured Rabelais, La Fontaine in prose." You could say the same about Toynbee. He's a denatured Spengler, a Le Bon, Frobenius, and Keyserling for spoiled children. He's taken everywhere, because he belongs to a species of laxative which takes effect gently without interrupting one's sleep. Western eggheads are in no position to swallow anything more potent.

I'm thinking about how Ricardo, with evident colored satisfaction, whispered the news from so-called reliable sources that "if Castillo Armas wins, no American will leave here alive." In this expansiveness, an American is *pars pro toto*. Each and every white man here is a *gringo*. I look him calmly straight in the eyes: "I'm not afraid. You know quite well that I don't consider myself in any way your superior and this business is no concern of mine." And at that moment I saw in his eyes the extinguishing of a spark, as though he were suddenly disenchanted. I didn't jump, I held out. Much depends on that.

June 17, '54

A war mood. Censorship of newspapers, the walls of houses along the streets pasted over with very patriotic and very Communist posters. Nobody knows what's going on. General excitement, nobody wants to work. The stores are open, but nobody bothers to raise the steel blinds in the windows. All private radio stations received the order to retransmit the uniform program of the official government station. Between one Prokofiev march and another the radio summons members of the syndicates and political parties to meetings, the heads of the Communist "Fridays" gather together subordinates by means of coded signals, telegrams from the provinces sent by various Communist organizations are read. Everything in a monotonous tone, in a monotonous jargon. The entire country has been pretty thoroughly worked over.

Around noon, shouts, and the drone of planes. People run out into the streets. From afar the sound of diving machines and the rattling of machine guns. Shops close, buses race for their sheds, in the space of a moment all life ceases. I return home.

Downpour in the afternoon, the punctual downpour of the rainy season. Around five it clears up and clouds hover only above the mountains. The distant sound of motors. I go out onto the veranda and a moment later two Thunderbolts fly low over the house. They circle the city like an arch. Uneven shooting from anti-aircraft guns. From the veranda I see how the planes spin over on a wing and dive. Through the drone of their engines you can hear their machine guns and see sparks along the edges of the wings. The attack is flawless. On the third pass over the city they drop bombs.

It's as though a draft passed over the entire city. The planes fly away and quiet returns again, the gentle tranquility of a wet afternoon saturated with humidity and fragrances. In neighboring houses the men crawled out onto the roofs and are exchanging conversation from roof to roof. Castillo Armas is beginning to make an impression. The sight of the planes pleased me. The antiquated AT-6's of the government can't measure up to the Armas machines. Perhaps they'll succeed after all. I return to my workshop and go on working. In the evening some planes flew over again. The lights were extinguished. War, complete with blackouts.

June 18, '54

Morning in the city. Empty. Stores locked up, quiet. I run into one of the officials I know from the Ministry of Foreign Affairs. He's noticeably upset. The first time in his life he saw or heard something like an air raid. He tells me that during the attack his wife suffered an attack of hysteria. He asks me seriously if we weren't afraid. I couldn't restrain myself and burst out laughing. He looked at me even more shaken than before. Laughing, I tell him that one can calmly observe such little air raids directed, by the way, exclusively at two military targets, and that it's nothing dreadful at all. But I can't calm him, which deep down actually satisfies me. If all of them are going to be afraid like that, then it's a good sign. I feel sorry only for the poor Indian soldiers attacked in their barracks, for they were doubtless seized by such a panic that they abandoned their gun emplacements and fled to the ravines on the outskirts of the city. O. asks me what I think about the whole business. I tell him that if the insurgents succeed in using and taking full advantage of air power, which the government is absolutely incapable of opposing, then the outcome of the conflict is decided in advance. I learn from him that the territory of Guatemala has already been encroached upon. How many of them are there? He doesn't know. About six hundred men.

If Castillo Armas manages to topple the red régime and liberates the country, there's only one thing to be afraid of: the wealthy people. If that worst of all elements here is given a voice in the management of things by Castillo and he submits to their will, everything that's happening now won't make any sense at all. The worst enemies of capitalism in these countries are the capitalists themselves. Every one of these little lords, of these *platudos*, trampling and despising everything beneath his income, is a hundred times better a propagandist of the Communist cause than all the trained agents of Moscow taken together. These people are the curse of Guatemala.

Investing a thousand dollars today, tomorrow they want to extract five thousand from their initial investment and send the entire profit to a bank in the USA. Investments? Raise wages? Better conditions for workers? Let the stupid Americans do those things. And when an American arrives and begins to get something going, begins paying the workers better, giving them protection, making things somewhat easier for them, then they raise a patriotic hue and cry and are prepared to do anything just so long as nothing comes out of his efforts. They'll even go so far as to cooperate with the reddest regime, just as they've done here. A good half of the wealthiest families and merchants quietly cooperate with the Arbenz government. That explains why the propaganda of the Communists here is not directed against them; the Communists know that these relics of a past capitalist mentality pose no threat to them, that they are cowards and can be easily persuaded to cooperate in exchange for transitory material gains (government orders, positions, and the like). On a certain level, the Communists even need them in the nationalistic battle against the greatest enemy in these areas—progressive American capitalism.

In all its shadings, anti-Americanism is, in the final analysis, a struggle against the new American capitalism. With its cold figures, its increases in workers' salaries (usually the highest of any in the country), its protection and general improvement of the lot of the working man, with its daily example and practice it confounds the theory and propaganda of the Communists among the element on whom they are most dependent. For the past six years all the strikes in American enterprises have been organized and directly forced on the workers by the government. In this lies the core of the conflict.

The new American capitalism (*ça existe, mon cher* . . .) is certainly far from perfect and certainly still has not yet resolved all problems, but it certainly possesses the possibilities to do so, if only for the reason that it is a product of a free climate and is not burdened with dogmas. In its own sphere it managed to solve many problems whose solutions the Communists are still daydreaming about. It often seems to me that at present only the Communists know what this modern American capitalism really is and the strength it represents. Only they seem to esteem it properly and know that in its present form its system is not yet finished and perfected. For us, American capitalism is above all an "exceptional phenomenon"; in the current judgement, it is the remaining organ of an outmoded system. Well, let us be convinced of the truth of what the Communists disbelieve. Still another economic-intellectual slogan without any basis in fact, entirely in accord with the wishes of the Communists. Is Moscow's fight against the unification of Europe dictated by the fear of war? No, rather by a panicky fear in the face of economic achievements, in the face of the possibility of creating an internal market so absorptive that because of it modern capitalism would begin operating in Europe the same way it does in the USA. This fear explains the red propaganda of irrational nationalism which was unheard of before, though it might have seemed that Hitlerism carried this aberration to its acme. Today small Guatemala surpasses in this respect the Hitlerite German and French chauvinism by a good ten lengths.

June 20, '54

Still no real idea of what's happening. Radio communiqués from neighboring countries, from the USA, and from Europe are hazy and attest to the complete lack of more precise information.

As of today a police curfew and blackout period are obligatory. The police are under orders to shoot at any window with even the smallest amount of light shining from it. Yesterday all lights in the city were extinguished for two hours. But it's pretty generally known now that the extinguishing of lights serves mainly for the transfer of anti-Communist prisoners from jail. In all probability, for mass execution.

I'm sitting by a candle with a Colt on the table and I'm afraid. It's all very romantic, but somehow it's difficult for me to be Gregory Peck in Technicolor. I try to imagine what I'd do if they came for me. Probably I'd make for the bamboo forest beyond the house. If I had to I'd defend myself. In front of Basia, however, I feign calm and resolve. In such situations a woman is like those "underdeveloped countries" looking on the free world from aside and anticipating energy from it. In that respect superficially I am like Gregory Peck. I walk about the house, jingle the cartridges in my pocket, smoke a pipe, drink some whiskey, and smile from time to time at my "underdeveloped country" so as not to lose her respect. Now I regret not having bought a few hand grenades. When fear crawls deeper under my skin, I have fits of courage. Well, let them try, let them come for me, let them shoot me, but before that I'll get in a few shots myself. If it comes to that, what would I really be defending? What would be the sense of it all? I have no idea. But I do know that if picked on, I'd fight back. I wouldn't negotiate if only for the fact that I feel myself a small part of that civilization against which war has been declared at this moment in this miniscule scrap of earth here. By no means as a Pole or as a member of the white race. Just, to put it simply, to defend my image in the mirror, to be able to look myself straight in the face. And also for the sake of setting an example and in order to defend the right of imagination which two hours ago five men from nearby houses had and continue to have after coming to me for advice and direction.

They're supposed to begin distributing weapons to workers' syndicates. Trucks are probably already loaded and just waiting for the assignment of the distribution points. All the people living in the so-called better sections are threatened with burning and murder. They're threatened by *Bogotá*, as they call it here for short. We've had a council of war. I dictated something on the order of a plan. We're pretty well situated as regards weapons because my next door neighbor confessed to me privately that he's got a submachine gun and more than seven hundred rounds of ammunition. My eyes bulged. It seems that he's got a small piece of land by the Pacific, an empty stretch of beach, and he goes there to hunt sharks with the submachine gun. It's his "hobby." Despite the seriousness of the situation and my familiarity with the customs here, I haven't laughed like I did then in a long time.

I think about them and I think—I don't know for how many times now—that Kali and Nel began to respect Staś Tarkowski from the moment he first shot the lion, then the Bedouins. When I contemplate the future of our civilization, and the Kalis who observe it from all corners of the globe, it seems to me that this one episode in Sienkiewicz's *In Desert and Wilderness* excellently sums up the problem of existence. Too bad that Toynbee never read it. No, we're not just one of the several civilizations that have come and gone. This is something greater and perhaps worth defending because nothing has ended in it. Rather it is just now beginning.

Single shots constantly throughout the city. No doubt the police zealously carrying out their orders as regards windows showing any light. Why was it these five gentlemen came to me, to my shed, trembling above a garage for buses? Why was it to me that one of them confided his possession of a *Schmeisser?* Why do they expect more from me than from others in the neighborhood?

June 22, '54

A complete lack of more definite information. The postal service has been discontinued for a week now and planes aren't coming in any more. Just for a brief moment I happened to catch a communiqué from the free station. It appears that Castillo Armas has taken Esquipulas, a small city with an air field situated about fifteen kilometers from the Honduras border and that he's pressing on in the direction of Chiquimula. Another blow is aimed at Zacapa. They want to cut the rail line to Puerto Barrios on the Atlantic. In the meantime, however, the papers assure everybody that in a few days time the government army will have the entire situation under control. Moreover, Guatemala has appealed to the U.N. Security Council and the Arbenz government is doing everything it can to convince international opinion that it is an innocent democracy, the only true one in Central America and that it is perishing under the blows of "American imperialism." And I'm quite sure that he'll manage to cause some confusion here and evoke sympathy.

A unique phenomenon: the downfall of a single Communist evokes protests throughout the entire free world. The Communists and the non-Communists shout, the intellectuals protest, issue manifestoes, sign petitions, condemn, and express their everlasting solidarity. But who condemned, who issued any manifestoes, who in fact knew that on July 12 two years ago the "democratic" Arbenz ordered an anti-Communist demonstration quelled by gunfire? Who protested anywhere over the fact that six persons were killed and more than forty wounded? Silence. Does anybody protest the fact that for two years now anti-Communists here are imprisoned, tortured, deported?

We perish in abstraction, dissolve in slogans. Agrarian reform, sewn coarsely with red thread, has blinded us completely. Is it necessary? Obviously, but what reform and introduced by means of what methods? Not this kind, to be sure. But what isn't understood is that if reform is necessary it makes no difference what kind it is, and besides we're talking about some Guatemala somewhere. A wild place. No, *mon cher*, your Breton or Norman peasant isn't the slightest bit more advanced than the Indian here.

What is being carried out under the cloak of this reform here, what is happening under the cloak of Arbenz's "democracy"? Undeniable results, they'll answer. And that's the kind of nonsense they spew out in liberal and enlightened circles, in the so-called progressive circles, without any real knowledge of the countries involved, the people, the conditions, the geography, the climate even. They keep on repeating the same old nonsense about Spain, Formosa, Guatemala, about everything. Now, here, completely cut off from the rest of the civilized world, in the center of a conflict of seemingly small significance yet anything but that today, I hear the commentaries from around the globe and I realize that there is no difference, after all: a familiar jargon from that side over there, and from this one here an equally dense and abstract liberal jargon, gliding ever so delicately through reality so as not to strike anything too forcefully, so as not to give the Communists cause to raise even a louder outcry. Freedom? They don't want it. They dream about chains called security. Just so long as they don't get their hands soiled, just so long as they don't have to let go of a pen ready for everything. Those specialists in freedom would be the first to become reconciled to its loss here the same way others managed to "explain" it to themselves over there. From total negation to total assent is the easiest transition of all. Freedom without a foundation, without the support of some truth or other (God's perhaps?) is nothing, it has no substance, it's of no use. And on what truths do they lean for support? Only on the one which states that there is no truth. Everything is constantly in flux, so why give shape to fleeting impressions? Come now. It's rather the impressions that give them shape. Coexistentialists.

At noon, my partner rang me. A telegram came from Chicago requesting the transfer of 3700 dollars because an order of ours is ready for shipment. I told him to comply. He was appalled. Fortunately, the telegraph lines are in private hands and still operating. In the afternoon an air raid. The streets empty as everybody crawls to the roofs to have a look. Shouts of joy and enthusiasm, like during a *corrida*, rise up from the roofs. There's no mistaking how each passing day, each air attack increases the sympathy for Castillo Armas. People are impressed with strength. The street has already baptised the Thunderbolts *Sulfato* and at the faintest drone of a plane engine joyful shouts of *Viene el Sulfato* can be heard. During today's raid, I happened to pass by a hotel in front of which stood a group of American correspondents. They were disoriented. "It's the first time in my life I've ever seen people enjoying being bombed," I heard one of them say. The army doubtless has opposed the distribution of weapons. The papers carry a denunciation of the attack and the promise of the liquidation of the enemy by means of an "outflanking maneuver." Meanwhile, I happened to hear today that yesterday the Thunderbolts played havoc with a troop transport headed for the "front." Barely fifty men were left from a unit of more than three hundred. The rest went over to the side of "General Montes," as they say here, which simply means that they headed for the hills.

June 24, '54

Things are getting better all the time. There's talk about universal mobilization, about the formation of teams to construct fortifications all around the city. In a few hours Mexico is supposed to send in planes. The brother of the Minister of Foreign Affairs and Arbenz's personal friend, J. Toriello, went there with around a million dollars for the express purpose of buying Mustangs. The initiated laugh maliciously and claim that that will be the best transaction he ever made in his life, although he always had a reputation for shrewdness. The matter is already arranged. The happiest news comes, however, from the diplomatic posts of the other Latin-American countries. Under pressure, undoubtedly, they are readying places for Communists seeking refuge. They say that the Mexican Embassy bought out one company's supply of chamber pots. But despite such auspicious news from the field of battle it's hard to laugh because the situation really is serious. The worst thing is the complete lack of any precise data. Nobody knows a thing.

I'm nervous; I can't find a place for myself. Now just when the hope of freedom is beginning to dawn the fatigue of the past two years starts oozing out. I felt from the very beginning where it was leading. But people didn't believe me. Later on, it was even dangerous to discuss it. Recently the situation looked so hopeless that as late as yesterday I had no hope of anticipating anything better. They've already started to make fun of the Americans. Their eyes on Europe and Asia, with some sort of fanatical farsightedness, they refused to see what was happening in their own back yard. And if one can speak of their erecting something on the order of a front (this still doesn't extend beyond much more than a barrier), the effort will be senseless until they first put up an "America Line." Until that happens, they won't lay solid foundations under the forward bastions anywhere on the entire American continent. The task certainly isn't an easy one, but it's high time to give it a thought. To the present day, they have no policy for the Americas. Guatemala is a signal.

June 26, '54

Spent the evening with friends. D. is a Pole, a long time resident here. The well-to-do home of cultured people. Mrs. D. belongs to the anti-régime organization but in the final analysis doesn't know too much either. We spread out a map and try to figure out how the situation really looks.

Castillo Armas will never enter into open battle, because his army isn't powerful enough. The complete concentration of the government forces, on the other hand, is also out of the question because the planes come in and break up any efforts along those lines. The Indian soldier can't bear air raids. They desert *en masse*. D. claims that at present everything depends on when the army decides to dump Arbenz. Nevertheless, the biggest complication is the honor of the army which under no circumstances can permit itself to accept the fact that it was defeated by five or six hundred students, deportees, émigrés, and peasants who join the ranks daily in exchange for a rifle, a uniform, and a good day's pay (around ten dollars a day). "The colonel is going to have a tough nut to crack," says D.

Somebody rings the doorbell. A young fellow comes in. There's definite information that Chiquimila has fallen to the rebels. We return to the map. D. recalls the "good old days." Once a revolution broke out here just because the widow of some dictator didn't get her regular allowance on time and didn't have enough money for her usual shopping. Angered, her majordomus went to the barracks, incited the entire garrison, and in a single day succeeded in toppling the whole unpunctual government. Those times have passed. Nowadays each revolution is going to be a splinter of a much greater conflict, like the skirmishes of knights before the main battles in the old days.

Later on somebody else rings and comes in. Whispers. Trucks with weapons are standing by in the sports stadium, but it's doubtful that anybody will come to claim them. The appeals of the leaders of the workers' syndicates are of no avail. I'm not entirely convinced that this will remain so, however, and would like to get home as quickly as possible. They're taking us back by car. The city is dark and empty. After my return, I "make the rounds," looking in on my neighbors. Now they too have heard about the trucks in the stadium. "If it begins, then it'll happen first in the southern part of town," they say. In all houses there are now refugees from districts situated in the vicinity of the garrisons and radio stations that came under air attack. They tell me that during today's raid a plane attacking the government transmitting station came out of its dive flying underneath the wires between the telegraph poles. If that's so, then it smacks of pilots—from the North.

The city is dark. It's damp and steamy. The fragrances of oranges blossoming below the house enters a window, one of the most wonderful scents I know. At dawn humming birds quiver in the small trees. Their flight is their song—a quieting trill. I sat up till late at night waiting to see whether or not some glow would splash forth in the South. The tranquillity of the night was shattered from time to time by single shots of unknown origin.

June 27, '54

From morning on the radio has been announcing an evening speech by Arbenz of "transcendental significance." Nobody's going into town. The atmosphere is heavy, the tension has reached its peak. One can sense that something has already happened. Only what, nobody yet knows. All appeals addressed to the populace, the workers and various organizations have ceased. They say that nobody's come to claim the weapons in the trucks in the stadium and that when the decision was finally taken for the creation of a people's militia, nobody put in an appearance at the designated mustering places.

In the afternoon my next door neighbor called me over. He was in town. He tells me that there are crowds in front of the foreign embassies and legations and that inside the buildings people are even brawling, because those who took refuge there from Communist repression refuse to leave while dignitaries of the government, envoys, and the entire red society have begun flowing in *en masse* in search of asylum. Must be pleasant there. There are also rumors that this evening Arbenz intends proclaiming universal mobilization and defense down to the last man. But when all is said and done nobody knows what's happening for sure. For the past ten days the sole source of news has been rumor. The Communists have such a hold on the country that I simply refuse to believe that this time it all could end relatively painlessly.

Evening slowly falls, and the magpies crowd the bamboo trees, making a terrible racket. The sight of vultures makes them hysterical. The radio plays only the national anthem now and at regular intervals asks everybody to stand by for the "transcendental address." At last it comes. First, the national anthem. Then the plaintive, trembling voice of Arbenz. For the good of the country, for the avoidance of further bloodshed (of people murdered by his police—my addition), defeated by air power which the government found itself incapable of opposing successfully, defeated by monopolies and by the United States (finally they defeated somebody), he is determined to step aside and to place all authority in the hands of Colonel Diaz. A tearful and touching farewell to the nation. Henceforth they'll weep for him at all convocations and congresses of eunuchs by conviction.

Now we're getting somewhere. The scales have been tipped, but it's not the end yet. Diaz, after all, is a Communist too. He went for his training to Moscow and in the capacity of Minister of Defense was responsible for the introduction of political indoctrination in the army.

I go off to see some acquaintances. They're already drinking to celebrate. For a while we manage to catch the rebel radio. They've made up their minds. They have no intention of entering into any negotiations with Diaz and announce an air raid for tomorrow. "Las hostilidades siguen." The most delicate moment of all now begins. The army forced Arbenz into retirement but it is trying to preserve its honor, and besides Diaz certainly must have a number of backers.

The first night is calm. It's hard to believe. The tactics employed by the Communists here were beyond reproach. The method of slicing salami. Day by day, slice by slice. And day by day, the closer I came to the moment when we'd all be living and thinking on two levels, the more I felt something heavy constricting my breathing. I go here and there, speak with this one and that one, and suddenly I get caught red-handed. I slip out of it, keep my mouth shut, answer no questions, and even smile. That's how it begins. Then mild contempt for myself, stifled by self-justification. What else can I do? Should I tell him straight to his face? They'll come, work me over, throw me in jail. After that they'll toss me in a car, cart me to the border at night, strip me of my clothes, and drive me naked into the jungle. And who'll concern himself about me after that? For the victims of "democracy," of leftist dictatorships, nobody intercedes, for such people certainly must be reactionaries. Entire parliaments are prepared to go to the defense of a single bull run through during a *corrida* in Spain. That's because it's in Spain. So I smiled. Ha—even a comparison can be found. Murders and the seizure of land under the guise of agrarian reform? Understandable: when a dam is opened sometimes pieces of a dike are ripped out. Little by little fear gnaws and crushes the spirit. It's a very different kind of fear, full of shame, abnormal, yet proud in its own way. You have to experience it to really understand it. The justification of everything begins with the justification of one's self. A great and general "Yes" so hard for us on the other side to understand.

June 28, '54

In the afternoon a big raid was greeted enthusiastically. A fine raid, indeed. They're attacking the old fort, which houses the quartermaster corps. The Thunderbolts sweep out of the sky like hawks, the missiles are released and fly faster and faster parabolically. Thump. Forgive me, but I'm glad. After the raid, I ride into town. At an intersection a car honks its horn at me. I go over. G., a pilot-major, motions to me to get into the car. Armed to the teeth, a submachine gun on a seat. G. is also a model plane builder; the hobby is more like a kind of religious order. He's slightly intoxicated and when I sit down next to him, he pulls out a bottle of whiskey and offers me a drink. I quaff some as though it were a breath of fresh air. Then I ask him what's really going on.

"There's nothing for you to worry about. This evening we're going to that . . . and if he doesn't step aside of his own free will, then . . ." and he points to the submachine gun.

He's suffering from a case of the jitters before the evening expedition.

"But *por Dios* don't breathe a word of this to anybody. Listen —I'm making a wonderful *Rayan*. As soon as all this shit ends, I'll bring it over to show you." There's nobody quite like a model plane enthusiast. A model, especially one under construction, is more important than just about anything else.

In the evening again the national anthem. Diaz places all authority in the hands of a military junta. The names this time are clean. They made a good job of it. Until late at night the radio transmits new decrees. About the abolition of the Communist Party, about the dissolution of Parliament. The end. The rest won't amount to more than the settlement of second rate matters of one sort or another. The most important has already been resolved.

After everything that's happened I feel as if some new element has bound me even closer to this country.

July 18, '54

I'm due to fly on Wednesday the 21st. Everything worked out, after all. Now I've got a case of *Reisefieber*. The whole business was settled at the last moment. On July 2, Castillo Armas entered Guatemala and was greeted by such crowds and so much enthusiasm that even his most ardent supporters rubbed their eyes in disbelief. The transition from one administration to the other was effected smoothly, without any undue complications. The army, however, constantly remains a puzzle.

Colonel Armas's forces have not yet been demobilized and are being held concentrated in the areas they occupied in the course of their activities. At the same time the regular army refused to give its permission to them to stage a march into the city and the colonel rode in himself under the protection of the populace. And this populace, it's hardly just the rich people. . . .

His first public address was reasonable and forceful. But will he be able to handle all the problems he faces, above all the economy? The Communists stripped the state treasury bare, stole everything they could get their hands on; even at the last moment Arbenz took out around a million dollars from the state banks. The foreign debt of the country exceeds thirty million. The plunder, thievery, and criminal activity that took place during the years of "democracy" here surpassed everything that had ever happened in this area. It was an internal *conquista* in the best Spanish style during which *los camaradas* made themselves fortunes. That was the one thing that really was democratic: everybody stole, on all levels, Party people and non-Party people.

When I look back on it all now, I realize that it was interesting. Now that the tensions have eased, when one can throw open a window more calmly after these years, certain suspicions arise. We are inclined to treat communism as a single entity, *en bloc*, from the point of view above all of the white man, of the person belonging to white civilization. It seems to us that the impact of communism on another race and the spread of communism among other races must follow the same course as among us. But now I see to what extent communism really is a creation of the white man, a mongrel of our own civilization.

The same way that Parish priests here in Indian districts not only tolerate—often openly—the celebration of pagan Indian rites under the roof of the church, but literally submit entirely to certain "liturgical" forms created by the Indians themselves ("They ring the bells when they feel like it," I was told by a vanquished Spanish priest, a doctor of two faculties who retained only the burning gaze from among all the attributes of this most fanatic of Catholic clergies), so the Communists too are engaged in a constant struggle with a completely different type of man here. We've been made responsive to many of the demands of communism by centuries of Christianity, but the colored man doesn't have such training. The sense of solidarity, discipline, ultra-Puritanical morality in certain areas is utterly alien to them. They are softer by nature; they submit, but often with the engulfing quality of shifting sand. Among the colored people communism is continuously exposed to the completely unexpected "ringing when they feel like it."

It's quite possible that under the influence of the recent events here—say what you will, it's the first instance of the spontaneous self-liberation of a country from the clutches of the Party—I tend to view everything too optimistically. But it does seem to me that there's something in what I say. Certain facts which are now coming to the surface enable me to understand to what extent I used to evaluate certain phenomena under the influence of a method worked out in an environment of whites and fair with relation to whites, but quite often erroneous with relation to colored or mixed colored-white peoples. The number of unknown, utterly unexpected flexions of an inveterate mentality is enormous, considerably larger than among the whites.

If Castillo Armas now reduces the thievery and even partly shrinks the monstrous bureaucracy that has grown out of all proportion in the course of these years, he may provoke a crisis, the sudden lowering of the level of purchasing power of a large segment of the population.

July 22, '54

Traveling by plane can be pleasant, but it certainly isn't taking a trip in the old sense. It's a kind of leaping. In this respect, a person closely resembles a flea, as Keyserling once observed somewhere or other. No flea would leap lightheartedly and sure of landing where he wanted, if he still had to devote himself to the culture of his inner life while leaping. After landing at the airport in Newark, I felt like a flea.

I took off yesterday from Guatemala at three in the afternoon. The weather was superb. There were a lot of friends at the airport to say goodbye to me and to Julio and Fernand, two brothers who are flying in the competition under my tutelage. A family atmosphere, everybody knows everybody else. In the plane our old friend, the American steward Carey, also a member of the model plane fraternity. He personally stored our boxes of planes in the belly of the Constellation as though they were glass balls. Afterward, we still had to wait a little while, because the Marquise B. was late as usual, but they made a special call to the airport to say that he had already left his house. In Guatemala he's what Prof. Dr. Ed. Pres. Józef Flach used to be in the old days in Cracow. He's an institution here and takes part in everything. He entered the plane in a very dignified manner, wearing a monocle on a black cord, and most charmingly begged all the passengers to forgive him for the delay. Waiting for the Marquise, the Constellation reminded me of Bełżec years and years ago when the entire train waited more than once for Ligowski or old Kiwerski.

The plane moved down the runway for the takeoff. The nervous tick of the model plane maker. Accustomed to small motors working at twelve to eighteen thousand revolutions per minute, it seemed to me at the takeoff that the plane's engines were working quite slowly and that we weren't going to have sufficient power to lift off. Carey confessed to me that he always has the same sensation as well.

We're flying in the direction of Mérida, in Yucatan. Down below, a thick jungle, monotonous in appearance. I try to read. I took along with me for the trip Hemingway's *The Old Man and the Sea*, in the hope that finally I'd manage to read something of his from cover to cover. But when I reached the half-way mark I stopped about where I usually stop when I pick up Tolstoy, Dostoevsky, Zeromski, and other monuments; I'm simply unable to finish. For completely different reasons in each case, of course, but the fact remains nevertheless that I cannot finish them once I've started. I don't know how many times I tried with Hemingway, but the end results are always the same. This time I had enough cruelty toward the poor fish and I got bored. Very pretty, doubtless beautifully written, but I just can't finish it. Bull fights and cock fights never could really get me excited. I was always upset with the bull for not spearing the toreador and "el divino" Dominguin was unable to move me. Why can't I stand Hemingway? I don't know. Maybe it's just because of my "lack of Latin," as my father used to call it. He raved about Tolstoy, but actually couldn't stand him. And I know that for his whole life the most courageous man is more afraid than not, just because he is courageous.

We arrive in Mérida, in Mexico. Scorching heat. The temperature of the fire-box of a locomotive when it's gone to a workshop, the fire and water are thrown out of it, and not long after somebody's got to crawl in and change the tubes. I was reminded of the good old days. After a quarter of an hour we take off again and in a little while are over the Gulf of Mexico. We fly high, the sun inclines to the West. Carey explains and then demonstrates the right way to use the life-jacket. Not a word about sharks, though. Then he brings around an early supper. It's fairly empty in the plane cabin and one can move around and change places and look out different windows. The sunset is unearthly. Here, up high, it's still quite light, but below you can see how quickly night alights on the water, thickens, and expands. Little lights on ships flash and immediately go out again. Then the lights of the shores of the USA begin to shine. We fly over an area in which many gas shafts are burning. They look like camp fires. To the right of the plane, the lights of New Orleans scatter for a moment; a great expanse, glittering like a shell, intersected by the darker belt of the Mississippi. We can already hear the whine of the flaps being lowered; there's a jolt, and at eight we make our landing.

I alight from the plane stupefied. The heat in New Orleans is worse than what it was in Mérida. Heavy, sticky, overcast. I wink my eyes because the excessive light irritates them. I've grown accustomed to that over the years. Behind me, on runways sunk in darkness, there's a ceaseless whirring. Planes taking off, landing; alongside, a gigantic Super Constellation rolls up and comes to a stop beneath a designated gate on a platform; on the side opposite, a smaller Convair starts moving, and it seems to me finally that I'm not at an airport but at the bus terminal at Bielany on a holiday. This alone was enough to convince me at once that I was in another world. On this hot night, in the blue light of neon signs, something was turning at a high velocity, like engines ceaselessly howling in the darkness. But not with a nervous rhythm. . . . Using terms from electricity, I felt no tension, but calm intensity, measured, cool, uniform. I began to wonder how they cope with this weird movement in the course of a full twenty-four hour day. Carey left the same time I did and was talking to me about it. He tells me that crowded skies, especially above airports, is already a major problem in the USA. After ten minutes I felt as though I had downed three "doubles."

Passport check and customs clearance. I didn't have a chance to get my shots before my departure so they gave them to me here right on the spot. The "vaccinator" (he's probably not a doctor) asks me questions about Guatemala, wanting to know how things really were down there and was it true that Communist influences were so strong in the country. In this dark West of ours, it's sufficient for any rapscallion to proclaim himself a democrat and enter into collusion with the Communists in order to do whatever he feels like later on.

We have nearly two hours before the continuing flight. First I go for a whiskey and then dinner. The restaurant is air-conditioned and at first I feel cold. But it's a wonderful invention, especially in restaurants. The food seems to taste so much better. I buy a few papers, write cards, crawl around the terminal. A fine feeling of "something different" and here there really is something different. A loudspeaker continually announces departures and arrivals, while the deadening roar of engines enters through the open windows; people coming and going constantly. There's no night here. They pushed it way back to the depth of the runways, where the unseen machines can be recognized by the blue flames shooting out exhaust pipes.

Around ten, Eastern Airlines announces the departure of our Air Coach to New York. The Air Coach is something on the order of a private train. It carries more passengers, it's cheaper, and the flight lasts all night, making a number of stops along the way. We board the plane. It's full and dark. I take a seat and involuntarily whisper something to Julio. There's a definite atmosphere here, a little "frightening." But doubtless I'm the only one who feels that way. The Americans act as though they were riding an ordinary streetcar. Some fellow gets himself into the most comfortable sleeping position, adjusts his seat, stretches out and falls asleep at once. Others adjust their little reading lights and get set to read or extinguish the lights and doze. I can't. The engines have already turned over and we start moving slowly, plunging into the darkness. It's pitch black on all sides except for the blue sparks streaming out of the engines. In the distance, the glow of the lights of the terminal and the glow of the lights of the city. We taxi down the runway, stop a while, move forward and in a moment I can feel the face of the wind. We pass over New Orleans, and I gaze at the Mississippi below, broad and shimmering. Afterward, everything is dark; blackness and the steady drone of the engines take over. I try to sleep. It's also dark in the plane cabin save for the occasional cigarette that lights up. I doze, but the plane starts shaking. We're coming in for a landing. Again the glittering lights of the terminal at Mobile. A small, hushed terminal. I go out to stretch my legs. A scorching July night. An indescribable feeling of delight, of flowing into everything around me. The years of exertion have fallen away somewhere and now there's only the present. Only the sensation of "now" gives me a real rest. I fool around first with an automatic machine dispensing bottles of Coca Cola, then with another one offering ice cold orange juice in paper cups. Stars buried deep in the sky, a light here, reflectors, and in their glare a slender, handsome machine. These too are works of art, harmonious and elegant.

I often burst out laughing to myself thinking about these poor people trembling with fear before the "technologizing" of culture and lamenting the disappearance of poetry. But poetry still exists, and if one wants to he can perceive it all around him. It seems to them that "phobias," that the creation of problems out of everything, at every step of the way, proves depth and the emphasis on the spirit. No—they fail to realize that it is precisely they who become sacrifices to the "technologizing" of culture, that it is they who have heartlessly stumbled into the technical intellect. Their "phobias" amount to a desire to stay where they are, to preserve an exclusive *cercle* by the light of candles and a subdued nocturn. They love what was; they are incapable of loving what is. And that's why everything seems to them dry and friable and they hurl themselves into even greater drought and friableness. They don't want to understand, they don't want to love.

Once again the darkness is illuminated by the blue sparks. Inside the plane cabin it's hot. I want to sleep but I can't. Anyway, we land again after a while. Birmingham. People get off and on. Then Atlanta. My legs have gone to sleep, I'm drowsy, but I really can't fall asleep. I get out. Scorching heat; the night is endless. After taking off from Atlanta, I finally managed to doze off. I awoke at dawn. The little windows lit up, the sun entered. We pass over Washington, D.C. For a moment I have a glimpse of the White House and the city. We land. The airport is situated along the banks of the Potomac and a refreshing cool wind wafts in from the river. My head aches from the heat and from the night's cigarettes and I think longingly of a bed in New York. After the takeoff, they serve coffee and in an hour we arrive at Newark. At last, it's all over; several thousand kilometers in an afternoon and a night. I get off the plane listlessly. A sunny day; the remains of the morning cold are still drifting about the airport, but you can feel the approaching heat.

We take a cab and of course the driver has a Polish name and speaks a perfectly respectable Polish. He's never been in Poland, but was born here and is married to a Pole. Right away he asks me if it's true about the Communists in Guatemala. From what he say it's obvious that he's seriously read the newspapers that taught him that things really weren't that bad down there and that the whole business is some dark story connected with the United Fruit Company. I swear out loud—even here. We race along some splendid new "highway," fall into a long tunnel, and as soon as we emerge New York looms up like some mountain chain. As hard and vain as it may be to say it, the view is—pretty. The skyscrapers in the sunny morning mist are wonderful. They have a style all their own. We enter a street. Here the heat is reflected from every wall; a huge city in summer with its characteristic odor of carbon monoxide, fermenting garbage, and exhalations from backyards. An environment to which I had become unaccustomed and about which I completely forgot in my "jungle."

We have a room reserved in the Claridge, in the center of Broadway, in the Times Square area. The hotel is old, but neat and inexpensive. The sun is scorching now and it's stuffy in the room. Any day of the week I prefer my tropics to this sea climate. We bathe and then go out to get a bite. I don't know why all of a sudden I don't feel tired any longer. The city animates me, like the heroes of Labiche's vaudevilles. *New York ventre à terre.* I hardly manage to come to, when I leave the hotel, grab a cab, and am off to pay a call on one of the companies I've done business with for years now and which I still can't teach how to draw up invoices in compliance with the demands of Guatemalan customs. I rush, because here you have to rush. I take care of my business, meet my boys, and take off with them together to "Jasco," another company, but a quite special one. Frank Zaic, a Yugoslav by origin, is the "pope" of model plane building to this very day, known the world over. Years ago he established one of the first companies specializing in model plane equipment, above all superbly cut wood and excellent sketches. He also wrote a few professional books on the subject. Later on, his sister and two brothers took over the company. They've maintained its high level to the present, although the competition from big factories and plastic model kits threatens them with serious difficulties. It's a family business, small, but well known to all dedicated model plane enthusiasts the world over. I use their wood exclusively. Five years ago, without ever having met me, they gave me exclusive representation for Guatemala. During the years we developed a friendship through correspondence.

When we go upstairs, everybody's in the shop. The sister greets us and we immediately embrace, like old friends. "Andy"—"Christina." Movement, fuss. Christina calls out to her brothers, "Guatemala's arrived." Christina is on the organization committee of the matches and she tells us they thought that as a result of the revolution in Guatemala we wouldn't be able to make it this year. She immediately puts in a call to the president of the A.M.A. (Academy of Model Aeronautics). In the meantime, I talk to Frank. In order to understand what these conversations are like, you have to belong to the model plane fraternity yourself. Frank asks me, for example, what you do with rubber in the tropics, what lubricant I use. Ha—years of experience, but I'll let you in on the secret: I use automobile brake fluid. A "Pirelli" with this fluid withstands the destructive tropical climate best of all. Frank laughs. While we exchange shop talk, Christina lays out lunch on the work benches, amidst the wood, saws, and machines. After all, we have to have something to eat with them. This directness of theirs is charming. This is also one of the traits which many people can't forgive the Americans for.

I settle the business I have with Christina, leave an order with her and arrange to meet at five in some hotel where they're having drinks for all the participants in the matches. I ask about the Argentinians. I don't even dream about victory, but I would like to put little Guatemala in a good position in relation to its powerful relative. The government covered the costs of the journey of the entire nine-man Argentinian team; model plane making is supported there like nowhere else.

Next on the agenda, a *ventre à terre* to the Empire State Building. We go there on foot and on the way I buy a pound of cherries. I'm convinced they're the best fruit on earth. Tropical fruits are one big hoax. The pineapple is edible, but I prefer it from a can. Mangoes, papayas, the others—enough to make you faint.

On the way to the top of the Empire State Building I thought I was going to drop dead and never get up again. I just about lost my senses in the elevator. But I came to when we reached the top. The view is impressive. New York from the top of its biggest skyscraper is a sight difficult to describe. It's undeniably magnificent and beautiful. And this is now the capital of the world. You can sense it everywhere around you here. And one more thing: it's perhaps the only place and city in which the styleless, gelatinous, inter-war period created a very distinct style of its own.

After this bit of mountaineering, I return to the hotel to take a bath and lie down for a while. Obviously, I couldn't sleep. Afterward, we change clothes and go off for the drinks. The hotel is wonderfully cool and we're given a tremendous welcome. I'm handed a glass of whiskey. Then they introduce me to General Doolittle. He's clearly one of the most outstanding figures in American aeronautics, a man who's become almost a legend in his own time. In the history of aeronautics his name comes up time and time again and one encounters his last feat at every turn: the first air raid on Tokyo. I spend a long time in conversation with him, because he seems to be quite interested in what's been happening in Guatemala.

Afterward, I meet the Argentinians, Swedes, Canadians, and the sole Japanese and Swiss entrants. The extremely pleasant mood of a sports evening. I converse with the American "proxies" who are to fly the models of two Guatemalans who couldn't make the trip. A council of war, and I am gripped with pre-match excitement. I bat down the whiskey and get good and stiff. And meanwhile M. is waiting for me for dinner. In view of that, I race to her *ventre à terre*. M. is extraordinary and although I didn't know her before, after five minutes it seems to me that we've known each other for years. With Polish women this tends to be rather a rare virtue. The whole time I'm with her I do my best to make sure she doesn't discover that I'm high. She made an enormous steak and a salad seasoned with something bitter. We talked for the longest time and arranged to get together again after my return from Chicago.

I return to the hotel by cab so exhausted I intend just throwing myself on the bed and going to sleep with my clothes on. Exactly! But no sooner did I enter the room, no sooner did I glance at the sea of lights on Broadway through the window than I immediately headed down again on the elevator. I crept around the streets until two in the morning.

July 23, '54

A morning reception at City Hall, picture-taking, speeches, the mayor of the city, a waste of time. In the afternoon we ride out to La Guardia airport. Hot as hell. All the time I'm eating something. I haven't had such an appetite in years. Toward evening, we fly in two military Douglases to the Suffolk County Air Force base on Long Island. We land at dusk, after sunset. From the planes we head directly for a simple soldier's supper right at the airfield. Some kind of soup, fried chicken, different kinds of salads, raw celery, crispy and crunchy, creamed carrots, cakes, ice cream, coffee. Like the Tour d'Argent. I have no sensation anywhere here of being on a military installation. *Une armée sans tenue et sans tenues,* as Malraux describes them. A lot of religious propaganda on the walls of the corridors. "Think of God, you are not alone," and things of that sort. Somehow that doesn't upset me. Much better than political propaganda. After supper they drive us to a hotel in Riverhead. I have an attractive room with air-conditioning. At last, I go to bed early and sleep peacefully.

July 24, '54

We leave for the airfield early in the morning. Ah, those breakfasts! In addition to eggs and ham there were even herring fillets. Besides everything else, of course. I stuff myself. I have an entire hangar at my disposition on the field. The morning is spent weighing and measuring the models by the judges' commission. From morning on all conceivable types of planes fly in for the exhibition tomorrow (and also because of us). An intercontinental B-36, an already antiquated monstrosity, a machine not of this world, lands. Slim jets. For the first time I have the chance to see them up close and in flight. And involuntarily I begin to recollect, involuntarily forgotten dusty memories begin asserting themselves. The airfield in Lida with the remains of Zeppelin hangers outlined against the background of the sky, several hangers, and German Albatrosses now with Polish markings on them. The smell of gas and oil, polished propellors, Captain Menczak who didn't have a single unbroken bone in his entire body stiff from the corset he wore and with his set of gold false teeth, Sergeant Choiński, forever promising me a tiny little plane with a little motor. How I waited for it. . . . Summer mornings, sandy tracks, little birch groves near Lida. I used to go horseback riding with my father and remain at the airfield until dinner. I sat quietly in some corner and watched the way mechanics repaired the wings of planes, the way they "stretched" them. During masses in the field, planes flew in so low that Father Antosz did squat-jumps at the altar out of fear. My father winked at me and the both of us laughed.

A Globemaster transport of monstrous proportions lands, while I sit in front of the hangar and recall the past. Wilno came after Lida. Here for a change I spent time in the Reduta on Pohulanka. Evenings, I went out the back entrance in the Rennenkamp Palace, up to the Smigłys. Napoleon's campaign, the concentration of artillery in the Battle of Wagram, the death of Lannes; the stories he used to tell. . . . He made me sketches of battle plans, drew pictures of soldiers. A Starfire taxis in, growling and howling. Toruń. And another airfield. The Moranes had arrived then and I fell in love with the actress Malinowicz. Every day I was on the firing range with father, a complete military preparation. I shot everything that could be shot, but best of all I liked the recoilless WB. rifles. The young officers used to say with the pleasantest smiles: "The colonel's son will certainly make a fine soldier." Father looked gloomy and muttered under his whiskers: "It's enough that there's one imbecile in the family." Three Sabres blinked by and disappeared. At the sight of these machines I suddenly feel old, I feel as though a slice of life passed by as swiftly as the flight of these Sabres. Somehow I could never recollect, but now here, in this hangar, amidst the roaring of turbines, I begin to recall everything in detail. I hear people's voices, I see faces, streets, houses, apartments; a whole life tosses itself before my eyes, a whole Poland lived in and traveled over from one end to the other. And in the end I'd like to get drunk on these memories, on those nights in the Lida forests, nights spent in remote rectories, on Easter in Wilno and the rolling of eggs, on that now famous double I gave General Skierski. The alarmed look of my father and a kick under the table. The malicious smile of Captain Keyser, my partner. After the general's exit the promise of a new bow as a reward from Boch. "What did you kick me for?" "I was afraid you wouldn't make it and that old fogy would think you don't know how to play." The entire 63rd infantry regiment, the 15th heavy artillery, and the Inspectorate talked for a long time afterward about that double.

An early supper and we return to Riverhead. I stop for a quick one in some cool nearly dark bar. I drink and recollect. In my head I've already written a huge book of memoirs. In the hotel room Julio eyes me suspiciously: "Julio! Do you know how the eighty-horsepower rotary Gnome-et-Rhône engine used to look?"

July 25, '54

Julio's in bad form; he got a stomachache from these simple soldier's *pommes frites*, hams, chickens, ducks, mayonnaise sauces, ice creams, and cakes. He tells me it's "fluid drive." But during the competition he takes hold of himself and fights to the bitter end. My drawing is good, even very good. It's worth developing further. At noon there's a break, a lot of people all over the place, television shows displays of the models and the efforts to break the Soviet records. In model plane championship matches the Soviets hold 90 per cent of the world's records. Although invitations were sent them, nobody showed up from there. In the afternoon, I sit in the hangar and get the rubber ready for tomorrow. Somebody chats with me in Polish. They read the name on my model. Naturally, invitations follow. You feel at home here. Tomorrow it's my turn and I'm numb at the thought. For the first time in many, many years I'm again taking part in some competition.

July 26, '54

Two rounds before noon with miserable luck. In the first flight I had a maximum in my pocket. The model took off nicely, reached its height, but in crossing over to a glide fell into too narrow a spiral. Upset, I fly a reserve model. Even worse. At dinner I have no appetite and I'm depressed. All the Argentinians are ahead of me. After dinner I pick up. The last two flights maximum and in the final tally three of the Argentinians are behind me. That's what I was after, though it could have been better. Got nervous, damn it. While I was winding up the rubber in the third round I heard a suspicious noise—"click"—and I stopped to check whether or not some belt broke. I wound up again and again the same noise. I didn't wind it all the way as a result and got off the mark on the edge of my nerves. Then I return and what do you think? In a motorcycle sidecar, nearby, a little boy was sitting, concealed, playing with a cap pistol. That's where the noise came from! I felt like . . . better not say. I adore children!

Spent the whole day on the runway, in the sun. I made up all right for the last six years. In the evening there was a banquet in the hotel. After the barracks "chow" the dinner was scandalous. Afterward, we made ourselves comfortable on the floor of the lounge and stayed up till late at night talking, exchanging sketches of models, and discussing plans and projects for next year. I grew young again.

July 27, '54

At five in the morning we leave by bus for some naval base near New York. I'm not yet awake. When I'm at the airfield again then I come to. A charming girl in a uniform shows us to a canteen for breakfast. Now we are guests of the Navy, which is taking us from here to Chicago for the "Nationals." A DC-4 is already waiting. For the past three days I've spent only small change for drinks and cigarettes. Beyond that, not a cent. We board the plane. I made a comfortable bed for myself out of parachutes and fell asleep immediately after takeoff. They woke me up just before we landed. For a change we are now at a naval air base, in Glenview, near Chicago. Beginning tomorrow and lasting to the first of August are the national model plane championship matches. The event attracts an enormous number of people and there are more than 1,500 participants. The organization is superb. The Americans have to pay a few dollars a day for entrance fees, and the like. Not us—we're guests. I receive my bed linen, towels, pillow, and soap and am assigned a bed in a huge gymnasium. A city of beds. Nearby there's a covered swimming pool and showers. Four sailors on duty move continuously among the beds keeping order, explaining things and helping out.

The Argentinians suddenly had the desire to call Buenos Aires from one of the phone booths. Naturally, they came to me. I thought I'd go mad. The telephone operator broke out in a fit of laughter; so did I, but anyway we scour the whole base collecting as many nickels as we can, transport them to the booth, and spend a good half hour depositing them in the coin box. The operator, a pleasant girl who spoke a little Spanish, was literally howling with laughter as she counted the money and tried to assess how much was left to be payed. But in the end we got Buenos Aires without too long a wait. Supper was awful; the cook is lousy in this Navy.

After eating, I'm off to the hangar-workshop. As light as day.

Rows of tables are set up in the huge hangar. In the middle there's a big shop selling whatever the heart could desire. An incredible sight. Hundreds of people, from small boys to grandfathers, bent over the tables, working at a fast and furious pace. Their mothers and sisters helping. The drone of engines and piles of models. Everybody's trying to enter the competition in as many categories as possible and many have begun work on their models only here at the base. They're so dedicated, they don't even bother going to sleep. I have my eyes open for anything new and am taking in everything in sight. It's all very impressive. In the USA model plane making itself is big business, but the turnover of motors, boxes of construction materials (kits), accessories, and the like, exceeds a hundred million dollars a year. And the young boys of today interested in model plane making become the engineers and mechanics, aeronautical designers, and pilots of tomorrow. The supply of fresh cadres of aeronautical engineers is a particular headache in the USA. Since 1949 the number of engineering graduates has been continuously declining and has fallen from 50,000 to 19,000 annually. And as with everything else, there's competition here as well with the Soviets. So there's really nothing at all surprising in the fact that an entire air base is put at the disposal for an entire week of people completely absorbed in aeronautics on this smaller scale. All day long, for example, four helicopters pursue models carried somewhat too far and return loaded down with them as though they were bunches of colored flowers.

I stop next to some individual in shorts polishing a handsome model. We get into a conversation. He's a surgeon by profession. "This is excellent relaxation," he said, "and besides, it keeps the fingers in shape." In Guatemala I've also got a surgeon in my group, and the Minister of Enlightenment has just become the attorney for our "Mafia."

I often get discreet visits from *señoras* who thank me because from the time of their friendship with me their prodigal husbands have stopped going out nights. But there are also some who hate me: "Now he's sitting up till one or two in the morning, never wants to go to a movie or anything . . ." Ha!

At nine I take in a film. A Disney short about Franklin. A work of art, an example of the truest art. But that isn't culture. No. In that case, what is it?

July 28, '54

Had a good sleep. Before breakfast, six laps around the pool. Awful breakfast. They ought to conduct an investigation, for certainly the Navy can't be provided for worse than the Air Force. An omelette of powdered eggs! The insolence. In Suffolk, the eggs were nice and fresh and fried to order. I ostentatiously toss the omelette into a garbage can. A sailor standing nearby smiled: "Don't like it?" "I'm not a PW." He roared and went off to tell the others what I said. They've probably had their fill of the cook too. Besides, don't forget the golden rule above the kitchen: "Take as much as you want, but don't want more than you can eat." I point out the inscription to the sailor and say that with such "chow" it's impossible not to want. He laughs even more loudly. After breakfast I go to the airfield and spend the entire morning observing the matches of the radio controlled models. They can go to hell! De Bolt performs acrobatic stunts with his model, all kinds of figures with the exception only of a corkscrew. Some magician even has the wheel brakes guided by radio. The model comes in for a landing, brakes, lets itself down and taxis in. The sky is full of model planes, a real madhouse.

I go for dinner in the first sitting, but walk out. Lamb! I make up my mind to have something to eat in Chicago and immediately board a bus. The whole lakeside area is impressive. After three quarters of an hour, I reach the city. I get off at the Loop. Terribly hot. I read in the paper that they forecast the same kind of scorching heat for the next three days anyway and that tomorrow it's even going to get hotter. Awful. Only somebody who's ever lived through a Chicago heatwave can understand what it means. It never gets so bad in the tropics. I take refuge in an air-conditioned cafeteria and have something to eat, but not much. I'm wearing cotton pants and a nylon net shirt and I'm still a little wet. I take a cab and head for a company I established contact with not long ago when I sent in the first big order. The manager greets me and right away starts calling me "Andrew." So I start calling him "Al." How simple that makes everything. From a pocket bar he extracts some whiskey. He tells me that my order has already been shipped. I explain to him how the invoices should be made out. He calls in a secretary and two workers from the shop. Introductions all around. "They handle Guatemala," he says, "and from now on will arrange everything for you. Please tell them what you've got to have." Then he orders coffee for everybody. That's what I like: a long conference. Sometimes they have a little trouble understanding. They seem to have an "anti-talent" when it comes to exports, nothing more or less than an aversion to all the problems involved in shipping goods out of the country. They're people who deal more with the domestic market. The entire United States doesn't export more than ten per cent of its general production, so in the final analysis export doesn't concern them greatly. I constantly hear the complaints: "What paper work" and "It's a lot of red tape." Fortunately, in New York I sniffed out a company that produces invoice forms specially for export to Guatemala and I have a sample with me. Faces light up. Besides, I import everything by air because it works out more cheaply than by sea. The packaging can be standard, in cardboard boxes. For one wooden box, which you have to use when you ship by sea, you have to pay here as much as an additional ten dollars. From Los Angeles it's even more expensive. For two regular boxes once I paid thirty-four dollars. That's because they were made of wood and there was a lot of manual labor involved. Then I go to the shop and place a new order. It's one thing to order from catalogues and another thing entirely when you have the chance to look things over yourself, try them out, get a look at the ready "display models." This business fascinates me. I can readily understand why Rimbaud could take an interest in the calico trade. Why not? Rubbing up against the hard edges of life can also provide considerable creative satisfaction. In any case, I prefer that to the lachrymose, hypocritical letters of Baudelaire to his mother whom he drained of money his entire life.

Toward evening Al invited me to his home because he wanted to introduce me to his wife. On the way, I see that there are a few trees in Chicago after all. On the ride out we give a lift to one of his workers who lives a bit beyond the city. American cities are now being built horizontally; the age of the blocks, of the gigantic ant heaps has ended. But even if it hasn't completely ended, at least it's ceased being an ideal. The centers of cities are becoming empty of people as the movement of the population is centrifugal, in the direction of the suburbs with their single family houses.

After a short visit at his home, Al invites me for supper to some very elegant restaurant outside the city. The customers looked as though they were in a movie. We speak about other things beside business. I tell him about myself, and it's pleasant for me because I see that he understands me and appreciates what I've been through. I raise the question of the possibility of competition. "Don't give it a thought," he said, "they'll only increase the number of your customers. The main thing is service." That's a word and a concept one meets in the United States at every turn. Here every function is a service, and what's more, a service with a social connotation, and the production of goods means above all "social service." Every new invention is a social good. Either this is hypocritical, or the Americans are by birth one of the most socially minded nations on earth and the only real Socialists of private initiative. I determined not to pass any judgments on America and the Americans for the reason that in the course of a short trip you can't get to know anything really well. The best you can hope for are very general impressions. One of them, from my point of view, is the prophecy that in this century of the "emancipation of the masses" a nation of the American type has the greatest chance for the least painful resolution of a number of questions related to it.

Our whole prejudice toward the Americans, toward the style of civilization and culture created by them, is really nothing more than an aristocratic contempt, an élitist disdain of *seigneurs* of the eighteenth century for the mass culture growing up in front of our very eyes. My second general impression is that this culture may prove to be something entirely different from our prophecies and complaints, for the reason that there is absolutely nothing plebian in the American. I don't know why it was that after spending so many days in a crowd, sleeping in a hall with a thousand cots, I didn't feel at all bad. Pushed here and shoved there in a line to get into the kitchen I didn't feel in the least insulted or, for that matter, impatient. And finally I came to the conclusion that it was due to a complete lack of plebianness, what we in Polish currently call boorishness (chamstwo). Americans are no *fine fleur*, to be sure, but they have lost nearly all traces of the plebian, that something which is so hard to bear in Europe in a crowded third class compartment or during the *heure d'affluence* on the Paris Métro. The American doesn't carry with him the smell of the rabble; he's lost almost completely the *arme Leute Geruch*. Almost nowhere here do you ever catch that odor mixed with the bitter stench of class hatred. The American is no Figaro—the rebellious boor with whom the streets, streetcars, and trains are crammed in Europe.

In one of his letters, Flaubert wrote: "This very fashionable phrase 'social problem' riles me to the core. The day when it's resolved will be the last day of the existence of our planet. Life is an eternal problem, and so is history, and in fact everything. New numbers for addition are constantly jumping up. How do you count the spokes of a wheel when it's revolving? In its emancipationary pride, the nineteenth century imagined that it discovered the sun." It seems to me that as regards the "social problem" the Americans share Flaubert's opinion and certainly for that reason have accomplished more in this area than those who are forever talking about it. And I don't think that they'd care to count the spokes of a wheel while it was held still or that they'd imagine that they discovered the sun. They prefer trying to count the spokes with the wheel moving, which is why they don't always do it well. Despite all its pretensions and theories of dynamism, communism dreams about restraining development, about petrification; it yearns to count the spokes of the stationary wheel. And that is the thing that repels, that has already cost it so much. To say nothing of the pretentious boorishness, ugliness, and plebianness which all the cultural undertakings of communism reflect in one way or another. They remind me always of the wife of the Polish worker who after making money in the black market walked around in furs and had a gold crown made for a healthy front tooth. In Europe everything that isn't truly elite is a hundred times more boorish, vulgar, and plebian than in America.

Generally speaking, it strikes me that the whole European-American conflict is nonsense. Asked once if there was a new direction in European culture, Malraux answered brilliantly that there is no Europe and never was. However, there has been Christianity and the quite nebulous European culture of the seventeenth and eighteenth centuries, alternating between the French-English and the English-French. What is understood today by the concept of Europe can be characterized only in a negative way: "Europe is what Asia is not, for if one wishes to say that it is what America is not, the question becomes very complicated." That's it—it becomes complicated.

What is culture? Frobenius insists that it's *Lebensgefühl*—a feeling for life; Malraux, that it's rather *un accord des sensibilités*, but it seems to me that it is the balanced use of the products of civilization. In accord with my definition I carried away the impression that the Americans are the people who in the present era make use of the products of civilization in a more balanced way than any other on the globe. And if not yet, they certainly are the best prepared to. And when people will be boarding atomic airplanes here the way they now do streetcars, elsewhere they'll still be choking up over the sight of a tractor and Bessemer's pears. That's what the difference will be.

July 29, '54

I'm boycotting the naval breakfast. In the morning I went to the city to take care of some business. I'm not sure if it's hotter; one way or the other, there's just no air. I take a cab and ride out to the Monogram model plane plant. I'm after the exclusive representation and direct factory supply because that way they give bigger discounts over the catalogue list prices. I arrive and enter. A harem of lovely stenographers. They're clean, bathed, elegant, and polished; all are almost a little "too." My pants are a bit dirty and my shirt isn't as clean as it should be and I don't feel myself in this environment. I ask to see the head of the concern. Looks. I give my name and add, "from Guatemala." They almost hit the ceiling. Now they're behaving differently; the exotic struck them. After a brief wait, they call me. An air-conditioned room, the president of the company sitting behind a desk. A cold stare. I begin timidly from the beginning. How I settled in Guatemala, how I began from nothing, I show him photographs, lard everything with details. Now I'm expanding my business, I foresee so much and so much, I know my stuff. I can see as I talk that I'm getting to him. In an entirely different tone, he asks: "Then what is it I can do for you?" I explain. He gets up, gives me catalogues, begins addressing me as Andrew, and I him as Jack, he shows me samples, calls a secretary, makes notes himself; things are beginning to move. We pass next to a discussion of the details, the formalities, packaging. Then we're alone again. Suddenly he says: "Andrew, it occurred to me that before Christmas you may need credit. I'm ready to help you. A thousand or two. But there's just one thing. If you can't pay on time, just write and tell me so openly and sincerely. I can't stand any fooling around." I assure him that I'm a "straight guy" and that I share his sentiments. I also don't like credit, but certainly the necessity could arise. I tell him that after I get through with him I'm going to another firm—Top Flite—on the same business. He picks up the receiver and phones there. He knows them. He speaks with the owner and beginning with, "Mr. so and so is here with me at the moment . . . ," he relates my curriculum vitae to the other fellow with unfeigned enthusiasm. "Please give him whatever help you can; he'll explain the details when he comes over." We part warmly and arrange to meet again in Glenview when the awards are going to be distributed. At Top Flite the ground is already prepared for me. I arrange everything in first-class fashion.

I'm truly charmed by this kind of approach, by the simplicity and straightforwardness of these people. Even though it represented profit for them, I still felt a recognition for me that was genuinely sincere and full of admiration. Beside profit, they *wanted* to help me. It's also to their advantage—of course—but there was something else at work in addition. A kind of feeling of solidarity with my efforts. Not pity, not the gesture of a wealthy man toward a poor one, and not help in our sense, but rather something like a lifting up of me similar to the lifting up of a weaker runner by a stronger one in a long distance race, full of the sportsman's camaraderie. Involuntarily I thought of the goods I had ordered from England which I've already paid for but am still waiting to get six months after the order was placed, and I can't wait any longer.

After dinner, I return to Glenview to lie down a while and rest. Toward evening, I head for the city again to see Cinerama. I like it very much. The three dimensional effect is nearly perfect. I'm sitting in a chair and when Venice is shown from the vantage point of a floating gondola, I have the feeling that I'm seated in the gondola and I have the desire to duck my head every time we pass under the bridges. Leaving the air-conditioned theater is like diving into an oven.

July 30, '54

I'm due to fly again before noon. More for sport than to achieve any particular results. It's a big mass flight, beautifully organized. I make the acquaintance of Donald, a young American dental student, and Jim, a movie projector operator from some small town. We have a lot of fun, and at noon, after five scheduled rounds, we ride in Donald's car to a restaurant for dinner. The whole day is spent roaming around the airfield and looking at the matches.

August 1, '54

Donald has become my shadow. Today the festive conclusion of the matches. I'm sure that all of a quarter of the population of the city of Chicago turned out at the base. The Navy demonstrates its planes. A Cutlass breaks the sound barrier. The chief item on the program is a display by the famed flying acrobatic team, the Blue Angels. It's as though they were bound by an invisible link; a distance of three feet between the wings. Five blue Panther jets dance the most modern ballet in the sky. I feel chills running up my spine when they change formation during a "looping." You get the feeling that they can't help colliding. It was worth coming here. The nearly full week I spent camped at Glenview was a better rest for me than a month's vacation. Something interesting going on from morning till evening. I went around all the time like a wound up alarm clock and something inside me kept on ringing and waking up.

August 2, '54

Morning. This time they took us to New York in a comfortable DC-4 with armchairs ("for the brass"). I'm sorry it's all over. At noon I return to the Claridge. Evening, dinner with M. and a movie. I buy a paper on the way in and I'm dumbstruck. In big letters on the first page: "Revolution in Guatemala." My beloved country. You can't leave it for two weeks. The army Polytechnic rebelled and suddenly attacked units of Castillo Armas's forces of liberation occupying a huge unfinished hospital in one of the suburbs of the capital. The army didn't hold out. As soon as I got back to the hotel, I put in a call to Pan American. Flights to Guatemala temporarily discontinued.

August 5, '54

The situation in Guatemala is rapidly clearing up and they managed to quiet this recent case of hiccups. But I was afraid. The embassies were full of "los camaradas" and if liberated, they might achieve in a frenzy of despair what they couldn't manage to do previously.

These days in Chicago are so pleasant I've lost all sense of time and now I don't even remember if it all happened yesterday or when. Meetings and conversations with people. After years of solitude I must get control of myself so as not to throw myself at everybody's necks.

One morning I called at a Polish bookshop. Picked up a few books. Wittlin, Lechoń, the last two volumes of Wierzyński's poems. When I got back to the hotel, in the very heart of New York, I lay the entire afternoon immersed in poetry. I had no desire to go anywhere. I forgot about the rest of the world. Gombrowicz once raked poetry over the coals and I jumped with joy. He was quite right.

Poetry is clearly one of the most difficult of all arts. It doesn't tolerate any bluffing. The smallest drop of graphomania in a poem leaves a stain like a blot on a napkin. In prose it's a lot easier to dispose of cheap trash and rubbish. There are a great many works in prose about which it's hard to decide whether they're *Hintertreppenliteratur* or something more. A poem is an act of decision or the work of a true poet, or more or less deft graphomania. And what's truly amazing is how this particular branch of art holds a particular attraction for graphomaniacs. As a rule, graphomania discharges itself usually first in verse. The worst thing, however, is that with many writers this form of discharge lasts their entire lives. With Poles, it's a national malady. How much of it weaves its way through journals. And usually they're the ones who shout the loudest that they're true poets. The aggressiveness of this gang of poetic snots is disarming. It seems to such a type that as soon as he slaps a few words together which the devil himself isn't able to understand, then he's great precisely because he's incomprehensible. His head is in the clouds. I can't abide that kind of greatness and as a rule I don't give a hoot for poetry. But this time I drowned in it. It's as though there was nothing to the poems I read. Simple? Too simple. Rhymes? Yes—and how. A scandal, in that case. Right away to the antiquarian book shop. Understandable? Still worse. One can say about so-called modern art (does it exist?) whatever one wants, but I do know one thing: above everything else, it's boring, boundlessly boring. When I listen to, read or look at these works, I'm always reminded of the fragment of a letter of Houston St. Chamberlain to Dujardin: "I recently sent my servant to a performance of *Tannhaüser*. She returned dazzled. "Oh, how pretty it is," she said, "but how prettier it'd be if there wasn't any music at all." Great poets, especially great lyric poets in the world today you can count on your fingers. Wierzyński is certainly one of them. No—violets don't blossom for him any more, and it's too bad they don't. But that's it. He didn't stop and he penetrated to the depths, without pretense, without any pseudo-philosophy.

August 8, '54

I overslept and missed the bus out to the airport. So I raced there with a cab and spent the rest of the money I had. At the airport I exchanged a few stamps so as to have some change, if only for a soda. An all-night flight; in New Orleans from one plane to another and then farther. I was home in time for dinner. My old friend, the punctual rain, greets me in the afternoon. The eucalyptuses smell fragrant, rolls of banana leaves stretch themselves out, it's quiet. The kittens have grown some in the meantime, the rabbit has once again chosen freedom and run off to the bamboo groves. So much work is waiting for me I'd rather not think about it. But the main thing is, I'm back in my hut again.

Translated by Harold B. Segel

Zygmunt Haupt

Lili Marlene

Sara, Sarusia, was the name of a Jewish girl who used to come around and wait for Wojciechowski at our barracks gate. This gave tremendous amusement to the rest of us, and of course prompted us to repeat a silly, trivial, popular couplet:

> Margot, unhappy girl, walking barracks street
> In hope and in despair, to find someone to meet . . .

We were hilariously amused by the spectacle of this persistent watch, but, as a matter of fact, there was something terrifying in all this. Taking into account the social circumstances, which made it somehow natural, it was at the same time abnormal, as this girl was really all the time on the lookout at the barracks gate, for hours, and in full view of strangers milling to and fro and of everyone aware of what went on. But she didn't give a damn, she just waited. There were rumors that she was the daughter of someone of importance, of a Jewish business man, a rich merchant, who was also a kind of rabbi and an official with the local Jewish community Kahal. So the affair acquired a scandalous air of some dimensions. A Jewess, infatuated with a "goy," and, to top it, at the barracks, and in full public view. So, if we were amused at this show, we were at the same time somehow embarrassed, and feeling quite awkward.

On top of that, Sara, Sarusia, was the type of female beauty, of woman's charm, which escapes all superlatives. As a matter of fact, she wasn't a woman, she was a girl, a very young girl. How old was she? Sixteen, seventeen? So any description—enchanting, lovable, marvelous—wouldn't do, but really she was *charming*. To consider her eyes—what were they like? Grey, framed by black eyelashes and delicate eyebrows, rounded cheeks, and hair falling on her neck and forehead, and her smile naïve and childish, and her bosom heaving with a sigh, and she wasn't embarrassed at all, she was shameless!

Of the Jews of this place it was said that they were of the utmost stupid species, of a proverbial, biblical stupidity, and there were many stories about it. For example, a saying which may not be very funny, but perhaps up to a degree: "As stupid as the Jewish Cantor of Chłąd turkeybird," which was supposed to express the essence of stupidity, the apogee of imbecility, of limitless simplicity of wits. Or there was a story derived from Jewish folklore, the case of "the Jews of Chłąd who Captured the Moon in a Well," if you please. According to this story, the Jews of Chłąd, espying a trembling image of the Moon reflected in the water mirror of a well, hastily covered the opening of the shaft and boasted that by this stratagem they had captured and held fast this heavenly body. Even in London the Jews of Chłąd acquired fame, because the Directors of the Bank of England, of The Old Lady of Threadneedle Street, keep in the Bank's stronghold and show with pride a five pound note, which once strayed far away to Chłąd in Poland, where the Jewish Kahal certified with several signatures upon it that this bill represented genuine money.

Well, enough is enough. The Jews of Chłąd were of a quite different species from, let us say, our Jews in my Galician part of Poland. Our Jews were a kind of Chassidim; there was something horrific in their extreme orthodoxy, and those of Chłąd were of another kind, akin rather to the former Tsarist Russian Litvaks. No long *chalats* could be seen here, like our Chassidim wore; the only attire distinguishing them was their dainty round caps with little visors, imposed on them in Tsarist times. But they were living, as Jews do in their Jewish way, tightly together, apart, by themselves in their ghetto, which really wasn't a ghetto but business streets, lined with shops, streets thronged by a black crowd, and "black" it had to be, gabbling and active in pursuit of business, a pitifully mediocre business indeed of big deals in coppers!

One day I happened to witness there the most pathetic Jewish scene I have ever seen in my whole life. Walking up the Main Street, one busy day in broad daylight, making my way through the crowd of businessmen, agents, merchants, and pedlars, I stumbled upon this spectacle: In the center of the thoroughfare a small unit of Shomrs, of Jewish Boy Scouts, was parading. They were marching in step, wearing some kind of uniforms and neckerchiefs, and, as all Boy Scouts do, they sported all kinds of regulation devices and insignias. I recollect now that their heads were bare, no caps, which was in pitiful and embarrassing imitation of the style of the Hitlerjugend. So they were marching, those Jewish boys, in step, their heads stiffly erect and their hair tousled by the wind. The downtown crowd was obviously excited and enthusiastic, to see their own youth boldly emerging from the ghetto, in such a martial posture, with such resolution, in such an organized way, marching in broad daylight through the main thoroughfare of the town, in step, in formation, with their heads up.

And then I noticed an old Jew who trotted alongside, infatuated with this spectacle, who trotted not along the sidewalk but in the gutter running by the curb, stumbling and trying to keep pace with this handful of youngsters, oblivious of everyone else but those boys, trotting along, not seeing other people, brushing past them, unable to perceive anything else but those youngsters, and his pale eyes shed tears into his dirty, tussled beard. What was he stricken with, here under the grey cloudy sky of this land, thousands of miles away from the Milk-and-Honey-flowing Land of the Lion of Judah and of the Maccabees, of olive and fig trees, of locusts and gazelles, of the Ark of the Covenant and of the Wailing Wall, in this land which he himself and his kin called Polin, which supposedly in Hebrew meant: "Here you will settle and repose." A poor old Jew, gulping air with his laboring Adam's apple, oblivious of everything but this handful of youngsters, trotting along in the gutter, with dirty tears flowing down his face.

And the town itself looked like this: On the top of the Hill, which also bore the name of Chłąd, was a post-Basilian Order Baroque church, formerly the Cathedral of the Greek Catholic Bishopric, and, close by, a cemetery. About the cemetery I will have something to say later on, as this will lead to associations which I feel awkward about discussing now, as this cemetery. . . well, we will talk about it later on. Up the Main Street, bordered with shops and boutiques, was a Classic High School *Gymnasium*, where, as is quite well known, well meaning liberal arts teachers and other fellows radiating pure enthusiasm were publishing quite irregularly a sort of little magazine named *Dikte,* a prose and poetry magazine of the province, and if you ask from whence came this strange name—sure, it was just to make the magazine more difficult to understand. Well, with the best wishes for this enterprising provincial avant-garde Pleiade, let's proceed with our story.

Our barracks lined one side of the street (and our barracks knew the old times, when they housed a Tsarist Horse Artillery Regiment in low, wooden, log structures, weathered and crooked, with rows of stables and a big riding-ring in the center). On the other side of the street, by-passing the barracks, the street where Sara used to wait, was level, empty ground, the location of our gunnery drills and horse-drawn caisson maneuvers—what larks! Further on were the grey and yellow walls of the Insane Asylum, looking inhuman and cruel, where our insane brethren, our unhappy brethren, were treated with the therapy of water douches and strait jackets, supposedly to be helped in this way, as they, contrary to ourselves, were supposedly abnormal.

And on the other side of the Hill was a different town, a new one. And it was a strange experience to stray there. A housing development of healthy, ruddy-colored brick, set there according to all esthetic, utilitarian, good city-planning rules, well planned and studied beforehand, and—empty. So what, why? You know, one of the big government establishments was to have been moved here from the central part of the country, so that's why it was so well planned, deliberated all over again, and this in very hard times economically, with no means, when other cities had to wait for months and years for credit opportunities, and meanwhile their jobless construction workers, getting their meager unemployment dole, were sunning themselves during the inactive summer, buying bread by half and quarter loaves, waiting and waiting. With the long, jobless summer over, nothing happened again, the credit possibilities were as futile as ever. Came the autumn, a fat one and plentiful, but somehow nothing happened. Eventually, with the end of autumn those slowly milling gods' millstones, those reluctantly turning cogs of the depression economy, at last gave some grist of achievement. In late autumn, in rainy weather, carts with building material began to roll, ditches dug out for foundations filled with stagnant water, and well into the winter construction works were under way. Here, somehow, suddenly, a new city grew up, a well-planned affair with streets, avenues, curbs, streetlights, with everything solidly set in, even street signs nattily displayed on their posts, marking avenues and streets, Mikolaj Rey Street, Romuald Traugutt Street, Avenue of The Roses, Avenue of the Chevaux-Légers—everything so trim and nice. Only wait! There was something askew here. A special commission called to review the whole enterprise and check the final results found some serious flaws, deficiencies as to the rules and standards of public safety requirements. Therefore everything came to a stop half done. And the town, grown up in such a very American manner, remained empty, uninhabited, condemned to a long wait for decisions which were to drag slowly, and so this new city was left humanless and haunted, with its empty streets, Traugutt Street, and avenues, The Cheveaux-Légers Avenue, silent, except for the rain and wind whistling along brand new tin drains of roofs and windows of the dwellings, black eyesockets.

So let us shun for a while this humanly abortive business and enterprise, let us find something of more cheerful interest.

For example, on our way back from a patrol of the Recce squad, or was it maybe from a hunt, a simple, improvised affair, going on horseback cross-country, through ravines, woods, at a gallop, in a swarm of riders, in pursuit of an illusion, when hooves thud, beating the exact rhythm of an anapest. (Whence this analogy with prosody? Didn't I say before, on some occasion, that the simple command of the corporal, the army buck sergeant, is pronounced with the rhythm and measured beat of, if I can put it so, almost a poetic phrase? When, if you please, this corporal utters a crisp command bark: "Kas-pe-rek! Take cover!" he does it by putting a definite stress, an accent on "rek!", and fat Kasperek, spurred by the unlearned but intuitive stress and rhythm of the corporal's command, jumps up to it, huddles to mother earth, involved, sharing and in full accord with the poetic stylistics of the corporal's command, which helps so much to drill (recruits). Now, what was I saying? Aha, about this horse's gallop, which sounds like an anapest, ta-ta-tam! for which we, from times immemorial, were always on the alert, putting our ears to the ground, listening for the sound of an oncoming raid, invasion, pursuit, for the thud of hooves, a portent of fear, disaster, things unexpected.

And now we slowed, going down the gentle slope of some field, with its wheat stubble, spreading farther on. Close by we passed a group of farm workers, some hired hands, harvesters, those "laborious" ones, bent over the local crop. The kerchiefs of the women, the men's white shirts, faces red with sunburn and toil and perspiration, movements round and somehow dignified, of those people bent over their fieldwork.

Amidst this group there was, I remember, a girl. I presume she wasn't a married woman, in Ukrainian *nevistka.* (Let us take note that Chłąd country is the terrain of an ethnic boundary, where a meandering invisible line marks the division between Poles and Ukrainians, where, as always with such ethnic abutments, the Polish is somehow very distinct, as if to make perceptive this boundary dividing Poles and Ukrainians. The population of this frontier region speaks a very correct Polish, devoid of any sing-song, stresses, dialect phonetics, just a pure, almost upper-class, literary Polish.) The girl straightened up, brushing the strands of tawny hair clinging to her eyelashes and eyebrows, her face rosy from sunburn and toil.

I pondered how it was that this fitted so closely my idea of the life design here, fitted so much the entourage, the landscape, this blend of the static posture of a girl and the kinetic movement of horses, which is reflected in all folk art, particularly in a folk tale, a folk song ("*Jasio konie poił Kasia wodę brala . . .*", "*Starsza soistra brata miała, no wojenkę go wysłała. . .*"). So I pondered the time of exaltation, of youth. (And, by the way, this folk song dispenses so easily and carelessly, when needed, with the usual Polish stress on the penultimate syllable, you know, moving it to the last one for the sake of a rare masculine rhyme, as otherwise the song cannot be put to the tune.)

And at the barracks gate Sara was waiting. This utterly amused us, and when Wojciechowski wasn't around we dared to sing:

> Margot, unhappy girl, walking barracks street,
> In hope and in despair, to find someone to meet . . .

But there was no cruelty nor maliciousness in it, we even probably liked the situation, in spite of the fact that it was scandalous. And the ditty was stupid, as usually such couplets from vaudeville or operetta are trite. Years later another song was to become quite famous, a popular ditty equally trivial, with the same theme of a girl waiting at the barracks gate, eager to meet a soldier of any rank. This other song was destined to make a success, a career, somewhere in the desert, amidst sand, trenches, and tank raids, this husky voice of a chance performer, some Swedish songstress's husky voice, made even more scratchy when reproduced by the much worn-out war booty victrola record, a song which was to add to this war a certain kind of shabby romanticism, cheap nostalgia, tearful wistfulness.

How odd it is that the history of this song repeated itself years later, returning in some peculiar cycle, spiral, resounding in an echo, on a different occasion, under a faraway sky, at the prompting of some other people. As if it were forseen by this so self-conscious philosopher, Giambattista Vico, who in his periwig, breeches, and ribbons, surrounded by stucco and cypress and pine trees against the robin's-egg-blue sky and sea of Naples, pondered over his parchments, thoughtfully rubbing his nose with a quill, an obsequious magician of old. Maybe, dipping his quill in his ink-pot, he hummed to himself:

Margot, unhappy girl, walking barracks street . . .

Well, these Jews of Chłąd. They differed from those of our section. Our Galician Jews were to me quite commonplace, even if they terrified others. Isaac Babel himself, a bold man, was horrified by our Chassidim. Babel, a Jew from Odessa, a tough, full-blooded rationalist, brought up among the Black Sea waterfront throng, on the abutment of the steppe, the Liman bayou waters, and the sea, where the shirtblouses and caps of peasants, watermelons and wine, Polish landowners, business exchange merchants and bandits of the Odessa suburb of Moldavyanka, Tsarist police, and rich merchants and speculators were mixed up, Babel, who followed the Red Cavalry, at its tail, and amidst slogans and banners of the Revolution was hastily setting propaganda prints, poring, with his myopic person's nose over the galley proofs—to him our Galician Jews were terrifying, with their synagogue windows sunk deep into the rubbish-covered ground and through which you could distinguish praying figures, with their *tales*, and *tefilim* on their foreheads, their *khedr* schools and their *melamed* teachers and little scholars, curls at the temple, swaying over books, the mezuzas on door sills, at the town boundaries "ajruv" wire strands marking the imaginary walls, and on the east side of *Bimah* in the synagogue, a *mizrah* with its scrolls of Holy Writing. A separate, set-aside world, from which only fragments of exotic language reach us, some of which we can make out, as with *pod Chajrem*, which means a kind of vow; *hutzpah*, impudence; *chazuka*, designating a certain monopolistic privilege, a right of possession; a *balagula*, the Master of a Carriage, or simply a Jewish teamster; and *shaibetz* is a slab of stone, marking a grave in a Jewish cemetery. Of course, the Jews of Chłąd used a similar vocabulary, but they were of a different kind.

One time, years later, in New Orleans, my wife told me about a local old lady who, while reading the morning paper at her breakfast table, first scanned the obituary page, to see if "anybody nice" had died recently. Now I have acquired the same kind of curiosity myself, and when I get hold of a weekly from Poland, the *Tygodnik Powszechny*, I look for the same kind of column. There you always find a score of well-known names, with their titles and short biographies. Lately, I stumbled there upon the name of Colonel Chmura. Thus it said, so and so, in 1919 he led a Troop of Artillery, in 1920 he was a battery commander, then he commanded such and such Regiment, eventually the Divisional Artillery, and he was a chevalier of many medals and orders, and he was also a member of many civic organizations, and in conclusion, at the very end: "a former employee of the state toy industry." Hmmmh. . . . When I was a youngster myself, an artillery cadet, after my military reserve officer's training school in Włodzimierz Wołynski, I was ordered to join for a time an artillery regiment stationed in Chłąd, at which time Colonel Chmura was commander of this unit. He was its ultimate lord and god, master of life and death over several hundred men and horses, over scores of heavy, olive-colored, greasy guns, protected by their steel armor, with their heavy rimmed wheels. Over the row of log barracks, numerous stables with their ruddy electric lights burning night and day, over horses, their shiny haunches groomed by gunners, over the elegant officer's mess, over a great riding ring square with its whitewashed horse-jump obstacles, "kopertas" and "triple bars," of a kingdom resounding at noon with a trumpet call to forage.

(So, this heavy officer, with his saturnine-featured face, Olympic, distant, and godlike, eventually finished up manufacturing toys for tots. About the destiny of another high ranking cavalry officer,

Polish émigré gossip whispers that he ended up in Canada, a helper to a *shames*, sweeping the floor of a nice, progressive synagogue there.)

The Regimental Order of the Day read as follows: "The Ront Patrol Service: Batteries will muster their Recce horse squads, who with Regimental Command Squad will report in full battle readiness, with live ammunition issued, and mounted, at the Stand To Regimental Alarm Post, at 21:00." It was the first of May.

I beg your pardon, I almost forgot about the Cemetery. Now, where were they to hide, Wojciechowski and Sara, where were they to seek privacy for their play, maybe to ponder over their troubles? Wait now, I didn't suspect Wojciechowski to be the troubled one. Anyway, the Cemetery was the only suitable place, shady, overgrown with a screen of greenery of gelder rose, lilacs, dogwood, laurel. Situated in the vicinity of the post-Basilian Cathedral, it wasn't used for burial any more, and, overgrown with bushes and getting to be quite a jungle, as usually happens with old cemeteries, it became an ideal, not-too-frequented parking place for those who looked for privacy, the kind of place very common to any provincial town. No Peeping Toms, maybe the only "voyeur" there was the black skeleton of the Greek Catholic Bishop, Vladyka Tzaslav Lutsky reposing there under the vault of black stones eaten by fungi, with his hand in its pearl-embroidered glove and an episcopal ring on its finger, blessing the union of this sinful couple.

And we, the other cadets, who were we? Short and puffy Księżycki, Góralczyk, in civilian life an embryo newspaper man, very smart, showing a set of bad teeth in his smile, Emil Milowicz, who sported a different set of rather horsy teeth—Emil Milowicz of Modryniec, from near Hrubieszów, who years later was butchered by Bandera partisans. We, we were discreet, except when humming for our own amusement:

Margot, unhappy girl, walking barracks street . . .

We were absorbed in horses, "łozy," willow cutting at sabre exercises, and playing poker, losing cash to some more experienced hands.

No one asked why they didn't look for solitude in the Jewish cemetery, the Kirkut. Maybe because the Jewish cemetery was at some distance, somewhere at the periphery of the town, kept in good shape, with its tombstones leaning in all directions, with their epitaphs engraved in Hebrew, in strange letters, trying to tell something to the passerby. Maybe those graphs told of the genealogy of the people buried there, repeating in monotone: ". . . and Amon begot Josiah, and Josiah begot Jehonias, and Jehonias begot Salatiel, and Salatiel begot. . ." or maybe quotations from the Book of Esther, or from Solomon's Songs, and, higher above, signs and symbols hewn in stone, nine-branched candelabra and The Lion of Judah, or hands held up in a gesture of blessing, or a ceremonial Horn Shofar. But the Jewish cemetery was protected, guarded by a "goy" watchman, whose duty was not to let anyone in. And then came the time of disaster and this Jewish cemetery was put to ruin, its tombstones torn out of the ground and used as paving, made into sidewalks in little provincial towns, flagstones to be trodden upon by sacrilegious crowds indifferent to human memory, and I learned from people coming from Poland that, walking the streets of those places, you might tread on a nine-branched candelabra, on the above-mentioned Lion of Judah, all this still distinct under your foot. Only children, on their way back home from school, as children do, hopscotching on one foot, tried to avoid stepping on those images in the stone slabs, and one ponders if they were puzzled by this strange, unexplained pattern which was unfamiliar to them, this human enigma so lost after only a score of years that it seemed to them as inexplicable as the stelas of Inca palaces dug out of the earth, or the proud Roman inscription on a pediment, SENATUS POPULUSQUE ROMANUS, or the faint, rubbed-out traces of suras on old Arabian arabesques.

Years ago, when I happened to pass the Plain of Salisbury, I visited there the famous Stonehenge, the circle, or maybe I should say the Grand Circle of enormous stones, hauled from remote distances and set up there, for some unexplained reason, maybe to measure something, an astrolabe on a gigantic scale, or for the sake of some cult, all this a matter of much speculation to those who try to solve the puzzles of the past. Now it happened that amidst this mute and enigmatic antiquity I almost trod, in the dusk of evening light, on an object lying in this English grass, on an obvious, trivial rubber product, a so-called contraceptive. As at the time I was quite inclined to philosophical contemplations, I mused over this paradox and contrast, what about those prehistoric stones, with thousands and thousands of years behind them, an abyss of time, ennobling everything, those stones erected here by the hands of human hordes lost long ago; and in the same setting a bawdy accent, rather an unintentional if conspicuous jest, left here, a joke played at the expense of time, by some careless couple.

Now, someone may ask, why am I overloading this simple story with so many digressions, hardly connecting with each other? There I am, telling about the Jews of Chłąd, setting them in such a provincial panorama, putting in also a quite meaningless story about a beautiful Jewish girl and a sturdy cadet, who takes her out to the privacy of a post-Basilian cemetery, I add to this an almost Gothic description of some modern gruesome ruins, and to top it off I mention even the name of the provincial poetry magazine, *Dikte* (of course it was taken from the name of the classic Greek nymph, someone learned in books explained to us), and for contrast, and as if to counter the Jewishness of this story, I am hinting at things familiar, Polish folklore represented by another girl. The same one who straightened herself up in the field, screening her face with her hand, having a look at the riders passing by. So I, to compose the situation nicely, to round it out prettily, make it smart and nonchalant and in tune, to appear a daredevil in the presence of others, to say something from the height of the saddle, to show myself, I called to her: "Don't be so shy!" To which she snapped back: "Why, shy? of whom?" She just riposted, and that's all. And why wasn't I able to tell it to Sarusia, to warn her with the words of the song:

> "O Danube, Danube, with your stormy water,
> Beware my girl, beware my little daughter. . . ."

But today it is too late, now it cannot be done. I cannot warn my young sister, who is on the way to being a fast girl. Even the memory of her darling beauty is getting obliterated, as if seen through a haze, and it is the same with her world, the world of her people, which was lost, leaving behind only *shaybezes*, tombstones with the likeness of the Lion on them, of hands raised in blessing, of the crooked horn called Shofar, sounded at the ceremony of the Jewish New Year, and even the signs on those flagstones, turned into sidewalk pavings of little towns, are being obliterated by the tread of human feet, losing their meaning, and to children on their way back home from school appearing enigmatic and incomprehensible as things which were a thousand years ago.

* * *

Black night, under black clouds, on the first day of the month of May, we were leading our horses out of the stables, hard, reluctant, ponderous. Blindfolded by darkness, putting on saddle-blankets, belaying the surcingle strap ends with our teeth, with a hand between the girth and the horse's belly testing if it is tight enough, putting on bridles and steel bits, while the beasts lay their ears back, close their teeth tight and viciously kick and squeal. A carbine strap pinching under the throat, hurt by the pouches loaded with ammunition, with sabres strapped to the saddle, beating the horses' sides—at the command "Mount!" black silhouettes of riders rise over dark shapes of horses into a dark sky.

In close fours, when horses heave at each other and push with their bellies, with top boots pressed tightly by neighbors, with creaking saddle leather and clang of steel stirrups striking one another in close formation, with carbine straps pressing at the throat, pinched by all these leather trappings, confused by the unfamiliar situation, frightened by the kicking of the animals being saddled, with bridle reins entangled awkwardly in our stiff hands blue with cold, with a bitter taste in our throats and darkness in our eyes, with chinstraps of our garrison caps tight under our chins, with darkness in eyes and nostrils filled with the preservative in our uniforms and with our stable stench, with the rough material of our greatcoats rubbing our necks, peering into the night from under the visors of caps set deep on our ears, in close formation of fours, squeezing through the barracks gate, we rode in a thud and clatter of horses' hooves over a cobblestoned street, downtown, to meet the stupid Jews of Chłąd.

Translated by the Author

Józef Łobodowski

I Was Not Born for Battle

I was not born for any earthly battle,
but fate spared me none,
and my rhyme vainly sought
to grow wings of melodious rhythm.

When hardly conscious I wandered through the town,
and dewy lilacs were blooming in doorways,
you were approaching like a storm in springtime,
lifting my feet into swirling depths.

And when my lips pouting like a bud
broke into a whistle of a naughty urchin,
you were crowding darkly into the guard-room,
thrusting a Phrygian cap into my hands.

And I came to love that poisoned hop
with which, wench of ill-omen, you slaked my thirst,
that every evening I should wake
the drowsy, deaf windows and take my aim.

In the sepulchral silence of teeming towns
I grew into a wail upon the barricades,
watching the skyline glow above the roofs,
but there saw nothing save the stars above.

The bitter drink spun in the head,
the fiddle caused the heart to sob
while beyond the panes silvery welders
hammered throbbing fiery rails.

The inn like a ferry upon dark night
lulled with hops into a musical stream,
what was she? . . . a poem? a cry of revolt?
What was she saying to future days?

The faint tread of a hesitant foot,
dreams burned out in a senseless fight
and a song battling against the span of time,
with a holocaust of youthful days.

So thus proclaim *non omnis moriar*
to bitter verses that mean nothing now,
when the whole of life is like a murky tale
told to scare a gathered throng.

Translated by Jerzy Baran

Józef Łobodowski

Horses in War (fragments from "In Praise of Horses")

Painted uhlans rode and thundered:
the dream of steeds chestnut and dun;
rosemary songs are still remembered,
still woven in the golden sun . . .

Is it dawn breaking or is the town on fire?
Sparks fly over infantry and transports,
swarming in dusty manes like fiery flies;
beneath heavy feet broad tracts shudder,
shattered glass crunches
like gravel on Vistula's banks.

Towards smoky conflagrations weary horses stumble
shrouded in a haze of poisonous vapors;
listening, alert on evening patrol,
decimated in wild lunatic charges.
In the dark I hear a plaintive, anxious voice:
Whom does your painful cry
accuse?

A broken sorrowful whimper,
that quiet animal moan more desperate than a child's.
Blue sparks leap over wounding wires,
missiles drop from above.
In a roadside ditch a horse tears at thickly growing clover,
a wise look in its dark lamenting eye,
as though it knew better than we the bitter seed of causes
growing in manly hearts
with a spasm of blood and pain.

An explosion shatters bricks and scatters choking lime,
a running soldier halts, stumbles and falls;
fleecy clouds sail aloft, a bouncing shrapnel
thuds into a bunch of horses tied up in an orchard
and blood from a gashed neck flows into the dark earth.
The horse rears, jerks heavily up, eyes now covered in mist;
still smells the moist juicy grass,
still with dull neighing calls his master,
tugs the stiff bridle
but the blue blood-drunken flies
crawl along the nostrils
and the foaming mouth.

* * *

By thy passion, Christ,
and Thy holiest wounds,
Thou, who comest on horseback in a silver armor to meet my dreams,
send Thy peace to murdered horses
and let light eternal
shine upon them hereafter!

Translated by Jerzy Baran

Czesław Miłosz

Magdalena

From the *Valley of the Issa*

A FEW days before the Feast of the Assumption they brought Magdalena's coffin. It was covered with a brightly colored blanket, and rested on a bed of hay at the bottom of a big farm wagon. The horses had stopped in the shade of the great lime trees, and now drowsily swished their tails as they dipped their heads low into their feedbags, nibbling oats from the bottom; they had come a long way. The news spread so fast that even before the man who had brought the body had tied the reins to the fence people had begun to gather and stood in a knot waiting to see what would happen. High up on the hill Father Paskva appeared. He stood motionless on the flat stones of the path, as if trying to make up his mind whether to descend or not. Or was he, perhaps, summoning up courage? At long last, slowly, he started down. Again he stopped, pulled out a handkerchief, and began to crumple and twist it in his fingers.

The scandal over Magdalena had lasted about six months, and it was she who had brought it about. It could have been avoided. Father Paskva had found her at the rectory when he arrived—she had kept house for the old rector—and what happened between them was nobody's business. A priest, after all, is human. But Magdalena began to carry-on quite shamelessly: she went about with her chin high, swaying her hips, almost dancing. She took perverse delight in coming up to the rector and addressing him in a way that plainly told all other women: you may kiss his hands and vestments, but he is mine, all mine. Which, of course, led people to imagine how he, the same man they saw at the altar, lay with her naked in bed, and what they told each other, and what they did. Now, everyone knows that a great deal can be forgiven in such matters, but only as long as it does not evoke fancies that can't be banished from the mind.

The people of Ghinye, after going over Magdalena's behavior in endless discussions, concluded that there had been something wrong with the wench even earlier, during those two years she worked for the old parson. Remember how her marriage had come to naught? And how the lad had married someone else almost at once? No, it was not just on account of her age (she must have been close to twenty-five) or because she was poor, the child of landless peasants, and a stranger in these parts. No. The lad, at first, would not even listen to reason; he was going to marry her against his parents' wishes. And yet at the last minute he took fright and changed his mind. A wanton, that's what she was; the girl knew no bounds in anything. And there had been other similar incidents, too, that appeared now in a fresh light. It all fitted together. And if anyone had doubts still—here was her coffin, now.

Because Antonina, Granny's housekeeper, spat whenever she uttered Magdalena's name, Thomas, too, had turned against her, although there was no reason why he should. Back in Father "Well-Well" 's days, whenever he showed up at the rectory, Magdalena would beckon to him to come to the kitchen, and there she gave him cookies. To tell the truth, he had thought her wonderful then, and his throat had contracted whenever she came near. Her skirts rustled, the tight band pinched her waist, and every time she leaned over the kitchen range to taste a dish with a spoon, a loose strand of hair slipped over one ear, and inside her blouse a breast dangled. Besides, there was a bond between them, because Thomas knew what she looked like, and she didn't know that he knew. That had been a sin, of course, and he had told it in confession. But even so—he knew. The tree that leaned far out over the water was easy to climb, and Thomas had hidden among the foliage, his heart pounding: would she come, or wouldn't she? The river shone all pink in the sunset. A fish shot out. He became engrossed in a flight of ducks, and before he knew it, there she was, feeling the water with her toes and already pulling her skirt over her head. She went in not the way most women did by squatting several times with a splash, but slowly, getting deeper and deeper. Her breasts opened to the sides, and she was not very black under the belly, just a little so. She plunged forward, and kicking up little fountains of water, she dog-paddled to the spot where water-lily pads covered the surface, then she turned back and on the shore washed herself with soap.

The scandal reached Thomas' ears only in snatches—never clear, yet horrifying. How could anyone who thundered against sin be a sinner himself? And if he who grants absolution is no better than anyone else, what is the absolution worth? Not that Thomas actually asked himself these questions. Nor would he ever dare to ask them of his elders. Magdalena acquired in his eyes the fascination of "things-you-must-never-mention." The grown-ups were furious with her, but they drew distinctions—something that Thomas was unable to do. To them Magdalena was one thing, and the priest, once he put on the chasuble, something else again. Nevertheless, she had upset the pattern, disturbed their peace, and spoiled their pleasure in listening to his sermons.

Father Paskva was coming down the hill, and everyone was agog to see what he would order done with the coffin. But then, as he approached the wagon, heads began to turn away—because he was crying. Tears streamed down his face, his mouth twitched. He clamped his lips tight, then opened them again, but only to ask that the body be taken up the hill—to church. He meant to give the suicide a Christian burial. They took off the blanket, and the white pine coffin appeared. Four men picked it up. As they climbed the steep incline Magdalena was almost standing up.

* * *

To take rat poison one must not only lose all hope but also give way to one's thoughts to the point where they obliterate the world so that in the end one sees nothing except one's fate. Magdalena might have lived to know many other things: new cities, countries, inventions, people, books; she might have gone through many a metamorphosis open to human beings. She might have. But it would have been useless to tell her so. Nor would it have helped if, with the wave of a magic wand, one could have shown her other women, millions of them, who were just like her, and had suffered just as she had. Even if a sudden flash of understanding had made her realize the despair of those who, at the very moment she was administrating death to herself, were struggling for yet one more hour, one more minute of life—what would have been the use? By the time thoughts ebb and the body finds itself faced with the ultimate horror—it is already too late.

Keep in mind that shortly before the old rector's departure, Magdalena had been plunged into a state of utter dejection. It was just about then that her betrothed had jilted her. The blow to that love had left her with an icy lump inside, and with a dull conviction that from now on nothing would ever change. Everything inside her rebelled at the prospect. No. No. Things could not stay that way. How was she to go on living, knowing that day would follow day, always the same, year in and year out, until she turned into an old crone. She woke up at dawn, and lay still with her eyes wide open, terrified at the thought of getting up and resuming her chores once more. She sat in bed, and cupped her breasts in her hands; they too had been rejected, left to share her spinsterhood and wither uselessly. What else was left? Was she to run after boys at Saturday dances, let them take her to the barn or out in the meadow, and have them laugh at her afterward? By the time Father Paskva arrived to take over the parish she was close to black despair.

When you are on a swing there is a moment of complete standstill at the very top; then you plunge so fast it takes your breath away. Suddenly heaven and earth changed for Magdalena. The old tree outside her window seemed different, the clouds quite unlike those of former days. All living creatures moved about as though filled with liquid gold that shone right through them. Magdalena had never imagined life could be so glorious. For all she had suffered a reward had been prepared. But even were she to suffer ever after, this was well worth the price. Much of this bliss came from gratified pride; the heady thought that she, so poor, hardly able to read or write, she whom no boy would marry had been chosen by a man so learned, so superior to anyone else.

And it was then, let us remember, that she had been suddenly deprived of everything, pushed out into the cold, this time forever. Father Paskva, aware of the scandal, and forced to make a choice, found her a housekeeper's post with a rector of a distant parish; so distant, indeed, that everyone could see the break was final. In that rectory overlooking a lake, left all alone with a crotchety old man, Magdalena had not remained long—just long enough to plunge back into the black night she had known before her time of bliss. While outside the wind whistled in the reeds, waves lapped at the boat moored to the landing, and white foam spumed on the shingle, she swallowed rat poison.

The old priest would not bury her. He preferred to give a wagon, a team, and a driver, and be rid of the headache.

Magdalena's last journey, ere she entered the country where fine ladies of yore were waiting to greet her, began on an early morning. Flocks of fleecy clouds glided across the sky; the horses trotted briskly. In the clearings men honed their scythes and whetstone rang on metal. Then along a sandy road they went among juniper bushes, past clumps of pine trees, uphill, always uphill, until they had reached the cross-roads from where one could see three bodies of water, like a necklace of bright stones set with a clasp of verdure. Then downhill and into the woods, where in a village street Magdalena was left through the noon hours to gaze at the leaves of an old maple until the shadows lengthened, the heat abated, and the journey could be resumed. Now over the long, paved causeway, where the wheels bumped and bounced even though the horses went at a walk. Then the evening concert of thrushes broke out on either side, and now the starlit sky opened overhead effervescent with the motion of distant worlds. An immense calm—a deep blue space—who was looking down from there? And could he (whoever he was) see this one tiny being who, of her own, had stopped her heart's beat, stemmed the course of her blood and willed herself to become a motionless thing? The smell of horses, the voice of the driver idly talking to the team—on and on they went late into the night. A brief halt. Then early the next morning on again: over low hills and into the oak forest. They hadn't much farther to go now. Here was where the descent into the Issa Valley began and there, across the river, sitting in a spot from where he could see the water gleaming through the osiers, Father Paskva was reading his breviary.

In the summer a body will decompose fast, and people wondered why he delayed, as if loath to give her up to the ground. Yet when at last they were carrying her out, they noticed no unpleasant odor, a detail they were later to recall. The priest had her buried at the very edge of the cemetery where the steep slope began and only tangled roots kept the loose ground from sliding.

The sermon he preached on the Feast of the Assumption was

brief, and delivered in a calm, even voice. He told them how She who had known no stain had entered heaven not in spirit alone but with her whole being, just as She was when She walked among men. He described how at first Her feet still touched the grass, then without taking a step She rose higher and higher while the breeze played with Her long robe (such as were then worn in Judea), until at last She was but a speck among the clouds. And that was how She obtained what to us, sinners, will be granted in Josephat's Valley, and only if we deserve it; forever young, and with all earthly senses, She contemplates God the Almighty.

Soon afterwards Father Paskva left Ghinye, and no one ever heard of him again.

* * *

Women talked about it among themselves with elbows propped on a neighbor's fence. Men kept mum; their eyes glued to a pinch of tobacco, they licked the paper, pretending to be engrossed in the task at hand. Nevertheless, apprehension grew, though at first people merely tried to find an explanation, probing for the right one, yet careful to avoid dangerous words.

It was the new rector, Father Monkiewicz, who contributed most to the spread of gossip. A rotund little man, bald-headed and high strung, he was frightened, and unable to conceal the fact. What was that knocking at the wall, he wanted to know, always three knocks at a time? He could not find natural reasons for it. The house gave him an uneasy feeling on account of all he had been told, and he bore ill the alien presence that manifested itself by knocking, and also by slowly pressing the door handle. He jumped up to open the door; there was no one outside. He had hoped these strange manifestations would stop of themselves; instead, they were growing worse. The verger was summoned to sleep at the rectory, and from then on there was no longer need to speculate as to what went on. Anyhow, it was not long before Father Monkiewicz, unable to cope alone, turned to the village elders for help. They took turns, a few at a time, keeeping vigil in the kitchen.

Magdalena's wretched ghost refused to leave the site where she had known happiness. Wielding an invisible cleaver it split invisible logs and lighted an invisible fire which hissed and crackled just like a real one. It rattled pots about, broke eggs, and fried them though the range remained empty and cold. What manner of tools was it using? Are such noises mere sounds, a kind of broad register of rustles parroting the sound of nature? Or has a ghost at its disposal a different kind of kitchen with a universal pail, a universal skillet, a universal stack of firewood, the very essence of all the pails, skillets, and firewood that ever were? These are questions no one can answer, one can only listen and, at best, refuse to accept the evidence of one's senses. Holy water did no good. The priest sprinkled; a short pause would issue, then almost at once the bustle resumed, getting bolder every night. Worse yet—the mischief had now moved into the bedroom. In addition to the knocks and the moving door-handle, footfalls resounded, books and papers tumbled to the floor, and something else had hatched, too—something like stifled laughter. Father Monkiewicz sprinkled one room corner—no sound came; another—nothing again; a third—still nothing. But let him go near the fourth corner, and instantly giggles would ring out and then whistling, as if someone blew into a hollow nut.

The news of these doings quickly spread to neighboring villages, and had not the inhabitants of Ghinye made it quite clear that, after all, these matters were nobody's business but their own, there would not have been just three men sitting at night in the rectory kitchen—three hundred would have tried to get in. Denied an active part, people wagged their tongues, and the parish was rife with fantastic rumors.

Then, partly due to Balthazar, came the realization that Magdalena's spirit would no longer confine itself to the rectory. Were it not for one detail, Balthazar's story would have met with nothing but laughter, or, at best, with that mock gravity with which one nods to a drunkard's tale for fear of hurting his feelings. For Balthazar claimed, if you please, that he had just seen Magdalena astride a white horse coming down from the cemetery and headed for the river. She was stark naked and both she and the horse glowed in the dark. He kept repeating his tale to the crowd that had gathered at his father-in-law's house, and he took offense at the mere hint that he might have been seeing things. Then someone got a bright idea; why not go to the rector's stable and see if the priest's grey was there? The grey was there, all right, but drenched with sweat as if someone had ridden it at a gallop.

As might be expected, the manor house was seething with all

this news, and Antonina brought fresh morsels every day. Grandmother Misia kept exclaiming "How dreadful!" and delighted with these other-worldly pranks, she invited the priest over, so he might vent his griefs. Father Monkiewicz noisily slurped his strawberry-leaf tea and with a woebegone look admitted he was at his rope's end; if the mischief did not stop soon he would ask to be transferred. So Grandmother Misia's triumph was complete, and her incredulous exclamations: "Oh, no! Not really, Father!" rang with rapture because, naturally, she sided with the spirits, not with men. Soon, however, something else happened; this time very close to home.

Thomas, who was admitted to Mr. Satybelka's bedside when the bailiff was just beginning to recover, felt his flesh creep. The sick man's beard spread like a fan on the coverlet, and he spoke in a feeble voice. On the bedside rug lay his little dog Mopsy. Mopsy's behavior had been a disgrace. At the critical moment he had simply fled, with the stump of his bobbed tail between his legs. And yet his master did not hold it against him.

But, let us first tell what happened. It was then threshing time at the home farm. The steam engine stood in a shed by the barn, and as soon as the day's work was done the precious transmission belt was removed to the shed which was then securely locked. On that particular night Mr. Satybelka had already retired to his quarters, put on soft slippers, and sat smoking his pipe, when all at once misgiving assailed him; had he or had he not turned the key in the lock? He could not recall, and this inability to visualize himself performing his duty kept preying on his mind. Finally, fearing that someone might steal the belt, he rose to his feet. Grumbling, he pulled on his boots, donned his sheepskin and cap, took a lantern, and left the warm room for the cold and rain outside. It was completely dark; all he could see was what the circle of his lantern encompassed. He found the shed—just as he had feared—unlocked. Squeezing through the narrow passage between the wall and the boiler he went in and checked; the belt lay where it should. But then just as he was starting back he saw coming right at him—a monster. Mr. Satybelka said it looked like a sort of thick log moving broadside, level with the ground. Stuck on this trunk were three heads—Tartar heads, he said—writhing in frightful grimaces. The horror pressed forward while Mr. Satybelka kept crossing himself and step by step retreated farther and farther into the shed. Then it dawned upon him he was cutting himself off from the only way of escape, so waving the lantern wildly he began to sidle around the monster. It was then that his foot trod on the monster's body. "It was soft like a bag of chaff," he said. Once out of the shed he wanted to run but dared not turn around. And so slowly, walking backward, he made his way from the out-buildings to his own door, while the three fiendish heads on that low-slung, legless trunk kept writhing, right at his feet. Mr. Satybelka could hardly draw a breath and collapsed right on the stoop. He was at once seized with a fever, though the whole thing could not have lasted more than fifteen minutes, and there had been nothing amiss with his health when he had gone out.

Perhaps, as Granny Misia suspected, it had been the ghost of a Mohammedan from a hill called the Tartar Cemetery. The memory of Tartar prisoners who once, long ago, had worked in Ghinye would have completely vanished were it not for the name, which still remained. But even so, why should the Mohammedan appear just then unless someone had made him bold, perhaps even ordered him to join in the nightly riots. And who else but Magdalena? She must have by now become a leader among the underground powers.

All these incidents led in time to a rift between Father Monkiewicz and the village. People reasoned that because all now agreed on what caused the mischief, it clearly followed that the cause must be removed. They hinted as much to the rector, discreetly at first, beating about the bush with parables and similes. When this had no effect, they came right out and told him that an end must be put to the mischief, and that there was a way to do it. But he hollered that he would never, never consent, and berated them for being heathens. He was very stubborn about it and would not listen to reason. Why wait for his leave, some said, let's just go ahead and do it. But everyone knew they would never dare. So nothing was resolved. In the meantime another priest arrived at the rectory, and he and Father Monkiewicz exorcised the place.

* * *

Thomas had been afraid to be out after dark, but that was before he had the dream. It was a dream of great sweetness and force, but terrifying too; it was really hard to tell which of the three predominated. Thomas could not have put it into words the next morning, nor later either. Words cannot capture a mixture of smells, or that something which draws us to certain people; how could they describe the sensation of falling down a deep well, right through to the other side of existence?

He saw Magdalena under ground, in the loneliness of the immense earth; she had been there for years and would continue to dwell there forever. Her dress had rotted and fallen apart, the shreds of the fabric mingled with her dry bones, and the strand of hair which used to slip over her cheek when she leaned over the stove, stuck now to an empty skull. Yet at the same time she seemed close to him, looking just as she had looked that day by the river, and this simultaneous presence somehow implied another kind of time, different from the one we know. The sensation that once tightened his throat in her presence permeated him now through and through, the shape of her breast and neck continued somehow to exist inside him, and her touch translated itself into a plaint that was like a chant: "Oh, why do I pass away; why do my hands and feet pass away? Oh, why should I be and yet not be—I who lived once, only once, from the beginning to the end of the world. Oh, the sky and the sun shall be, and I shan't be ever again. Those bones alone remain after me. Oh, nothing is mine, nothing." And Thomas, too, was sinking along with her into the silence under layers of earth, where pebbles slide and worms inch their way; it was now he who was turning into a handful of rotten bones, it was he who was complaining with Magdalena's lips, and he who was asking himself the question: Why am I me? How can it be that I who have a body, warmth, hands, fingers, must die and stop being me? Perhaps this wasn't even a dream, because even while he lay at the very bottom, deep under the surface of reality, feeling his bodily self doomed, disintegrating, already beyond death, his own self that was participating in this annihilation knew that he here and he there were the same. He screamed and woke up. But the vague outlines of the surrounding objects had become part of the nightmare—they refused to stand out more real and strong against the murk. Instantly he relapsed into the same self-consciousness, and everything kept repeating itself with ever-new variations. At last dawn set him free. He opened his eyes fearfully; he was returning from a far-off land. Now, however, daylight was bringing out sharply every object: the table, the stools, the chair. What a relief to see the real world of solid things made of wood, iron, and bricks; so bumpy and rough. Thomas' heart went out to every piece of furniture he had treated so off-handedly the day before. Why, he had hardly noticed they were there. Now they seemed like treasures. He gazed at the cracks, knots, crevices. And yet the other thing had left behind a delicious giddiness, the recollections of worlds whose existence he had never suspected before.

From that night on he decided that even if Magdalena came up to him in the dark drive he would not scream, because she would not hurt him. Sometimes he even wished she would appear—though the very thought gave him goose-flesh; but it was not an unpleasant goose-flesh, more like the kind you get when you stroke a velvet ribbon. As for the dream, he never mentioned it to anyone.

* * *

It was all done in secret, and not until much later did Thomas, to his immense sorrow, learn of the horror they had perpetrated.

Only a dozen or so village elders, all wealthy free-holders, were in the plot. They assembled toward evening and drank a lot of vodka, for deep inside they all felt a little queasy, and in need of extra courage. Permission had been granted or, to be more precise, Father Monkiewicz had said: "Do as you please." This, however, was as good as an admission on his part that all means at his disposal had failed—as indeed they had. Shortly after the other priest's departure (as it happened only the verger and the old housekeeper were at the rectory that night, because everyone thought that after the exorcisms Magdalena would leave the place alone) the verger heard a scream coming from the bedroom; then Father Monkiewicz appeared on the threshold, his long nightshirt so badly torn, it practically hung in tatters. Magdalena had pulled off his coverlet and had started to rip his shirt. When shortly afterward he came down with erysipelas he and everyone else ascribed his illness to fright. For erysipelas brought on by fright there is no remedy save to cast out the spell. So a medicine woman was brought to the rectory to mumble her incantations over the sick priest. Little is known about these incantations except that they contain orders bidding the sickness to leave the body; these orders are reinforced by threats and snatches of prayers, some Christian, some even older than Christianity. However, the words once revealed lose their power, so that whoever knows them can transmit them only to one person—no more—before he or she dies. The priest submitted to the crone's ministrations unwillingly enough, but is a man apt to quibble when his health is at stake? Not likely. He thinks then that—perhaps—who knows? A similar fit of weakness, combined with a faint hope that the harassing manifestations would stop at last, had induced Father Monkiewicz to give his consent in that other matter, too.

The thing had to be done in the dark. Also (even though this, perhaps, was not a hard and fast rule), it seemed only proper to go about it piously, that is in silence. No idle onlookers; just a small group of serious, trustworthy men. They checked their spades to see if they were sharp, lighted lanterns, and singly or in twos stole out, moving silently through the back orchards.

A gale was blowing and the oak trees rattled their dead leaves. The lights in the village had already been put out, so there was nothing but blackness and this harsh rustle. As soon as all had reached the little square in front of the church they set out in a body and headed for the spot. Then they posted themselves in a circle as best they could on the steep slope. The flames of lanterns inside the glass funnels protected by metal bars leaped and tossed, driven by gusts of wind.

First, the cross. It had been planted here to stand as long as its wood would last, until, many years hence, the part stuck in the ground would moulder and let the cross tip over. They pulled it out, and carefully placed it to the side. Next, with a few shoves they leveled the little mound on which no one had ever planted flowers. Now they began to work with feverish haste because, say what you like, it was a frightful thing to do. You commit a body to the ground for all eternity; to go prying after a few months to see what has become of it goes clear against nature. Like planting a chestnut or an acorn and then scratching the ground open to see if it was already sprouting. And yet, perhaps, this was the whole point of what they were about; they had to summon all their will and determination to do a thing contrary to nature in order to counter something that, in itself, ran counter to all that was normal.

Gravel rattled. The moment was at hand. A spade rang out.

Lowering a lantern they peered in the hole. No. It was only a stone. Then, at last—the boards. They swept off the rubble, uncovering the coffin completely so they could lift its lid. A good thing they had drunk all that vodka. There is nothing like vodka to give a man that warm glow which makes him feel somehow more alive than anything around him; he will stand up to any adversary then, let alone trees, stones, a howling wind, and mere specters of the night.

What they found confirmed all their suspicions. In the first place the body was not in the least decomposed. They said afterward that it looked as if it had been interred yesterday. This was proof enough; only the bodies of saints and ghosts possess that attribute. Also, Magdalena was not lying on her back but turned over, face down, which too is a sign. To be sure, even without these proofs they were ready to do what needed to be done. Now that they had the proofs it came easier, without doubts or misgivings.

They turned the body over, then one of them using the sharpest spade and standing back for greater impact, cut off Magdalena's head. An aspen spike had been prepared beforehand. Now they stood it upright on her chest and with the back of an axe drove it until the point had pierced the bottom of the coffin and had sunk deep into the ground. Picking up the head by the hair they placed it against the feet. Then they replaced the lid, and with a sense of relief shoved dirt over it. They even laughed now, as people often do after moments of great strain.

Maybe Magdalena had been so terrified of physical disintegration, so desperately afraid to enter eternity—a new time completely alien to her nature—that, willing to pay any price, she had consented to haunt, and in return for that dreadful bondage had been granted the right to keep her body intact. Maybe. Her lips, they all vowed, had remained red. By cutting off her head and crushing her ribs, they had put an end to her carnal pride, and that pagan love she had for her own lips, hands, and belly. Pierced like a butterfly stuck on a pin, with her skull touching the soles of the shoes which Father Paskva had given her, she was bound to realize that she too, like everyone else, must now dissolve into the sap of the earth.

The disturbances at the rectory stopped right away, and nothing more was heard of Magdalena's pranks. After all, she had already found a way to prolong her earthly existence far more effectively than by cooking on an invisible range or by knocking and whistling. By entering Thomas' dreams, she had made sure he would never forget her.

Translated by Rulka Langer

Czesław Miłosz

Brognart

A Shotglass Story

QUITE a while back, in the 'fifties, I once stopped over in Marles-Les-Mines. That's a village in Pas-de-Calais, in black coal-mining country. Winter is wet there, with bright-green, short-cropped grass on the meadows, ink-black coal piles, and movement in the air: the turning wheels of the coal mine lifts. It rained incessantly. In Marles walls were blighted with the damp, mud oozed from between cobblestones, the trees were mere skeletons. The first passerby I asked for directions, a miner with coal-dust tatooed skin, returning from work carrying a lamp, answered in the language I spoke to him, because I've got a sharp eye—he was a Pole. Altogether, probably half the inhabitants there could communicate in Polish. The hue of the light there is muddled and foggy. When the doors of the little café opened, a bolt of steam burst forth. (Perhaps I'm unjust, spreading the smoke and steam all over that light.) Bicycles were parked in front of the cafés, and inside every café people behind shot glasses of *calvados* were gabbing about the Brognart affair.

In Marles itself, there on the spot, this affair struck me forceably and moved me. It's not for me to judge how my scales will balance when I am weighed for good and evil. Sometimes it seems to me that the one definitely outweighs the other. There are moments when necessity impels me to run or to yell out, because it's an impossible situation, because nobody, nobody else will, so I should —the responsibility rests with me. I decided that at least I wouldn't bypass it, so I inquired among the natives, and went to neighboring Bruay. The two villages are only divided by a sort of ravine.

From a young teacher I got Brognart's school notebooks: analyses of *Le Cid* and the *Iliad*, written in the poky hand of an assiduous student. To this day that teacher believes I was some sort of quack or spy, for I did nothing about carrying out my strong decision. If hell is paved with good intentions, then the scale is turning against me, all the more so because on my part there was no intention of runing around the world with my tongue hanging out, defending all the tortured people. In a country like France there are plenty of writers and journalists generally sensitive to the fortunes of their fellow countrymen, but none of the Frenchmen had the slightest notion about Brognart's lot. No one was capable of identifying with him; their imagination didn't stretch that far. A training of the imagination was necessary here—mine, from the east of Europe—and I knew well that I'm the only one who could do it.

I tried several times, but each time found a pretext (various obligations) that allowed me to shove Brognart's matter aside. And what were these obstacles? First of all, Brognart was no longer alive. That is, he was now part of the numberless mass, crowd, of those beaten, trodden upon, injured, in the eighth century before Christ or in the twentieth century after—time plays no role here. So why he, specifically he, why sorrow for him, why the complaints in his case?

Even if limited to my life-time, the reason is immediately insufficient, because millions like him died, and "the shirt is closer than the jacket," as the old Polish saying goes. I'd rather have taken someone from among my close acquaintances than a Frenchman. It's true, there was a certain mystery in my emotional response to the talk in Marles-Les-Mines. I almost guessed that Brognart interested me so much because he was a sort of a stand-in, tied by various unnamed strings to this and that person tangible for me. Nonetheless, the reason is insufficient, all the more so because cars, theaters, flowers, trains crammed with passengers, formed a human whirlpool that healed all of the losses and didn't want to hear of things uncomplimentary to it, so what the heck did one Brognart mean? To get up on a soap box and remind them, just so that they would turn away yawning from the boor addressing them or would wink knowingly: another wise guy, quite sharp though, multiplies his political assets.

But Brognart's affair had already became a political matter, though not of his own will. What could a teenager, with his analyses of Corneille and Racine, know about politics? It was a local matter in Pas-de-Calais, utilized in the election run-offs, but elsewhere it had already passed into philosophy, or into literary salons where it was untactful to blurt it out without some cutting remark. And though I didn't worry about tact, that taboo paralyzed me in a direct, specific way. I had engaged myself too emotionally in this story, so out of pure respect for its main figure I preferred remaining silent so as not to precipitate, at least in my own eyes, the suspicion that I employed Brognart as yet another argument for my self-justification or for the defense of my own virtue. Even the plan, the various chapters of the book I was capable of writing, outlined itself clearly. But supposing that it was published, it would have been of no use to anybody. Some would boo it down, pointing it out as an example of its author's "falsified awareness." Others would reject it politely, or praise it in some commonplace way, for what is an abyss to me is to them only weaponry in a political brawl, to be participated in for reasons other than cases like that of Brognart. And I do admit that the whole story is altogether fantastic and absurd. That's why everybody else would tend to bypass it, embarrassed.

But I won't beat around the bush any longer. Brognart, Gilbert by name, the son of a miner, was born in Marles. His father's family and his mother's family were both peasant families from the area and had grubbed in the earth for generations, when nobody yet suspected coal underneath. Later their land holdings (and they didn't diminish them by divisions) went up in value. They relinquished the plow and got hold of new jobs in the mines, but always with that backing in the deed books, so that it was said in Marles that these families were doing quite well, this house belonged to them, and that one, and that lot, and the other. But, as always in France: No showing off! Niggardliness! Moans rather, that there wasn't enough for wine and bread. Gilbert's father left his mother when Gilbert was small, got a divorce, and then married a third time. The boy saw him rarely, because he grew up by his mother's side in Marles, with his grandmother and aunts, while the father lived in Auchel, where he died. The mother guarded her one and only, perhaps more than mothers normally guard their only sons, with a desperate love, because of the divorce and, who knows, because of certain dramas in the seemingly dying-out family.

For instance, one of her sisters was slightly crazy: English "Tommies" had raped her when they were stationed there during the First World War, and then something had snapped in her mind. But it doesn't look as if Gilbert was especially spoiled. He was a completely normal boy: attentive, realistic, serious, liked by his friends, good in sports. He had no proclivities toward extravagance nor toward overly florid dreams, nothing beyond the necessities of the closest surroundings. He wasn't a climber: after the *École Primaire* he continued attending the same kind of school which was, according to the French nomenclature the *École Primaire Superieure*, then the *Collège Moderne*. He was preparing for mining school, to get his engineering degree there, and then to return to Marles. He was good in physics and mathematics. I developed, I think, an accurate idea of him from what his school-teacher told me. A typical peasant from northern France: phlegmatic, surreptitiously ironic, introvertive, and on top of this he had stubbornness, a strong will, independence. He never played the two-handed game, but always spoke his mind—that's what the teacher especially emphasized. In a team, in class, or on the sportsfield: dynamic. He first got to school in Bruay by bicycle. For his sixteenth birthday his mother bought him a motorcycle—the only sign of spoiling, though even then not so much really, because a bike or a motorcycle is necessary in those parts. An accident proved his cool: His front tire went, but he didn't lose control. If he got any allowance from his mother, his greatest pleasure was to do something nice for someone else. When he saw a friend of his desirous of something, he would buy it for him right away. Sociable to the correct degree, he belonged to one organization: *Jeunesse Étudiante Chrétienne*.

Brognart's photos tallied with his teacher's description: He had the pleasant face of a stable teenager, with strong chin, delicate mouth, prominent nose a bit childishly pug-like, and an open glance, careful, somewhat lyrical. And, I think, his eyes and mouth struck me, because they reminded me of the eyes and mouth of someone dear in my family. It is true that in some photographs Brognart had his glasses on, and then the resemblance faded.

But, with all of his stability he wouldn't have been a fledgling if he weren't attracted by running about, sniffing the world, visiting places. Naturally, he loved touring and expeditions into unknown parts. He found a good traveling companion in Marles, the son of a butcher; his was a Polish family that had come from the town of Torun in Poland. It so happened that relatives invited the Polish boy to Torun for a vacation, and he immediately suggested to Gilbert that he go along. The opportunity was exceptional, for Gilbert up until then had never been outside France, actually, never outside the *Nord*. He persuaded his mother to let him go. She most probably didn't want to—there's that French distrust of foreign countries—but it was difficult to refuse; he had just finished his *bachot* exam and was to begin mining school in the fall. This happened in 1939. Brognart had just turned eighteen; he was born June 1, 1921. I don't know if anyone in Marles really knew anything about international politics; Marles isn't Paris. It's probable that the mother had some fears, because it took him a while to get his way. He left for Poland in the latter part of August.

Torun is a beautiful city. He found a group of boys his age in his friend's family. Everything was novel, the architecture, the river, the kayaks, so time flew by pleasurably, and that's how the war caught Brognart in Poland. I use the word war, but it's stiff and inaccurate, because war can also denote the Greeks at Troy, as well as gigantic newspaper headlines read while drinking coffee when we're not directly affected, and, for that matter, the ups and downs at the stock market. There, however, it wasn't traditional. Instead, it was annihilating fire from the sky. The sky buzzed and shook with moving machines, while below, on the open spaces, the red centers of fires blinked through smoke, and one human society was dismantling, denuding itself, showing that which underlies every human society. Let those who haven't experienced this go along with me. Brognart started out on foot with three of his Torun peers, fleeing before the German army. They walked along bombed-out roads. His colleagues soon turned back because the German tanks were everywhere, and had encircled Warsaw. He, however, after a number of days and nights, ignorant of both language and terrain, got to Warsaw, aimed for the French embassy, and probably had pangs of conscience, thinking about his mother.

I've mentioned that this story fell into book form in my mind. It would have contained not only Brognart's adventures, but also those of his three colleagues, informative for some people, uninteresting to the majority. For I had also inquired at the butcher's family in Marles. They had answered unwillingly, but I did squeeze something out of them, and something had moved me to ask what fate had befallen the other three. They had returned home, to the occupied city. One of them, obviously the most adventurous, didn't remain long, but went south again, to Warsaw and farther, into the mountains between Poland and Slovakia. Young people sneaked out there on skis during the first war winter. He got to Hungary and from there to France, where he joined the ranks of the growing Polish army. Evacuated with his unit to England, he took pilot training there and flew bombers over Germany. Now *he* was the punishing fire. Near the end of the war he died of shock from landing in a damaged plane. The second fellow, rather differently, was mobilized and incorporated into the German Wehrmacht. (Let me explain that the Germans considered Torun German and its citizens Germans.) He found an opportunity to surrender to the Allies in Italy. He next wore the Polish uniform and when, after the war, this army was transported from Italy to England he could have stayed there, but he didn't want to, and returned instead to Poland. He studied, and was already taking his finals in engineering when he was jailed. The new authorities were very careful in weeding out those who had belonged to the Polish army in the West, but not necessarily those who had been in the Wehrmacht; they were more lenient with the latter. The third—Brognart's friend from Marles—got stuck in Torun, longed for his parents and France, worked in a factory. The Gestapo arrested him for belonging to an underground organization and he landed in the Stuthof concentration camp near Danzig. He spent only a short time there, because he got caught when the German Empire was nearing the end of its tether, but he returned home inwardly broken. In seeming good health, he registered at the university, but climbing the stairs one day he fell and died of a heart attack. A digression—three variants of the fate of one generation in one country. I didn't have to make anything up, or add anything. Still, none of the three met with as great a misfortune as Brognart. The first fellow had his masculine triumphs, his joy; the second, unless they racked him up too fast, probably got out of prison after a couple of years; while the third, even if he suffered much, didn't suffer long.

Brognart found out in Warsaw that the French embassy was no longer there, that it had been evacuated East. How he shifted about there, how he made out, what he ate in that alien city of chaos, contradictory rumors, and panic—the wind there blew about documents of already nonexistent offices and bureaus—how long he remained there, I don't know. He survived the siege, and quite a siege it was, with whole streets streaming up into the air in fountains of brick, and horse carcasses on the street from which people carved out the round steaks, etc. Next, in November, he was caught by the German police in the already-occupied city, but they let him go after holding him a while—probably didn't have time to take care of such minor matters as the citizens of other countries snared in the sack anyhow. Brognart must have figured, no doubt logically, that instead of waiting around until they lock him up in a prison camp, he should get through to some neutral country where his consulate would be located. Of the two countries that had divided Poland's territory between them, one was neutral; it had received what it did as payment—interest on its neutrality. The border that lay between them on the strength of a pact ran not far from Warsaw, and in November Brognart crossed it, detouring the guards, as many did at that time.

Supposedly man can learn everything, only not immediately—his imagination is fettered with habits. Brognart probably thought he'd find a French consulate right away or, if not, that he'd board a train and go to Moscow, as he used to travel from Marles to Paris. When it became obvious that that was not allowed, he quite naturally turned to the authorities for help. He was well acquainted with the bureaucracy of his own country, the country of Europe's oldest bureaucracy. He didn't know however—had never pondered—that the bureaucracy, even before the French Revolution, was quite democratic in relation to others. Now he had to find out what happens when nobody moves a finger because the individual has no so-called natural rights. He was enraged, and told himself that if this was the way things stood, he didn't need anybody's help. He gleaned information here and there, and found that French consulates were located in the neighboring Baltic states, at that time still independent. So he simply went. It's difficult to accuse him of frivolity. The trip from Warsaw made him bolder; it shouldn't have. It was much easier. Besides, the Poles, seemingly called upon to know the customs of their neighbors, were also naive, venturing out in whole groups, like Brognart, just to get out from under the authority imposed upon them without asking their opinion. Some made it; some didn't. I would have probably let the whole Brognart thing alone in Marles-Les-Mines if concrete images had not linked me with such border-crossings. But they did link me—very much so. I assure you that to go through that experience is really quite something. Later on whole years pass, but life still remains wonderful, every day a gift. Well, they caught Brognart on the Latvian border. They held him in various prisons stuffed with a flea-infested human mass, youths just as he, who wanted to go West to the army, and with old people and women, Polish Jews, Lithuanians, Byelorussians jailed for various improprieties, mainly for belonging to an improper social group.

In such a situation an astute and stubborn youth naturally remembers that the castaway should transmit news of himself in a bottle intrusted to the sea and shouldn't lose hope; there's always a chance that someone will fish the bottle out. So Brognart, and here his conscientiousness becomes mainfest, carefully wrote his name and plea for informing his family of his plight on the wall of every cell he was in. He didn't miscalculate. Only that his bottle was knocked about by various currents for six years, and not so much the bottle as those who fished it out. It was only after the war that letters came to Marles from Polish officers and soldiers of that army which was in Italy, the sometime tenants of the same cells. They had either read the signature, or some had had the Frenchman for cellmate.

After months of prison they read Brognart his sentence. No one could say that they didn't abide by the law there. The respect for the law was even there very great. Lawful ruling is an attribute of culture, and it was invented in the same place as other cunning tricks such as brushing teeth, the steam engine, electricity, and parliamentarism. They didn't go so far as to make any use of the law or the elections, but the fictitiousness even added a desire for celebration. Brognart probably didn't catch a single word of the whole ceremony, but some connection or proportion was established for him between guilt and punishment—this had sunk into him through literature, school, and environment. He didn't understand the language they spoke to him anyway, and if they indicated to him by finger-count how much he got—eight—he didn't catch on at once that it meant eight years. And if he despaired he was wrong here as well, because it didn't matter where it was five or eight since, as the weaker prisoners died out, the goal was to keep the same number of hands working in the concentration camps. He was taken to one of these camps near Archangel.

This descendant of assiduous and hard-working peasant generations was hardy. To last there four winters in a row is quite a feat, even for people accustomed to a harsh climate from birth. That was the average expectancy of healthy males, but the seasons kept on passing and Brognart did not give in. He kept on throwing his bottles into the sea, believing in a rescue. After the war not only did his mother know that he was somewhere in Russia, but the French embassy received a letter from him, smuggled through somehow, in which he precisely repeated his condition and whereabouts. Attempts were begun, and when his place of stay at the mouth of the Pechora became known, the Russians quit denying his existence. This denial had lasted quite a while, it is true, but they finally did admit that he was there, sentenced justly and legally, with an additional ten-year sentence "for the spreading of provocative rumors," and that a review of the trial was impossible. In other words, Brognart had not learned humility in the camps of the North; he still spoke his mind, as he had done in school. The answer to attempts to allow him at least to write home was always the same: No.

I won't even try to guess what his mother had to go through. It is not difficult to break down when you send letters and applications every day, travel from bureau to bureau, and even go to Thorez, literally kissing his feet, begging him to bring about a rescue—when such attempts last for years and years. Finally, when I was in Marles, the mother was living in a psychiatric institution, placed there of her own request.

Brognart died in 1951. That's not a bad achievement, eleven years; the families of Russian and Polish prisoners would nod their heads to this. Not many dragged their feet around that long in the *lagers,* almost an eternity. The official announcement of his death was passed on to the French embassy with the proper delay (about a year later) and then the sensational magazines in France related Brognart's story in the *faits divers* section. Only in Marles and its vicinity did the thing take on a more widely echoing significance. The Communists and Socialists especially fought over the votes up there in the *Nord;* the Socialists forged an argument out of Brognart that was quite uncomfortable for the Communists. For of course the Communists wanted to deny all slander against Russia; yes, there were corrective prisons for political trespassers, fascists, hitlerites, and the like, but who could ever have any mercy on such criminals—only some agent of American imperialism. They had a strong point, for wasn't it necessary to punish the *collabos* in France? So every person who held even any unclear doubts tucked his head in between his shoulders. It was far away anyhow, so who would check it out; both the countries and the people were without faces. Now, unfortunately, there was one man with a face, and that works stronger than ten million abstract ones. Brognart? He was far from politics, a fledgling, everybody in Marles knew him. That's why it was necessary to find a way. The Communist press dragged out the mixed-up aunt connected it with the mother's illness and *the* hypothesis was ready-made: Brognart was handicapped genetically and all those reports, as it were, that he had passed on about himself were the imaginings of a madman. I think the articles had their effect; at any rate I know that shortly thereafter, when I returned to Paris, talk of Brognart began dying out, until finally it died out for ever.

Now I'll admit to the emotional tie. Brognart's photographic likeness resembled my cousin, and the moments I spent with these relatives of mine in their house are important to me to this day. This cousin, also an only child, is quite enigmatic to me. I often wonder what he'd be like if he had grown up. He was sensitive, lyrical, musical—besides this his parents' personalities were contrary, and they were somewhat like the heroes of Thomas Mann's early stories. He was fifteen when the Nazis took him from Poland to a concentration camp in Germany, and seventeen when he died there. I can't talk about it. If they had at least shot him . . . But that span of time had been imposed especially upon him—yes, upon him.

I would like to stress that essential difficulty a bit more, the one that caused the necessity of remaining silent about various Brognarts. Sure, one was free to cry over the victims of Hitler's camps. This didn't lower anybody's literary prestige, and if the reader was bored, he was respectfully bored. Nonetheless, that is the past. Nothing could now help either my cousin or those like him, so there was a lack of inspiration, and masses of people like Brognart—enough to populate a medium-sized west-European country—kept on going to work every morning and the same sun shone upon us. There's ridiculousness, yes, in taking the defeats of every stranger upon oneself. Am I my brother's keeper? True, but then why did the Parisian cafés feel they must accept universal responsibility, why did they plunge in constant excitement from one matter to the next: they're torturing Negroes in Mississippi, Madagascar can't obtain its independence, the villages of Indochina are burning? They weren't ashamed of sentimentality here. So other criteria were at work here, other springs balanced the scales unevenly. A big aspirate "aaah" issuing from the mythical East, or from a gigantic mountain. That's where progress is, the direction of history, and one shouldn't expose oneself dangerously, but should guard one's name before posterity. And the endeavors they undertook—noble and guaranteed by the future. Just like the other endeavors, undertaken by Lamennais or Victor Hugo or Zola, always afterward warmly remembered by later generations. Because there's no heaven, let there at least be the heaven of good fame. And anyway, there were many in Europe who made anti-communism a profession, just to squeeze money out of the Americans; generally, they were excluded from decent intellectual society, in other words, others were afraid of catching their leprosy. There's nothing straightforward here. French rationalism is a legend, unless we consider rationalism bringing everything down to eloquence. It is rather a ritual, like ants touching each other with their feelers.

Though I could have regarded him ironically, I by no means treated lightly the cunning and the high sensitivity toward convention that sets the fashions for the enlightened ones at the eternal dinners at Madame Verdurin's, and then those fashions infect Japan and America. The direction of history they carted around for show was a stupidity not only in my book, though it is true I suspected that it hadn't come out the way they had planned it safely, with growing room provided. However it was, my ambition suffered. If it wasn't Brognart it was some related theme I'd toss up and thus ruin my good name. In other words, my work was underpinned not so much with regular cowardice as with a constant wounding of my ambition. I tried to guess how they saw me: a maniac, an emigrant, i.e., a reactionary, and my tone would take on shades of desperation. Now that all that is behind me I wouldn't want to repeat it for anything in the world. I was fixing up a face-deforming mask for myself which was political, though I never had any strong political interests and never claimed any erudition in this field. I showed surprise, rather, that one can't show surprise at people's lightmindedness. They swam around me in fogs, babbled, as if these weren't matters of fatal seriousness lying deeper than any politics. My surprise, I think, reached its climax a bit later, when the ban was suddenly lifted, supposedly because one bad man was responsible for all the crimes. From whence the breakdowns, the disillusionments, from whence the feigned naïveté of two-year-old children? Either a state is regarded as an institution whose individual members delegate a part of their privileges and exercise control, or else one believes in a messianic state and then, in the face of the greatness of the aim, all tears shed over the breakage of some odd number of human machines are truly nothing but crocodile tears. Ancient Mexican priests, who offered human sacrifices to keep the sun in motion and assure good harvests, would have been rather downcast if it were proven to them that the sacrifices were unnecessary because they had no influence on the motion of the sun. As far as I was concerned, I happened to dislike the monopoly state—the Messiah state—and that quite independently of the question of whether it has a tremendous future before it. So I was surprised—no, not true—I most disliked not their breakdowns and disillusionments, but the ease with which they immediately glued their wisdom into the motion of history, not drawing any consequences.

These problems were just on the surface for me, however, and I held it against myself that by stopping there I fall into falsehood, represent myself not as I am. I had to return to myself, learn how to outline my hidden beliefs, my true faith, and testify through this. It's a lengthy task; I haven't learned yet. But once I began it Brognart was of little use, because he would have directed me toward that which because of his dazzle would have attracted too much attention, overshadowing things both more difficult and more essential for me. Some—few in number anyhow—those against fashion, seeing a valuable ally in me, screwed up their faces at me, for the world's divided into two blocs. If you're in one you've got to beat the dickens out of the other, and I was slipping out more and more, leaning away. But what kind of a politician am I anyway; that sort of a mask doesn't fit my measure—unauthenticity, the slavery of circumstances. In human fate I sought sources, not rivers that spilled forth from these sources.

So I buried Brognart, which doesn't mean that he didn't haunt me. He haunts me to this day, ever more closely grown together with my cousin, so that I can no longer distinguish them. Not even faces, these are weakly discernible, but more their insides, the imagining of this or that one in their moments behind the wire. Peace to their poor souls.

Translated by Albert Juszczak

Czesław Miłosz

Two Poems

I sleep a lot and read St. Thomas Aquinas
or *The Death of God* (that's a protestant book).
To the right the bay as if molten tin,
beyond the bay, city, beyond the city, ocean,
beyond the ocean, ocean, till Japan.
To the left dry hills with white grass,
beyond the hills an irrigated valley where rice is grown,
beyond the valley, mountains and Ponderosa pines,
beyond the mountains, desert and sheep.
When I couldn't without alcohol, I drove on alcohol.
When I couldn't without cigarettes and coffee, I drove on
    cigarettes and coffee.
I was courageous. Industrious. Nearly a model of virtue.
But that is good for nothing.

Please, Doctor, I feel a pain.
Not here. No, not here. Even I don't know.
Maybe it's too many islands anad continents,
unpronounced words, bazaars, wooden flutes,
or too much drinking to the mirror, without beauty,
though one was to be a kind of archangel
or a Saint George, over there, on St. George Street.

Please, Mr. Medicine Man, I feel a pain.
I always believed in spells and incantations.

Sure, women have only one, Catholic, soul
but we have two. When you start to dance
you visit in your sleep remote pueblos

and even lands you have never seen.
Put on, I pray you, charms made of feathers,
now it's time to help one of yours.
I have read many books but I don't believe them.
When it hurts we return to the banks of certain rivers,
I remember those crosses with chiseled suns and moons
and wizards, how they worked during an outbreak of typhus.
Send your second soul beyond the mountains, beyond time.
Tell me, I shall wait, what you saw.

A SENTENCE

And yet it's too great a responsibility to lure the souls
From where they lived together with the idea of the hummingbird,
the chair, and the star.
To imprison them within either/or: male sex, female sex,
So that they wake up in the blood of childbirth, weeping.

Translated by Czesław Miłosz and Peter Dale Scott

Józef Czapski

Cedar

A. M. Remizov is dead. I wrote about him in *Kultura* in 1951. Looking through it now, I find a fragment of a poem by Norwid which I translated for him.

It delighted him, and later he often recalled:

> The cedar is born of the desert and not of the garden . . .

During one of my last visits, I found him sitting hunched over, blind, short of breath—this affliction bothered him nearly every night and every day. I had the feeling that physically this was only a whisper of a man, when he said to me with sudden force: "I need solitude, silence, *the desert*."

His translator and most devoted friend for the past twenty years, Natalya Reznikova, was still writing out the last texts of this almost totally blind old man. She told me that when she arrived for her few hours of work with him he shook all over in his eagerness to dictate still more and more to her of what he had thought during the sleepless nights and solitary mornings—thoughts that he was able to put into unexpected, sophisticated, and yet fresh words whose cradle was the Russian land and the depths of his own soul.

How many artists search frantically for originality, how irritating this forced originality is, and how it falsifies everything. Especially during his youth, Remizov suffered a great deal because he was different. He tried to be unnoticeable, to be like the others, but he *was* different, and all his life he searched for words that would really express this uniqueness. I will never forget how once, as he listened while I read my French article about him, he caught me using a few words about the Soviets, dictatorship, or totalitarianism, which were banal, basted together in journalese. Waving his arms, he called out: "Don't use these words, they are already covered with dust." By his very style of life, by his every remark, not only the written word, Remizov was a protest against all jargon. No wonder, then, that it was just this arch-Russian master of language who headed the list prepared by Zhdanov of harmful and banned formalists.

A whole epoch has gone with him, because this man in his eighties had been a friend of Rozanov and Blok. Remizov's last book, *Circles of Happiness,* published in 1957 by a handful of friends from Paris, consists of four legends about King Solomon. The very introduction to these tales expresses the strangeness of this style: "My four novels are the eternal voice of the Russian land: the Russian fable, the Russian novel, and two legends about the building of a temple. The novel—I cannot do without this—I modernized, I moved the legend of the flying camel to the Middle Ages, and I 'amplified' and 'interpolated' the apocryphal work on the centaur and dressed it in Byzantine finery. I gathered these elements of the folk novel like pebbles, matched them, and set them into the 'golden frame' of the likeness of King Solomon. *My conjectures and my words—that is my whole art.*"

Remizov does not call himself a "word-maker" or "neologist" in vain. His tremendous knowledge of linguistics and history, his familiarity with remote sources of Russian and Russniak traditions, with myths, legends, Russian fables, currents, and links with the West through Poland and Byelorussia, with India, even China, Persia, through Byzantium or again through the West—all of this contributed to the curious word formations where the writer blends the words of yesterday with currently used words and those just being created, bringing into the Russian even colloquial expressions heard in French, so long as they are eloquent and richly resonant. This baroque structure, these combinations based on complete freedom and profound knowledge of language, can perhaps be compared to the style of Audiberti and to his degree of erudition and his neologisms.

The starting point of Remizov's literature is always the word, the rhythm of the sentence liberated from a dead weight, almost a *graphic drawing* of a sentence. Illustrations, drawn by Remizov himself for some of his books, his albums of drawings, of which he is said to have done about two thousand, even his penmanship itself, including a stylized seventeenth-century design of letters—form an indissoluble whole with his word. Rozanov's books were usually published almost like manuscripts. "Gutenberg licked all of literature with an iron tongue and its manuscript intimacy disappeared," wrote Rozanov, and he would be happy today to see that this intimacy in literature was regenerated by his friend Remizov, and at a time when literature in Russia had to be for the masses.

Great poets appear when there are none . . .

As I looked at this sage's head, his great brow bent, this gnome, child, or dwarf, I always realized anew that Russia, after all, borders on China. His strange cutouts or abstract paintings with which, as with precious Chinese tapestry, he hung his humble walls in the hungry times of the occupation, these weirdly shaped bones, gilded pine cones, fish bones, or roots which, suspended by string, divided his room, shelves made of old boxes, filled with books and manuscripts—the already blind Remizov knew perfectly well the location of each—the tales, the fantastica that this son of Gogol and Dostoevsky rearranged, blending them with Norman, Scottish, Persian, or Russian legends—all of this created, on the quiet Boileau Street, in the least interesting quarter of Paris, a magical island. Not only an island of magic, but an island of goodness as well. Remizov could never have created his work if it were not for his Russian friends. These people, many of them old, mostly women, all, if not bordering on destitution, at least poor, still found enough strength and heart to take up collections not only to support the writer in conditions in which he could work, but even so that out of these collections his writing could be published in a few hundred copies. We are far from Françoise Sagan and the countless laureates of innumerable prizes, whose names are plastered all over the papers.

It always struck me how this sick old man, who could express the poignancy of pain, abandonment, and loneliness better than anyone, to the end kept his joyfulness, how he loved life, voluptuously and hard. Even in his last book humor gushes forth.

But then the humor, the magic, the "association of apemen" which he formed and presided over, giving each of his friends the most fantastic monkey sobriquets—all of that was not completely in fun; the joke was treated most seriously, half magically. At the same time, how Remizov was tied to the Orthodox rite, its prayer, its whole liturgy, its customs; how well he knew the Orthodox tradition. And when over his body, over his face tied with a dark-cerise kerchief, a face white as chalk, thrown back, as if left uncovered by the great thoughtful brow—the clergyman stood, surrounded by a handful of Remizov's remaining friends and in a low, familiar chant intoned prayers for the dead, it struck me what Rozanov always wrote: to what a degree the Orthodox religion warmly and even joyfully greets *death*, the beginning of a new life, a life at last in peace, light, and truth.

In Remizov's last book there is a bibliography that is hard to believe—eighty-one book titles. Between 1907 and 1921 Remizov published thirty-seven of them in Russia. From Tibetan fables, apocrypha related by him, to short stories, novels, and even plays. Between 1921 and 1957 he roamed the world as an émigré. First Berlin, then Paris. Abroad he published forty-four volumes. Remizov had followers not only among Russians. Poets and surrealists were very much interested in him; the editors of the *Nouvelle Revue Française*, Paulhan and Marcel Arlan, had been his friends for years. Many of Remizov's books were translated into French or German, but not one into Polish. *With Trimmed Eyes*, recollections from his childhood (1951), is being published by Gallimard in French in the next few months in an amazing translation by Reznikova (several chapters of this book have already appeared in *Nouvelle Revue Française*.)

From among Remizov's many works I would still like to call attention to his tales of the perishing city of Petersburg. There is a 1918 poem by Mandelshtam from which I recall only a few lines: "*Na strashnoy vysote bluzdayushchyi ogon*" (At a great height stray flames appear). Every stanza ends with: "Your brother Petersburg is dying."

This verse, by a poet of the same era as Remizov, of the same generation (news of Mandelshtam's repeated deportation and death is whispered about), could serve as a motto for the most beautiful stories by Remizov from *Russia in Storm;* the tonal quality is similar: deeply sorrowful, and yet "controlled." Stories of the beloved city dying in hunger and misery, of the confusion, hopelessness, the little man swept away in the deluge, the Revolution seen through his eyes.

Stories written many years later are similar in tone—stories of wretches begging in the Metro, of crippled children, of mice and rats, of a gnawing loneliness in glittering Paris. And probably, rather than the brilliant Nobel laureate Bunin, a post-Tolstoy classic, also an émigré, now published and accepted by the Soviets, it is Remizov who has carried Russia in him from the oldest myths through the cruel years in which he lived and wrote—who will remain as a monument of the rarest metal in the great Russian literature put to death or driven out by the Revolution.

And when the last heart attack came to Remizov at rue Boileau a few days before his death, in a language understandable only to those closest to him he still spoke of the dreams he dreamed, created words—the word-maker.

And today those who knew him think of his humble and beautiful death with emotion but without bitterness. All of us can envy his fulfilled destiny.

Translated by Maria De Gorgey

Aleksander Remizov

The Rat's Portion

"Crédit Municipal," or pawnshop in our language—how familiar the way that leads to it.

I carried two Moscow quilts brought from Petersburg twelve years earlier, together with all kinds of rags and tatters, and the inevitable, always scrupulously guarded kerosene stove; the quilts were somewhat worn but still strong and spotless. I was afraid all the time that they would only give me three francs for them, the sum at which they appraised my ten-year-old coat from Berlin, so I shuddered a bit when they called out my number—but now, I heard right, five francs. Relieved, I sat down on a bench to await payment.

As I stood at the window unrolling the quilts, someone sat down on the very edge of the bench, his feet dangling, fumbling; I felt it right away, but did not glance his way, and now I saw him: a rat. Yes, it was a young, hungry rat; he installed himself near the window, diligently observing the pawns, all the time shaking his paws in the air; but no grub came around: cameras were just being pawned.

And now some woman came in, walking very strangely; perhaps she had a headache, or felt embarrassed by something, or maybe she was reluctant to enter, or, like me when I came in, she was worried that they would give her three francs, so that after deducting the Metro fare nothing at all would remain; she sat down on the edge of the bench the same way; she had with her two packages and also a little basket shaped like a sugar-bowl—everyone noticed, and the rat stared at her intently.

Her packages were tied securely. Frowning, she began fretting at the string with her fingers, polished fat nails shaped like almonds, but the knots would not budge. She was dressed too lightly—well, what of it, a free body is heaven, because toward evening it grows stifling after the daily toil!—she had on a pistachio dress so tight-fitting that it seemed she wore nothing under it, only grey silk stockings and shoes with buckles. On her head was a faded knitted cap, and she herself was rather grey all over, lightly sprinkled with powder, her hair painted to a somewhat greenish tinge. At last she managed to untie her packages—we saw fabric of some kind—very soft—some pieces of dark blue material: velvet. Yes, velvet, I became convinced, as I looked at the rat, at his beady eyes which suddenly lighted up—and I already saw bloody meat with a thin layer of warm fat—rumpsteak. The woman handed over her basket also: some trinkets, little elephant figurines and picture post-cards in thin frames—wall, just a little something to get offered as a separate item.

The velvet was appraised, just as my quilts, at five francs.

"Spots and holes!" explained the appraiser.

And for the elephant figurines and postcards—nothing.

How can that be? The woman did not want to take back the basket.

The boss, a heavy set man with padded shoulders, came out—his glasses straddled his beak of a nose, his eyes and nose worked unerringly and simultaneously. I was reminded of the usurer from the "Petersburg alleys"—nothing would move a type like that—and so he was not moved, neither by the trembling mouth, nor the empty eyes, grey-white like deadly nightshade.

She sat down on the bench, holding her number and the rejected basket.

"Where is it from—the beach?"—I wondered idly, or perhaps her light pistachio dress made me think of the season.

"Or maybe straight from a night spot?—no, probably her lover abandoned her."

Suddenly she winced so pitifully, as if she wanted to sneeze, but decided that it would not be dignified, and stopped herself.

"Yes, of course, abandoned. And the dark blue velvet—rump-steak—the last thing she owns: five francs."

Again a grimace crossed her face, but different than before, and the fingers with nails like fat, painted almonds twisted in a shudder.

She has nothing more to pawn.

I suddenly felt very sorry for her. And I seemed to take on myself all of her fate, her desertion; without thinking, without reflecting, I gathered her to me with the emotion that all at once welled up in me, not knowing why or wherefore.

She adjusted her cap, trying to appear different; she arose, holding the light little basket with both hands—elephant figurines and picture postcards—she moved to another seat.

I sat with my back to her, facing the rat, but still I saw her, frowning and shaken, even more faded under my fleeting glance than a moment before. And I could not get rid of this feeling of pity and sorrow.

I do not know whether she felt this, but she rose suddenly and sat down on the bench opposite.

How can I help her? My worth is five francs too. And what good will my glance do her, even magnified a thousandfold? Would I be able, even if I took upon myself everything she went through until the last disastrous night, and even until the hardest dawn of this unbearably toilsome day, to take this damnation off her shoulders?

She stopped frowning—did she turn to stone?—did she calm down?

And I suddenly recalled the look given me by an unknown woman when once, getting up from under a car that had hit me, crumpled, bruised black and blue and, above all, scared, I made my way home with faltering steps, and her look was—I remember—like outstretched hands. And recently in the Metro—I remember that look too—some woman got up and offered me her seat—I was so weary then.

The rat was called. I rose as well.

And when the rat leaned over the counter, showing his "papers," I noticed how the hair on his back was standing on end. He carried his five francs off between his paws, and such appetite burned in his eyes as if he were carrying a slab of cheese to his rat hole. And after I received my rat's portion, I too left, without looking back.

At that moment a woman leading a little girl entered the pawnshop; the little girl hung back behind her mother, and when she saw me she became frightened and ran off. I saw her mother calling her and smiling. "How could I have scared her?" And suddenly my eyes met the other woman's: after receiving her rat's portion she also walked to the exit.

I can imagine how the children ran off at the sight of Dostoevsky, who had a "demon in his heart and a demon in his thoughts."

Walking along the corridors of Madeleine station, I met a woman with one child at her breast, and two more at her side: a boy and a girl. I had already noticed them going the other way; not a drop of blood in her body, like a leaf, wearing dark glasses—my heart bled for them, and as usual I asked myself: How is it possible, that mothers with children stand in corridors of the Metro and beg for alms?—and my exasperated heart answered, without considering whether this would help or not, that there is no other way to put an end to this cruelty but to blow up all these corridors. But immediately I remembered the "Petersburg alleys."

"And are the children real—I asked myself—or are they changelings, rented out?"

Cursing misery and corruption, I dragged along on my bleak way. The whole dread of suffering engulfed me, I could almost smell it. Or perhaps it was the smell of the cheese that emanated from the rat's portion? And there was no pity in me.

Trembling, half-open mouth, lips that never close—I had such a neighbor in the Metro—is this a human being? And that one—across from me, the faded one with eyes the color of deadly night-shade—is that a person too? And I myself—rolled into a black ball—who did I seem to be?—that I tried not to think of.

Editor's note: This is a fragment from an unpublished book entitled *The Music Teacher* (1923–1939).

Translated by Maria De Gorgey

Aleksander Remizov

In Bondage

It suddenly dawned on me that we are all serving a sentence, and a life sentence at that. I saw the many things we do in a new light, things that can be explained by this life-sentence state of ours.

Everyone hates everyone else. Enemies everywhere. If not openly, at least in secret, everyone tries to trip up everyone else. They are always whispering, always looking askance. There is a universal fear that someone will appear, spoil things for you, wrench them out of your hand. And not out of greed, but from a gnawing wretchedness. Honor has disappeared—honesty has burned out in the course of time so that no trace of it remains. It is as if the words "to stand up for someone" did not exist. Hypocrisy flourishes—but no one is fooled by it: for a long time now no one has trusted anyone else, while bootlicking and adulation are on the rise, and hit on a sure-tried way, possibly the only way to reach a goal.

The convicts who have managed to grab power act wisely and torture those who must depend on them. It is just their vile nature. Or it may not be a question of nature, but of demoralizing association with dullards and no-talents who always acquiesce meekly; there is nowhere to turn, and, without meaning to, you agree to everything.

I am one of those convicts who always depend on someone else. I am forever standing back to look at my suffering; I do not know how much I can stand, but I do know that my feelings cannot, but somehow must spill over to the surface, and come out in some coarse and vulgar way, which will be a new source of anguish for me. I was never a slave before, and if I have become one now, after all, the hour of slave revolt will strike. People say only nasty things about each other. Their greatest pleasure is to invent some disgraceful story, to slander someone. It has already become our second nature, our convict's nature. This is where unceasing deceit comes from. In short: Russians try to avoid other Russians.

But is it possible that only the dregs inhabit Russian Paris? No, it is just that the bondage has done its work: after twelve—fifteen years of exile, these are the seeds it has sown! But essentially man does not change—this is confirmed by all the upheavals we have witnessed—as he was born, so he will die, despite everything, while the circumstances of his life only help his inborn traits to develop; even though I say "dregs," although I refer to bondage, even without bondage the roots of these dregs must have sprung from somewhere.

And somehow everything goes awry. I recall that a certain friend of the fabulist Kukovnikov—you know him, ladies and gentlemen—of whom it could not be said that by nature he belonged to the Paris dungheap, once told me amicably of someone's mean deed. Naturally, it would seem that to clear up the matter he should have indicated the villain, but I could not get him to divulge his identity. "I gave my word that I would not tell!" he told me. So tender in his purity—he would not go back on his word—but for all the friendship he professed for me, he did not stop to think that I would be smeared with mud? And does he not understand that because he had "soiled" me, his own "purity" was worthless?

Always be watchful: you can expect anything. Many things have stopped bothering me altogether: habit. But not only habit. What once would have burst out into indignation and repeated cries of: "What contemptible baseness!" now is shrugged off with a hollow and impotent "Rascals!" or the vile excuse "It is not my business!" or most often by a meek silence. Meek silence! There is an ominous sign that life has been crushed. What more can be expected of slavery, once you know there is no escape anyway.

Yes, only death will open for us the door to freedom.

I must admit that I have often wanted to turn on the gas, but was stopped by the thought that that swindler Kozlok would immediately sit down and write reminiscences about me: "A. A. Kornetov in Music and Calligraphy." Kozlok has stopped busying himself with developing amateur photographs, and has become specialized in a new literary genre: in the wake of countless memoirs—the main capital of émigré literature—he was the first to write his—what should I call them?—"shreds and tatters," yet this aptly describes his gossipy remembrances of the dead.

Even now, he has nested near me, hovers around me, drinks up my every word—he does not care from what a very broken heart flow these words, my most bitter confessions and, who knows, maybe even despair; in his posthumous writings there will always be all the filth that people have grown accustomed to saying about each other, and generally everything "they say."

So this miserable life drags on. And it is all happening in magnificent, dazzling Paris! A hopeless, beggarly life fenced in by inflexible dates and deadlines: rent, taxes, electricity, gas, water, insurance, registrations of all kinds. In this slavish life, the only moments that my careworn eyes rest are meetings with children.

Most often this happens in the Metro. I greet them, we exchange glances and, if we can manage it, we talk. Children understand all languages, before them I am not embarrassed about my pronunciation, nor do I become flustered if I begin to speak Russian. They are not embarrassed with me either. How pleased I always am that they are not afraid of me; how glad that the dark storms that tear at my heart have not carried me off yet, that there is still light and tranquility in my heart: it is because of this light and tranquility that my eyes do not terrify. But more and more often I become aware that our common bondage and my own gift which enables me not only to look, but to see and remember, this gift that lets me see the bondage under the surface of a dazzling Paris—are blowing away and extinguishing the last remaining light in my heart.

Translated by Maria De Gorgey

I. Ivanov

Foreword to "Does Life Exist on Mars?," published in 1961

WHEN I arrived at the decision to publish this play far from the borders of my fatherland, I wondered involuntarily, as does each author, giving his work over to the printer: And who exactly will be reading it?

I realize that the readers of a play about events occurring on Mars in the year 1956 will be very diverse persons.

In my fatherland it will be read exclusively by those elect few whose obligation it is to hide in safes everything that, for the most diverse reasons, may lead into temptation the imagination of the Soviet people. The reaction of this group of readers is well known to me beforehand; therefore, in order to escape personal troubles, I wish to remain anonymous.

On the other hand, it must be assumed that my foreign readers will be a great deal more diversified.

The leaders of Communist parties should anathematize me. (As a matter of fact, they may act immediately after having read the foreword, without wasting time reading the work.)

For rank-and-file Communists, I will not presume to take on myself the responsibility for any categorical statement; as one of our dignitaries has said (of course not publicly, but at a small gathering of intimates and friends), "Communists in the West are increasingly undependable recently."

Readers belonging to the opposite camp—adherents of ruling circles in the West and in America, not to mention the government of Israel—should praise me. And if they do not, then it will be common discourtesy on their part.

What, however, will be the reaction of that reader who forms his opinion independently of innumerable *Times*' and a few *Daily Workers*'s? Those readers are probably strongly diversified, and in this milieu two logically valid questions may arise: (1) Why did the author write this play? and (2) Why did he publish it?

Because the opinion of this third set of readers is not unimportant to me, I want to answer both questions.

To the first question—Why did I write this?—I want to answer as simply as possible: I am a writer and I write about everything I have lived through, what thoughts occupied my mind, what moved me. But it is important to add at this time that the events that prompted the writing of this piece moved not only me but even those as well who today will be prepared to cover me with slime and declare categorically that these events never happened at all.

It is more difficult to answer the second question: Why publish the play? And at a time when relations between the two blocs have worsened to such a degree that a spark would suffice to set off a conflagration. Why, then, at such a time give to the enemies of one's own fatherland yet another pretext for strengthening their propaganda, when it was already sufficiently unconscionable? But in the end, I do not at all wish victory to the generals of the Pentagon and the revanchists in Bonn. Not only that, but if it comes to the outbreak of war, I will find myself in the ranks of the Soviet Army, and if I perish, I perish as a Russian soldier. In that case, then, why am I publishing this book?

We live in times when the fates of nations of the whole world are so closely interwoven, one with the other, that it is impossible for a Mongolian to be indifferent to what is happening in Egypt, and for an Italian to ignore what is going on in the Soviet Union. All of us, inhabitants of the Earth, are so interdependent on each other that, for example, the Algerian affair to one degree or another rebounds off the personal fate of each of us, irrespective of what nook of the planet we may inhabit. The close interdependence of all nations, the interweaving of our fates—this is one of the most characteristic marks of the mid-twentieth century. Therefore we ought also to know as much as possible about each other.

But at the same time, the epoch in which we are living is an epoch of the moral bankruptcy of, in the first place, bourgeois democracy, seeking salvation through fascist bayonets, and in the second place, the bankruptcy of that which calls itself the dictatorship of the proletariat, but which in reality has turned out to be, as Plekhanov has already said, a dictatorship over the proletariat.

In such circumstances, the role of each honorable Soviet writer consists of demonstrating that the Soviet horseradish is no sweeter than the bourgeois radish. If the discrediting of this bourgeois radish is a matter of conscience for writers of bourgeois lands, then the Soviet horseradish altogether burdens our consciences.

In the course of the several months after the historic Twentieth Congress of our [Communist] Party, it was possible to think that the cult of personality with all its marvels was essentially the error of a madman. But today only the blind do not see that in its substance everything has remained as of old, and what has changed is only the form, under which they attempted to cover the old content; but nowadays one can no longer think this way.

The Twentieth Congress brought complete victory to Khrushchev and his creatures. Of all of that which a Marxist-Leninist ought to have discredited, Khrushchev, at the Twentieth Congress, actually discredited precisely that much which was necessary for him to discredit so that, controlling the previously-existing government machine, he could seize power after sweeping the remnant of the Stalinist leadership from his path. At the same time—and this is understandable in itself—Khrushchev undermined the faith of millions in Soviet socialism. And it is precisely this on which his historical merit rests, for in this manner did he jolt the course of history from a dead end. But not in the least did he do this from some basic ideological consideration. He wanted power, and he has this power in his hands. Out of stupidity he himself chopped through the branch on which he was sitting and the existence of which he wanted to ensure forever.

That Khrushchev did not intend to alter the bases of the machine that produces the atrocities and crimes of the Stalinist variety received sufficiently eloquent testimony by his return to the cult of personality. Of course nowadays Khrushchev himself has become the object of that cult. It can be concluded that, once again after ten years (or perhaps significantly more—Khrushchev is a healthy fellow and will not die soon), there will be talk, defrauding the masses, about the consequences of this pleasant cult. I speak of "defrauding," because the cult itself represents the consequence of the bureaucratic system of the Soviet governmental machine.

At the present moment the prediction, expressed in the anecdote narrated immediately after Khrushchev accomplished his complete victory, is being realized; in this anecdote Stalin supposedly left his heir this testament: "Discredit me, and afterward behave in all things exactly as I."

Marx began his *18th of Brumaire of Louis Bonaparte* with the words that the current best friend of the Kazakh, Kirghiz, and many other peoples (as it had been declared during many decennia of national arts) ought to hammer into his memory: "Hegel somewhere observed that all the great events and figures of a world-wide scale appear, so to speak, twice. Hegel forgot to add: The first time as a tragedy, the second—as a farce."

Fate so decreed that it would fall to the lot of people of my generation to be the witnesses of the realization of yet another version of the cult of personality, but this time of that version which is realized as a farce. It is necessary, then, to hope expectantly that all the basenesses that, at the present moment, indicate a tendency toward its regeneration do not drag after them such tragic consequences as they brought in the Stalinist epoch.

In order to prevent a repetition of this tragedy, writers may do several things. Let my play, then, become yet one more reminder of that truth, that the leadership of the Communist Party of the Soviet Union did not want to say even a single word about the ignominious years 1947–53, and continues to persist in the old line. Let us unmask and discredit this "most democratic system" so praised by Khrushchev. Let it become worthwhile for all those who, standing on humanistic positions, equally cast aside the bourgeois state, as well as the Soviet dictatorship; for those who are seeking new paths of social development.

Translated by William J. Sullivan

Andrey Sinyavsky

Thoughts Taken Unawares

You live like an utter fool, but now and then some first-class thoughts do come to mind.

*

How do you have the gall to fear death?! That's just like turning coward on the battlefield. Look, people are falling all around you. Think of your old parents; they're dead. Remember your cousin Verochka, who died when she was five. Such a little girl, and she went to her death suffocated by diptheria. And you, grown-up, healthy, educated, you're afraid. . . . Well, stop shaking! Cheer up! Forward! March!

*

The life of man is like military service. It is short and full of responsibility. You can't depend on it as a permanent residence, and settle down to serious housekeeping. But neither will it let you live any old way and pass the time as if you were on leave. You have a set time to serve and an allowance has been given you. And you are not alone. Here on earth we are all neither guests nor hosts, neither tourists nor natives. We have all been drafted.

*

If I were to become a eunuch, I could get so much done!

*

To make our lives less offensive to us, we comfort ourselves with death beforehand and are forever saying: I won't give a damn after I'm dead!

We shall probably have to pay dearly for this arrogance, which sees death as a way out of the game. Nature does not provide ends as easy as the departure of a guest who can take his hat and say: "Well, I'm leaving, but you stay and do what you like." Probably death (even in the form of simple physical annihilation), like everything else in the world, must be earned. Nature does not permit us to indulge our whims in her house.

*

We must trust God as a dog trusts his master. Whistle and he'll come running. And wherever you go, he'll follow you, to the very ends of the earth, without any questions, without even thinking about it.

*

I was sitting in a restaurant and looking around. It was during the day, there were few customers, and those that were there had gathered quite by chance, people who had just come up from the country or who wanted to eat in elegant surroundings for once in their lives. Being there by chance myself, I found it interesting to observe others who had come together by chance.

I happened to notice a young girl, homely, with loosely waved hair and an unnecessarily wide, open mouth. Unaccustomedly tipsy from the sweet wine, she was laughing loudly, showing off immense teeth. I looked at her and thought how ugly she was, and resented her ugliness, complacent and unaware of itself. It seemed to me that not only had she no right to sit there at the table, but that she had no right to exist on earth at all; how could this girl not be ashamed to be so ugly, how could she still laugh, faced with her own ugliness? . . .

And suddenly I thought, and was rather surprised by the idea, so surprised that even now I keep going back to it, although it is time it was forgotten—I thought: "And what right, really, have you to judge this girl if God Himself tolerates her presence? If he allows us all to exist, who are just as unattractive, just as miserable. Here we sit and despise each other, ready to wipe each other from the face of the earth, while He, Who plainly sees all our lack of beauty, nonetheless permits us to live even though He could cut short our impudent, free-and-easy existence at a stroke. What is your authority for not tolerating this ugly creature, if He, Whose beauty is ineffable, has tolerated her?!"

This recognition of my unfairness, so obvious in the light of His tolerance, put me in an unexpectedly comic mood. I laughed at myself and, while I shook with inward merriment, maintained external decorum, because I was not alone in the restaurant, but in the company of friends. But in the depths of my soul I was rolling about and holding my sides, and it was as though I felt a condescending but tender gaze upon me. When I looked at the girl, who had not become any more attractive as a result of it all, I felt more cheerful than I had in some time. But my cheerfulness at that moment contained no malice; rather, it was full of gratitude for the thought that had revealed all this and that was laughing at me and at all of us with bright, inoffensive laughter. And to this day it seems to me that God was blessing me then in that laughter.

*

Art is jealous. Taking its point of departure from certain uncommunicative "facts," it depicts, with the power of fiery imagination, a second universe where events unfold at a heightened tempo, in plain view. The artist must love life jealously, that is, must not trust the picture before him, and, turning from it, must suspect the presence of something in men and nature that no one else can see.

*

"I was her sixty-seventh; she was my forty-fourth."

*

My fuses were burned out. I felt very sad, thought myself lost, and asked God for help. And God sent me an Electrician. And the Electrician fixed my fuses.

*

It is only when you contract a venereal disease that you begin to understand how chaste everyone is.

*

There is something pathological in sexual relations. A repulsion that attracts, an attraction that repels. This is no "piece of bread" which one would like to eat up. Here desire is based on the fact that one must do it, and the more one "must not," the more one wants it.

Anatomy is elementary. But what darkness, what a glow in the darkness?! A woman who previously was accepted as a perfectly normal creature all of a sudden acquires a supernatural aura. From being "Lyudochka" or "Sofia Nikolaevna," she becomes a priestess guided by dark forces. In the sexual act there is always something of the Black Mass.

The very pleasure achieved in this manner is deeper and more terrible than the ordinary joys of the flesh. To a significant degree, it is based on the commission of a sacrilege. Beautiful women, apart from anything else, are successful because the sacrilegiousness of the act increases with them.

This is the cause of fickleness and infidelity. From a strictly physiological point of view, there is little to distinguish the new love object from the old. But the whole trick is that the new object seems "sweeter" beforehand because you are breaking the law with her for the first time, and, consequently, behaving more sacrilegiously. You turn an unknown Donna Anna into a tart, and it affords you particular satisfaction that she is a "donna" and "unknown": "So pure, so lovely, but just watch what I'm going to do with you!" With her you relive the sensation of the Fall that you had lost with the "old object" from force of habit. In that case repetition had legitimized the act of sacrilege and it ceased to appear so attractive. The history of Don Juan is the eternal search for the One, still inviolate, with whom the illicit can be most pleasantly achieved. In relations with a woman it is always of more significance to take off her pants than to satisfy your own natural desires. And the more lofty and unattainable the woman is, the more interesting she becomes.

It is the same impulse, obtained from moral law, that makes the debauchery of husband and wife in their lawful bed far more inventive than that of casual adulterers. For strangers, the shame of being strangers is enough. But for loving married couple, before whom can they be ashamed, with whom can they be lascivious? Nothing else remains for them but to break the law within its own limits and to furnish the conjugal union with such shamelessness as to give it at least the appearance of the Fall.

*

Women start eating their pastries in pastry shops without leaving the counter. For some reason men don't do this. But women—they run into the shop as if it were the ladies' room and in a herd, in front of everyone, gobble it all up on the spot! They all have a sweet tooth. From young to old. Watch how they eat—there is a hint of something improper, something immodest in their postures, their gestures, their nibbling, as eager as lovers' kisses. She'll finish stuffing herself, turn, and go on her own way. . . .

*

Women's pliancy is depressing. There is in it something of our common human imperfection.

*

Women are more sinful than we are, but better. It's very odd, but perfectly true: both better and more sinful. A wanton woman becomes virtuous, a hypocritical woman becomes sincere, an evil woman becomes good, with barely a change in her feminine nature. Such transformations are as natural to women as walking to the other side of the street. She stopped, crossed the street, and went on, quite different, and yet just the same.

*

Somehow, filth and rubbish are concentrated around man. There is none of that in nature. Animals do not make dirt if they are not kept in stalls or cages, that is, again by the act and will of human beings. And if they do make dirt, it is not disgusting, and nature herself very quickly tidies it up without any effort on their part. But man must work at keeping himself clean all his life, from morning till night. At times this process becomes so tiresome that you think: I'd sooner die than soil and be soiled any longer. The ultimate piece of rubbish is a dead body, which also demands to be taken away as soon as possible. What's left is a heap of dung.

In addition to this we are to master the role of the cleaning woman who sweeps up after everyone and can never stop; the piles of trash will continue to grow. She identifies people by the mess they leave behind them: that man doesn't wipe his feet, while this woman always leaves a lady's trivial debris—hairpins, a perfume bottle, discarded puffs of cotton that stink of eau de cologne, scattered all over the room. This is what happens in a hotel.

*

The location of sex is fatal—right next to the organs of excretion. It is as though a squeamish, sarcastic grimace had been foreseen by nature herself. Whatever dwells side by side with urine and excrement cannot be pure and spiritual. Physically unpleasant, foul surroundings are evidence of the mark of disgrace on our private parts. The shamelessness of sexual intercourse, apart from our shame and fear, must overcome the feeling of nausea caused by something unclean. Common pleasure resembles a feast in a sewer and makes one want to flee the source of filth.

And yet, imagine a girl, ignorant, timid, who works and works and patiently waits for the time when someone will at least want to amuse himself with her in passing. And still nothing happens. One fellow did give her a squeeze in a dimly lighted club, but his drinking got the better of him; he abandoned the idea, fell asleep in the middle of it, and remembered nothing in the morning. Then some peasant, lame, I think, with a wooden stump instead of a leg, considered marrying the girl, and again she was willing, but he either was run over by a tractor, or just went away and never came back. And her life went on in monotonous work, while she quietly wondered why no one found her desirable, with a guilty smile that no one was even tempted. The question is: wouldn't it have been better for her to sin than to languish in this unhealthy, useless chastity?

In our life, in existence, the idea of the Fall is seldom set forth in all of its metaphysical nakedness. There are so many side issues, circumstances, and motives involved that it all seems to be much sadder and funnier than it is. It happens that a man has no place to call his own, and so he attaches himself to a woman who also has to find a place for herself. A tedious and meager life, with nothing at hand but one's private parts which dangle like a baby's rattle, and why shouldn't a bored man play with it a little? Or why shouldn't a woman forget herself with a man she doesn't know—it's just the same as going to a new movie. Here there is not even always the attraction of forbidden fruit, of sex, of dangerous pleasure, but simply the attraction of "the other side," self-pity, the desire to have fun, to go away, to make a change, and even love for a fellow creature for whom we have no other way to show our affection. All this triviality of human life does not remove or justify sin, but side by side with it sin, taken separately as such, in its own primordial nastiness, is less frightening and appears to be a safety-valve. Sin implies the end, crime, the abyss, hell, death—in other words, all of the maximal limiting concepts—but here in reality, in life, ours is a dull existence compared to which death itself would be better.

*

A man actually becomes closer and dearer when he loses his badges of office—his profession, his name, his age. When he no longer is even called a man, but turns out to be simply anyone at all.

*

The accumulation of money. The accumulation of knowledge and experience. The accumulation of books that have been read. Collectors—the kings of numismatics, plutocrats of candy wrappers. The accumulation of fame: just one more poem, just one more role. Lists of women. A swarm of admirers. Notches on the butt of a sniper's rifle. The accumulation of suffering: what I have lived through, what I have borne. Journeys. The pursuit of vivid sensations. Discoveries, conquests, the growth of the economy. Whoever has accumulated the most is better, superior, more cultured, cleverer, more popular.

And in the midst of this universal accumulation:

"Blessed are the poor in spirit!"

*

It makes us feel secure to understand that our fate is predestined.

*

Our death should be such that we can cry (whisper) before it: "Hurrah! We're setting sail!"

*

It is a good idea in going away (or dying) to leave a clean place behind you.

*

Lord, take my life!

*

For lack of a word or gesture, for want of something better and more important, we concentrate on women and make various indecent propositions to them so as to have something to do, something to talk about.

*

When every secret stands revealed—you understand?—every one!—then we'll really be in trouble.

*

If we are doomed to die from some sort of radiation, it will be perfectly logical. An idea can evolve to the point where it overwhelms itself. But of what are dogs and frogs guilty—creatures that had no desire to evolve?

*

And yet the main thing about a Russian is that he has *nothing to lose*. This accounts for the unselfishness of the Russian intelligentsia (outside of its bookshelves). And the outspokenness of the people: drunk, for Russia, with breast bared! Shoot, you rats! That's not hospitality, it's despair. A readiness to offer the last morsel, because it is the last and there is no more, to the limit, to the very end. Their thoughts and opinions come easily. What chaos. They have saved nothing, learned nothing. Who dares to pass judgment? They have already been judged.

*

Drunkenness is our fundamental national vice, and, furthermore, our *idée fixe*. The Russian people drink, not from need and not from sorrow, but from a primordial longing for the miraculous, the extraordinary; their drinking has a mystical quality, if you will, which tries to raise the soul from its earthly equilibrium and return it to a blissful state of disembodiment. Vodka is the white magic of the Russian peasant; he definitely prefers it to black magic—the female sex. The ladies' man, the lover must model himself on a foreigner, a German (Gogol's devil), a Frenchman, a Jew.

We Russians will hand over any beauty for a bottle of spirits (Stenka Razin).

In combination with robbery (the lack of a firm belief in substantial, objective ties) drunkenness offers us the freedom of a tramp and puts us in the suspicious position of a *Lumpen* in the eyes of other peoples. As soon as the "age-old principles" and class hierarchy tumbled down and were replaced by amorphous equality this criminal quality in the Russian emerged into the light of day. Now we all belong to the criminal class (who among us does not feel that there is something of the scoundrel in his soul and fate?) This gives us an indisputable advantage in comparison with the West and at the same time stamps the life and aspirations of the nation with the seal of instability and capriciousness. We are capable of taking over Europe or of infiltrating it with an interesting heresy, but we simply are in no position to create a culture. We are unpredictable, like a thief or a drunkard. It is easy to dominate us, to govern us by administrative measures (a drunkard is passive, incapable of self-direction; he follows where he is led). And at the same time, how difficult it is to handle this unsteady nation, how painful it is for our administrators to deal with us!

*

How pleasant it is when a casual passerby says "please" or "thank you." And says "thank you" so cordially, as though he really wishes you salvation.[1] Only by such sincerity is the world upheld—especially the Russian world. Words like "buddy," "pop," "do me a favor." Without any urbanity, but said from the heart.

*

In earlier times man's domestic life was far more broadly and simply connected with universal—historical and cosmic—existence than it is today. Although we have newspapers, museums, radio, communication by air, we hardly notice this all-encompassing background and are not particularly impressed by it, think little of it. Wearing Czech shoes, with a Mexican cigarette between my teeth, I read an article on the emergence of a new state in Africa,

1 The Russian word for "thank you," *spasibo,* originally had the literal meaning "God save you."

and went out to have some bouillon made from French meat. All this external, apparent contact with the world has the character of casual, unconnected information: "an elder's in the garden, but Uncle's in Kiev." We can hear about this uncle in Kiev many times a day without attaching particular significance to these facts. The quantity of our bits of knowledge and information is immense; it overburdens us without changing us qualitatively. Our entire world can be encompassed in a few days—one can sit in an airplane and travel around it without gaining anything for his soul, only increasing the amount of information to be dealt with.

Let us now compare these chimerical horizons with the bygone way of life of a peasant who never traveled any farther than the hay-mowing, and spent his entire life in home-made, traditional bast shoes. His scope seems limited to us, but how really extensive it was, this compact area within the confines of a single village. For even the monotonous ritual of dinner (in comparison with French bouillon and Jamaican rum) was involved in a circle of concepts with universal significance. Observing fasts and holidays, a man lived by a common historical calendar which began with Adam and concluded with the Day of Judgment. For this reason, incidentally, a half-educated sectarian could occasionally philosophize as well as a Tolstoy and achieve the heights of a Plotinus with no other aid than the Bible. The peasant maintained a continuous connection with all of creation and died in the depths of the universe together with Abraham. But we, after reading our newspapers, will die alone on our narrow, worthless couches. And then we will have no use for information. It's like a pair of trousers made of imported material. We show off in them, and that's all. What become of all our broad outlook, our wealth of information, when we take off our trousers or have them taken off? Or when we pick up our spoons to eat? The peasant, before taking up his spoon, used to cross himself, and by this single reflex action made himself one with earth and heaven, with past and future.

*

We are obliged to urban comfort and technical progress for the fact that faith in God is on the wane. Surrounded by the things created by us, we have considered ourselves the creators of the universe. How can I see the Lord God in a world where I come across man at every step? The voice of God resounded in the wilderness, in silence, but silence and wilderness are precisely what we lack. We have shut out everything and become engrossed in ourselves, and then we are surprised that God does not appear to us.

*

Any personality is repulsive if there is too much of it. Personality is always a kind of capital, even if it is a combination of virtue, wit, and talent. "Distribute your riches . . ." Christ loved those who were "nobody." And wasn't He Himself a "Nobody?" As a personality He was rather inscrutable (and therefore ineffable) and in no case was He original. "The personality of Jesus Christ" sounds blasphemous. His was a Personality in the reverse, negative sense. You would not call Christ a "genius." A genius is full of himself; a genius is a capitalist. There is the vampirism of genius, the worship of geniuses, which began with the Renaissance, and then there is the altruism of sanctity, forever shining, not with its own light, but with Yours, Lord.

*

Enough repetitive talk of man. It is time to think about God.

*

The theosophists are afraid of the words "devil" and "God." They are always worried that they will be suspected of ignorance, and want to discuss matters scientifically. Such caution does not inspire confidence in them.

*

Why did Christ never smile? Perhaps because laughter is inappropriate in a prison where men condemned to death await their executions?

*

It is not impossible that hell exists on earth. That would explain everything. But if not? Lord, what then? . . .

*

It is possible that sinners grouped in hell according to different classes and parties also envy each other and put on airs before each other. One who is being roasted on a spit makes fun of those who are strung up by their feet. Insults abound, conflicts threaten; each one thinks that he is worse off than the others. And then there is the snobbishness of a few sufferers (pederasts, for example), who constitute a special caste with a refined method of torment. There are sudden fads, when all dream of getting into the gas chamber reserved for the murderers of children, and back-date their uncommitted crimes; they would all be glad to kill a child, but there's not one to be found in this infernal darkness. The eternal struggle for precedence in the underworld, and quarrels over freedom, equality, and brotherhood.

*

I do not understand at all what is meant by the "freedom of choice" liberal philosophy talks so much about. Can we really choose whom we love, what we believe in, what illness to have? Love (like any other strong emotion) is monarchical and despotic, acting from within and taking prisoners without exception, without a backward glance. Of what freedom can we be thinking when we are totally absorbed, when we understand nothing, see nothing, except the Object that has chosen us, and, having chosen, torments or delights us? As soon as we wish for freedom (whether from sin or from God—it's all the same), we fall under the sway of yet another force, which whispers about freeing us only as long as we have not surrendered to it completely. Freedom is always negative and presupposes a lack, an emptiness, which is anxious to be filled as soon as possible. Freedom is a hunger, a longing for domination, and if there is so much talk about it nowadays, it means that we are in a state of interregnum. A tsar will come and put an end to all this spiritual parliamentarianism which goes by the name of "freedom of choice."

*

Imagine a genius in the other world. He runs from corner to corner—in hell—and points out to everyone: Look how talented I am!

*

It's a good thing when you are late to slow down your pace a bit.

*

Still, I do love snow better than anything else in the world.

*

Sometimes (very rarely) we have dreams about the dead which are quite different from our dreams of ordinary people. That is, they speak and look like the living, yet the dream is not of their past life with us, but of a present meeting with them, suddenly revived and come to see us. Perhaps they have only temporarily taken on their previous appearance in order to make it easier for us to recognize and understand them.

We feel joyfully surprised at seeing them and sob in our sleep with happy tears when we realize that it was all untrue and they are alive. We do not at all forget that these are the dead, but their appearance takes place in an annihilation, as it were, of death. We are terribly excited and exultant ("he didn't die! she didn't die!"), and want nothing more than to live with them and never part; we promise them something, beseech them, and settle or try to settle something with them. And they—who are also happy at this moment—for some reason are very quiet and not at all excited, but only attempt to calm us gently, as if they know more than we do, as if they are stronger and more patient than we. And they smile and nod at our fervent words.

But then the meeting is over and they fade away, not wishing to sadden us with farewells and goodbyes, they fade away and leave us in a profound and blissful childlike sleep. When we awaken all is peaceful and quiet in our soul, and the dream—as distinguished from other, ordinary dreams—is firmly impressed on, imbedded in our memory. The remembrance of it is like that of a real meeting. It is as though eternity condescended out of a kindly regard for us and let the members of its household go home on leave. Everything, everything, even his shabby coat! So that we should not be lonely, so that we should not forget, so that we should feel encouraged until the next time.

There is no doubt that they succeeded in giving us a hint of something during the dream. That is why we do not grieve when we wake up, why we are not tormented and do not yearn helplessly after the fleeting images. The only sad thing is that we don't remember precisely what it was we settled with them, what arrangements we made; could we really have settled *everything* with them? . . .

*

Death separates the soul from the body just as a butcher separates meat from the bone. And this is agonizing. But it is thus and only thus that freedom comes.

*

Every time I fell asleep I always hoped that while I slept my body would become well and recover its strength. And when I saw that it still ached, I fell asleep again until the next time. It was like going away when I fell asleep, going away expressly in order to give my body time to come round and pull itself together. As though I had had some disagreement, some quarrel with it, and from time to time would leave and come back, bargaining with it and abandoning it on the premise that without me it would be better able to fulfill the conditions of our agreement and that, upon my return, I would find it in accord with me. But it continued to be obstinate and complain and ache, until I wanted to give up on it and never return to it again. Let it do what it pleases without me.

*

What is the body? An outer capsule, a diving suit. And perhaps I, sitting in my diving suit, am wriggling like a worm. . . .

*

The Lord prefers me.

*

If even the reading of books resembles theft, then how can one not feel somewhat romantic?

*

Lord, You see—I'm drunk. . . .

*

What tenderness you can suddenly feel toward a piece of soap!

*

My whole life is made up of cowardice and prayer.

*

Waiting for the end of my life, I have been able to accomplish much. Oh, how slow the approach of death is!

*

Death is good because it puts us all in our place.

*

One must believe, not from force of tradition, not out of fear of death, not just in case, not because someone tells you to and something frightens you, not from humanistic principles, not in order to save yourself, and not for the sake of originality. One must believe for the simple reason that God exists.

*

Our natural surroundings—forests, mountains, the sky—are the most accessible, most tangible form of eternity, its material imitation, image, embodiment. The very extent of nature in time and space, its great duration, its immensity in comparison with our bodies, inspires thoughts of the eternal and shakes a man's confidence in his limited existence. Consider the combination in any one tree of age and youth, complexity and simplicity, movement and stillness, wisdom and naïveté. What about the inexorable change of the seasons, of day and night, which repeat themselves and yet reveal something new each time? And the indifference of nature to good and evil, indifference which stems from the conviction that in the end all will turn out to be good. This completeness of existence, which foreshadows eternity, allows us, who have no other escape, to run to nature as in other times men retreated to monasteries.

*

When you sail on an ocean liner and around you there is only the sea, you begin to understand that, no matter where we have been, no matter where we go, we are always in the same place in relation to the sky.

*

For some reason it is supposed that what is begun *here* must be worked out and resolved in some other *there* (in the future or in eternity). That we are to be compensated for our sufferings, efforts, sins, virtues. However, it is possible that we are not the ones who must be paid, but that we will ourselves be the pay or retribution to someone for something. Looking at the universe from our corner, we see ourselves as the beginning and mentally select for ourselves a fitting end. But in the balance of the world we are not the starting point, but a curve traced between immensities unknown to us, and so it is inappropriate for us to demand that *we* receive justice.

*

We flush our excrement into sanitary toilet bowls and think that we are saved.

*

Why do you feel such dread when you turn and see your footprints in the fresh snow? . . .

*

A conversation between two old ladies:

"Is your pension enough for you? There isn't anything left to spend on clothes—it all goes for food."

"Yes, it's enough. . . . Honestly, I even manage to feed the *cat*."

*

"Do you have a husband?"

"I have one at night, but, no—I don't."

*

He was walking along in the forest. Three men in bast shoes were coming toward him. He walked up to them and said:

"You frighten me, brothers. It's three to one."

"Come on," they said, "we'll sit down on the grass so you won't be afraid of us. Now you can stand over there, ten steps away, and we'll talk."

The three sat down and asked:

"Got any bread? We haven't eaten for three days."

He gave them some bread he had and went on. Later they were arrested and shot in the town.

*

People turn their backs so as not to see. Happy that they still have skin and bones—a defense. They make a shield out of the body, a walking barricade, and hide behind it. If the soul were all alone, would we be able to endure? Where would the soul turn, how could it cover itself? The soul can't even close its eyes. It's always on view. But things are nice for us, quite convenient. We can stop up our ears and withdraw into ourselves. And when it gets really bad, we can turn our faces to the wall and protect ourselves from behind with our trusty, impervious backs.

*

An old woman came back from the bathhouse, changed her clothes, and sat down to rest. Her son wanted to cut her toenails. monstrous, horny nails.

"What are you up to, Kostya, what are you doing? It's time for me to die. How will I climb up the mountain to God without any toenails? I have a long way to climb. . . ."

The old woman can hardly have forgotten that her body will decay. But her mental pictures of the Heavenly Kingdom have an earthly realism. And she thinks of her immortal soul realistically—with toenails, wearing underclothes, in the form of a barefooted old woman. Our philosophical and theological structures frequently lack this kind of conviction. Everything is conceived so spiritually that it is unclear whether God actually exists, or whether He is only the symbol of our humane tendencies. The savage who imagines God as a bloodthirsty wild beast is less blasphemous than the philosopher-idealist who replaces Him with a gnosiological allegory. Christ literally rose from the dead, in tangible form, in the flesh, and manifested Himself in spite of the abstractions of the Pharisees. He ate and drank at the same table with us and made his appeal with the help of a miracle, that is, with material proof.

*

Lord, reveal Yourself to me. Let me know that You hear me. I am not asking for a miracle—just some sign, however faint. For example, make a beetle fly out of that bush. Right now. After all, a beetle is perfectly natural. No one will suspect anything. But it will be enough for me, I will be able to guess that You hear me and are telling me that You do. Just say: yes or no? Am I right or not? And if I am right, make a locomotive sound its whistle four times. And then I'll know.

*

Nature is beautiful under the influence of God's gaze. He watches the groves of trees silently, from a distance—and that is enough.

*

The laws of nature are a miracle which extend through time and space. It is thanks to them that snowflakes, mammoths, sunsets, and other *chefs d'oeuvre* of creation are able to exist for greater or lesser spans of time, periodically emerging, developing, following the tradition laid out for them (the tradition of the conservation of energy, the tradition of earth's gravitational pull, and so forth.) A new miracle can destroy tradition, a miracle that happens only once or one that is also firm and established, like a law, in some other universe, epoch, period.

Divine cosmogony has nowadays become the subject of the humorist (the Lord God cuts flowers out of paper). But suppose you approach this subject seriously. Every flower takes your breath away, amazes you—just see how it's made! And every tiny seed, each insignificant grain of pollen already contains the future of a dozen petals.

In nature we are constantly coming across art. The architecture of mountains, forerunner of the Gothic. Pools and clouds executed in the style of *tachisme*. In the creation of man we see the principles of figurative art (in the image of the Creator and yet entirely "different"!) There are singers and musicians flying through the air and crawling in the grass. The change in styles that comes with the advent of glaciers, the eruption of volcanoes. A living museum, where everything is restored and preserved, where, as in art, everything is just realistic enough and just illusory enough.

*

Truly Christian feelings are contrary to our nature, abnormal, paradoxical. They beat you and you rejoice. You are happy as a result of the misfortunes raining upon you. You do not flee from death, but are drawn to it, and begin to resemble a dead man before your time. This seems bizarre to every healthy, normal person. Nature teaches us to fear death, to avoid suffering, to cry when we are hurt. But in Christianity everything is the other way round—unnatural (say the humanists), supernatural (say the Christians). And none of your provident calculations (I would rather suffer *here* in order to be blissful *there*—the calculation of a money-lender). Contrary reactions arise without premeditation, against one's will. But "to forgive him who has offended you" is worth doing; your soul will become lighter, as if a knot which you struggled in vain to untie had been cut in two. And if you take this lightness and gaiety of soul to be, not a result, but a reason, then forgiveness and other contrary reaction to an injury done to you will rise to the surface irresistibly, effortlessly, involuntarily. Not the overcoming of our natural tendencies, but the substitution for them of another, unfamiliar nature, which teaches us to bear pain, suffering, and death, and delivers us from the need to fear and hate.

*

Man lives in order to die. Death lends a thematic direction, unity, and purpose to life. It is the logical conclusion arrived at by the path of life's evidence, not a breach, but a pact drawn up long before, beginning at our birth. In comparison with the dead (particularly compared with historical figures and literary characters we seem incomplete, unfinished. We feel half lost in a problematic fog. This is why we have no confidence in our own worth, in our understanding of our role, fate, and position. Until we die, there is always something lacking in us. The end is the crown of our entire existence.

We unconsciously envy the completeness of the dead; they have already escaped from their ambiguous position, acquired clearly defined characters, lived out their lives, become embodiments. This accounts for the interest in one's *own* end, the guesses, the predictions, the blind pursuit of the final period, the decisive stroke. We are attracted to suicide, fascinated by it, because it promises a good bargain, permitting us by our own choice and decision to draw a short allowance and sign a receipt for it. But it is a better idea to accept the death sentence as it stands, which offers the victim the extraordinary right to be present when it is carried out, knowing that he is truly ready, that he has fulfilled himself. Those condemned to death immediately increase their stature by half, and, if they can keep their wits about them, a better method of settling accounts is hard to imagine.

Man's fate in the ideal is portrayed in the genre of tragedy, which is wholly directed toward death. In tragedy, death becomes the goal and stimulus of the action, in the course of which a character manages to reveal himself unstintingly, and, on achieving completion, fulfills his destiny. We watch this headlong and fateful approach to catastrophe and rejoice that the hero was worthy of being chosen, that he, almost from the time of his birth, was provided for and insured, with his entire biography furnished as preparation for the finale. Death has been planted in his fate and character like a seed, and when it germinates before our eyes, we are enraptured by this faithfulness to destiny, which transforms the forces of life into the heroism of death.

Tragedy in its conception is similar to an execution, but the sentence of death is extended to the limits of natural human maturity, which creates an illusion of freedom and lack of constraint in moving along the shortest, predetermined path. The downfall of the hero is justified, won, earned by life, and this balance produces a feeling of harmony. In contrast, the death that is the lot of the "man in the street" is almost comical: he was taken by an apoplectic fit, he choked on a bone. Such a fate is pitiful because it is casual and extraneous (he lived and lived, and then he suddenly died from something or other), and because there is no inherent connection between his life and his death. But the most terrible of all is for Providence, as a mark of punishment, to turn its back on this tiresome person and allow him to die a disgraceful, obscene death, according to his own taste: he drank himself into insensibility and choked on his own vomit; he died in a moment of passion so that it was difficult to free the poor woman from the old man's clutch. . . .

We shall ask fate for an honorable, worthy death, and go forward to meet it as best we can, so as to carry out in a fitting manner our last and most important assignment, the assignment given to all life— to die.

*

Thoughts of God are inexhaustible and as great as the sea. They are overwhelming; you can submerge yourself utterly in them without touching bottom. In our consciousness God is a concept so broad that it can play the role of its own opposite even within the confines of a single religious doctrine. He is unknowable and known everywhere, unapproachable and closest of the close, cruel and good, absurd, irrational, and completely logical. No other concept gives such scope to the fluctuation of meaning, or presents so many possibilities for comprehension and interpretation (together with a simultaneous strong confidence in its absolute precision). This in itself bears witness to the significance of the Person and Object of our beliefs and doubts Which stands behind the concept. One's belief in God can take various forms, one can think about Him endlessly; He encompasses everything and exists everywhere as the Principle One, for Whom there are no limits. This is the greatest phenomenon in the world and It is unique. Other than It there is nothing.

*

Perhaps life consists of a cultivation of the soul, yes, that very same immortal part that will take over from you and fly forth. To be more exact, the soul does not grow, does not develop, but bides its time hidden within you until you have matured to the point of coming into more or less close contact with it. Your soul must commit you to memory, become your intimate, and retain a portion of your personality from its acquaintance with you. This is the meaning of the expression: "It is time to think about your soul." In other words, it is time to be concerned about establishing a firm relationship with your soul so that your soul can think about you.

There can hardly be any people with vile souls (unless an alien, inhuman soul should settle in someone). The very worst scoundrels are convinced that "in the depths of their souls" they are still good. And it is said of a thoroughly bad man that he "has no soul." It is indeed possible that his soul still remains within him, but has retreated so far down that it no longer has any contact with him.

You cannot "destroy your soul," but you can destroy yourself after losing your soul. The soul does not depend on you, but you on it, and it will be your guardian if you are able to see that.

*

The charm of solitude, tranquility, and silence is that at such times one can hear what the soul has to say.

*

We must not understand the truth, but comprehend it. To understand, to know means to break in, to ravish. One can know a woman (violence and struggle). To comprehend (the very same woman) is to find room for her, accept her. Understanding is always aggressive and implies a taking by force. In comprehension there is a burden laid down from above. In comprehension we are the captives.

*

The Church cannot help being conservative as long as it wants to maintain its fidelity to tradition. It does not have the right to say one thing today and another thing tomorrow, depending on the interests of progress. No religious reformation, no matter how serious and profound, has been equal to the present, but has yearned for the past, for the source of origin of its teachings, even though this leads to confusion in its tracts. But apart from wishing to preserve the ancient holy ways and keep to the legacy, the Church in its immutability "lags behind life" so that, being outside of time, it can convey to us a whiff, a taste of eternity. With its set forms, the archaism of religious rites corresponds to and resembles the heavens, which are not inclined to evolve with the speed of history. This essential slowness of reaction to contemporary events threatens the Church with stagnation and decay.

But even so it is an incorruptible mummy, awaiting the hour when it will be said: "Arise and walk!"

If only it could hear. . . .

*

Today's Christianity commits the sin of gentility. Its only thought is how to keep from soiling itself, how to avoid seeming indelicate. It is afraid of dirt, crudity, bluntness, and values a precise middle course more than anything else in the world. The spineless have brought it to the point where holy oil has changed into sweet syrup (that one little word "oily" is enough to make your gorge rise). They purse their lips and wait for God to give them a check mark for their exemplary behavior. Like prissy young ladies, they blush at every insinuation of illicit pleasure: "Oh, you, I'm not like that! You can't be serious; I'm an innocent maiden." They have confused the Church of Christ with an institute for young girls of the nobility. As a result all that is bright and lively has passed into the hands of vice. Virtue is left to sigh and hide its tears. It has forgotten the fiery invective of the Bible.

But Christianity is obligated to be forthright and to call things by their right names. It is time to turn away from garlanded cherubs, so that real angels can become more powerful and substantial than airplanes. "Airplanes"—not in imitation of the contemporary, but in superiority to it.

It is possible to fall into heresy on this path. But at present heresy is not as dangerous as a shriveling at the core. Lord! Better that I err in Your name than forget you. Better that I destroy my own soul than have You vanish from sight.

*

Side by side with the other religions, Christianity plays the role of a shock battalion, a penal brigade, rushed to the hottest and most dangerous part of the front. Somewhere there may be artillery and air support, but these condemned men alone have been thrown into hand-to-hand combat, into the inferno, their bridges burned behind them, to carry the fight right up to the trenches of the enemy. This accounts for the determined character of their attack, their readiness to go on to the end, the difficulty of their exploit and its narrowness, the intolerance of their doctrine (at least, compared with that of the Hindus); in other words, the concentration and direction of all their forces on one blow. Take a look at Christianity's heroes. There are few sages here, but a great many zealots who have won honor by preserving and dying. The lives of the saints are a long list of tortures and executions endured by militants following the example of their God Who was put to death. These are soldiers who exhibit their scars and wounds to the world like decorations for valor. And from whom is this army chosen?—from all nations, from the masses, even from criminals who have taken on themselves the burden of the cross. Everyone can enlist. Everyone, the very lowest, the most uneducated, the most sinful of men—if only he is prepared to hurl himself into the fire. Everyone, together with others or in single combat. It is a religion of the highest hope, which originates in despair; a religion of celibacy, strengthened by a keen sense of its own sinfulness; a religion of the resurrection of the body in the midst of foulness and decay. Nowhere is there such intimate contact with death as in Christianity. In it, the fear of death has been, not vanquished, but developed into a force capable of breaching the tomb and leaping to the other side. It is not contemplation of eternity, but the winning of it in battle, armed with only one weapon—a readiness to die.

*

When we go to sleep, we adopt the fetal position. We draw our legs up, curl ourselves into a ball, make a nest—a snug and safe maternal lap. We become children, snuffle, and smack our lips, as we kick off our later stratifications. This slipping back into childhood, a universal and daily occurrence, has in it something of a return to oneself, to one's original position, which was and will be the most important in life, while all the rest amounts to nothing. When we fall asleep we sever our connection with the world; discard the mask of profession, age, culture, nationality; return home and revert at last to our original form, ridiculous and defenseless. This is our root, our innermost "I," which is hard to call an "I," since, infantlike, we are all identical here.

From another point of view, sleep is a rehearsal for death. When we fall asleep, we die: we lie down, close our eyes, lose consciousness of self, and it is not impossible that we exist partly in some other world. Echoes of the day's life can be heard there, but in the untroubled depths of sleep there is a sense of something different, which bears no resemblance to our usual existence—the maternal cradle and womb from which we are born again in the morning, refreshed and rejuvenated. Sleep, like death, gives a hint of non-existence, of oblivion, peace, and childlike bliss. It is said that before death memories of childhood are particularly strong. And so they should be; it is not "Count Tolstoy," the writer and thinker, who is dying, but "Lyovushka"....

A man's childhood accompanies him throughout his entire life as its unique and indispensable foundation. In recalling our second, or fifth, or seventh year, we clearly acknowledge our connection with those former selves, although logically there is no similarity between our adult personalities and ourselves as children. But memory, which does not depend on the arguments of logic, makes no great distinction between the one and the other, and each of us can say of himself: I remember how they used to wash me in the tub, and I would say "myaoo," looking at the little lamp. And that certainly was I who said "myaoo," and not someone else; this "myaoo" is firmly linked to me, it is I. Regarding our youthful and mature selves, it is sometimes simply unbelievable that we could have done such-and-such, said such-and-such (the change in convictions, interests, and the like). You often remember your behavior and feelings as an "individual" as though they were something quite alien. Only childhood retains its permanent authenticity into old age.

*

Even in the creation of children there is an element of return to childhood; we acquire a child because of our inability to become children ourselves. Of course, the pretensions of our adult personalities, which would like to continue into posterity, are also involved here. But still it is a child that people want, and not a thirty-year-old uncle "who looks like me;" they dream of a *little one*, a tiny baby. In women this feeling is even more clearly expressed; devoid of our ambitious tendencies, they simply want a *little one*, without any particular desire to secure their "unique individuality" in it. Even grandmothers long for grandchildren and play with them like dolls, abandoning themselves to childishness and talking babytalk in their enthusiasm. Why don't they act the same way with half-grown children? Isn't it because the newborn baby is more desirable to them and closer, because they recognize and find themselves in him?

And so, if we compare all of this—sleep and childhood and death—it seems that life, which is lived as a "development of conscious personality," vanishes without a trace and has no purpose. Whatever we become, whatever we learn, we are left with the same resources that were ours as children and are ours before sleep. With them and them alone we shall go forth from this place, having forgotten forever all other acquisitions—knowledge, money, fame, works, books, which have made their impression on our personalities, but have no value in the eyes of childhood, sleep, and death.

*

Thoughts end and come no more as soon as you begin to collect and ponder them.

Translated by Elinor Hewitt

Yuri Daniel

Hands

HERE then, Sergey, you're an intellectual—polite. Therefore, you're silent; you ask nothing. But our factory boys come right out and ask you: "What is it?" they say. "Has Vaska turned into an outright drunkard, drinking his hands off?" This is what they say about my hands. Do you think I didn't notice that you glanced at my hands and turned away? And even now you're still trying to glance past my hands. Yes, indeed, I understand everything—you're doing this out of politeness, in order not to embarrass me. But look, look at them. It's all right. I won't be offended. I'm sure you won't see a thing like this every day. This, my dear friend, is not from drunkenness. I seldom drink—mostly in company or on some occasion, like for instance when I'm with you. We can't not drink to our meeting. I, dear fellow, remember everything: how we were scouting, and how you spoke French with the White officer, and how we took Yaroslavl. Do you remember the speech you made at the meeting? You took me by the hand—I happened to be next to you—and you said: "With these hands . . ." you said. Ye-es. Well, Sergey, start pouring. Or else I'll just spill it. I forget the medical term for the shakes. Good, I have it written down, I'll show it to you later. . . . Well then—why did all that happen to me? There was an incident. But speaking chronologically, I'll tell you: When we were demobilized, after the victory in '21, I immediately returned to my old factory. There, of course, as expected, I was honored and respected as a revolutionary hero. Moreover, I was a member of the Party and a conscientious worker. Of course, it didn't happen without my having to straighten out somebody's mind. All kinds of talk began, like: "Well, you've fought, and what have you managed to accomplish—you have neither bread nor water. . . ." Such words I'd cut short. I was always very strict. You couldn't fool me with this Menshevik nonsense. Well, there, pour it, don't wait. But I had been working longer than a year when they called me to the District Office. "Here you are, Malinin," they told me, "your trip-ticket. The Party," they said, "is mobilizing you, Malinin Vasily Semyonovich, into the ranks of the glorious Special Committee to fight against the counter-revolutionaries. We wish you," they said, "the best of luck in your fight with the world bourgeoisie, and please give our humble greetings to Comrade Dzerzhinsky, if you see him." And I—what did I do? Of course, I was a Party man. "Ye-es sir, I accept the order of our Party." I took my trip-ticket, went to the factory, said good-by to my comrades, and was on my way. Off I went, and I could already imagine how mercilessly I'd catch all the counter-revolutionaries, so they wouldn't be able to contaminate our Soviet government. . . . And so I arrived, and indeed met Dzerzhinsky. I repeated the wishes of our district comrades. He shook my hand, thanked me, and later he took all of us who were present, and there were about thirty of us there mobilized by the Party, and lined us up, and told us that one cannot built a house on mud, and that one has to dry the mud up first, and that in that process many an animal like a frog and a snake has to be destroyed, and therefore, he said, an iron will is required. And for this job, he said, we all have to put our hands together. . . . He said it, of course, in the form of an anecdote or fable, but, of course, it was clear. He himself was strict, never smiled. Later they started to classify us. Who is who, from where. "What is your education?" they asked. You know what my education consists of—the German and Civil wars–besides my work behind the workbench, that's my education. Two grades of elementary school I had. . . . And so they assigned me to special service—speaking frankly—to execution. This job one wouldn't call difficult, but one couldn't call it easy, either. It has an effect on one's heart. It's one thing at the front line, you know: either you get him or he gets you. But here. . . . Well, of course, I got used to it. You step behind him in the courtyard, and you say to yourself: "You must do it Vasily, you M-U-S-T. If you don't finish him off now, he'll corrupt the whole Soviet Republic." I got used to it. I started to drink, of course, couldn't get along without it. They gave us liquor. As regards to some "special rations," it's all nonsense, bourgeois inventions, that Cheka members eat white rolls and chocolate. Our rations were the same as a soldier's—bread, grain, and fat. Liquor, indeed, that we got. You had to have it, you understand. Yes sir, I worked this way for about seven months, and that's when it happened. We received an order to exterminate a number of priests. For counter-revolutionary agitation. For their provocations. They aroused their parishioners. Because of Tikhon, I think. Or due to their anti-socialism—I don't know. In other words, they were considered enemies. There were twelve of them. Our boss gave the order: "You," he said to me, "Malinin, will take three of them, you, Vlasenko, you, Golovchiner, and you. . . ." I forgot the name of the fourth; he was a Latvian—some strange name, not like ours. He and Golovchiner went first. We had it arranged in the following manner: the guard-house was right in the middle. On one side, that is, was a room, where they kept the condemned, and on the other side was the exit to the courtyard. We took them one by one. You'd finish off one in the yard, then drag him to the side and go back for the next. You had to drag them away to the side, or else when you entered with the next, if he saw the dead one, he'd start tearing himself away. The trouble sometime was endless. But, of course, this is understandable. It was better when they were silent. And so, that Golovchiner and that Latvian finished off their victims and then it was my turn. Before that I had a few drinks. It's not that I was scared or a sort of religious person. No. I was a Party member, tough, I didn't believe in all that nonsense—gods of various sorts, angels, archangels,—no, I didn't—and yet I felt kind of strange. It was easy for Golovchiner, he was a Jew; they, I heard, don't even have icons. I don't know if it's true, but there I sat and drank, and all kinds of nonsense came to my mind: how my deceased mother back in the village would take me to church, and how I would kiss Father Vasily's hand, and how the old man would call me brother by name. . . . Ye-es, indeed. And so I went to get the first one, took him out. Came back, had a smoke, took out the next. Came back, had a drink—and became nauseous. "Wait a second, fellows," I said, "I'll be right back." I put the gun on the table and went out. I'm drunk, I thought. I'll shove a finger in my mouth, get some relief and I'll feel much better. And so I did what I had to, but I didn't feel any better. All right, I thought, I'll finish everything I'm supposed to do—and off to bed. I took my gun and went to get the third one. The third was a young stout fellow, such a healthy chunk of a priest, good-looking. I take him down the corridor, and I see how he raises his long robe over the threshhold, and I began to feel miserable, I don't know why myself. Out we went into the yard. And up he looks at the sky and raises his beard. "Go ahead, father, don't look back. You yourself have prayed for this kind of heaven." I wanted to joke, to raise my spirits. Why, I don't know myself. Never did I talk to the prisoners before. And so I let him walk three steps ahead of me, as required, I placed the gun between his shoulders and fired. As you know—a Mauser fires like a cannon! And it kicks back so strong that it almost tears your arm out of your shoulder. But all of a sudden, what do I see? My victim turns around and comes at me. Of course, sometimes there are complications: some are knocked off immediately, some swirl on the ground, sometimes they even take a few steps and swing as if they were drunk. But this one comes straight at me with small steps, as if he was swimming in his cassock, as if I never shot him. "Stop, father, I say stop!" And again I put the gun against him—his chest. He tore his robe at the chest, a chest full of curly hair, then goes and screams at the top of his lungs: "Go ahead, shoot," he screams, "go ahead you anti-christ! Go ahead, kill me, kill your Christ!" I got all confused, and shot once more and once again. But he keeps on coming at me! Neither blood nor a wound anywhere, he goes and prays: "O Lord, You have stopped the bullet from black hands! For You will I endure all tortures! . . . Do not kill a living soul!" And something else. . . . I don't remember anymore, I know that I must have shot him— I couldn't have missed, I shot straight where I aimed. There he stands in front of me and his eyes burn like a wolf's, his chest bare, and around his head there seems to be a halo—later I realized that he stood sheltering the rays of the sun from my eyes, it was right before sunset. "Your hands," he screams, "are full of blood! Look at your hands!" I threw my gun down, ran into the guard-house, knocked somebody off his feet at the door, ran in, the fellows looked at me as if I were a psychopath and roared. I grabbed the gun from the pile and yelled: "I'll finish you off if you don't take me immediately to Dzerzhinsky!" They grabbed the gun away from me and took me in a hurry. I entered the drawing room, got loose from my comrades, and in a stuttering voice I told him: "Go ahead shoot me, Felix Edmundovich, I can't kill a priest!" I said that, and fell on the ground, I don't remember a thing more. I came to in a hospital. The doctors said: "Nervous breakdown."

They treated me well, I must say, with care. The care, the cleanliness, and the food, for those times, were pretty decent. They cured everything, but my hands, as you can see for yourself, they always tremble. Probably the shock passed into them. I was discharged from the Cheka, of course. They need different kind of hands there. Of course, I couldn't go back to the workbench either. I was assigned work in the factory supply-room. There, of course, I do my business well. True, I can't write all those reports myself, my hands can't. I have an assistant for that purpose, a smart little girl. That's the way I live now, my fellow. What happened with the priest? I found out later. There was nothing divine about it. Our boys, when I went out to vomit, took out the real bullets and put in empty shells instead. They tried to make a joke. Well, I am not mad at them—it was a youthful prank, they didn't have it easy either, so they thought of a joke. No, I don't blame them. But my hands now . . . are no good to work with.

Translated from the Russian by Vera von Wiren-Garczynski

Ilya Zverev

Sedov for the Defense

To Attorney Vladimir Lvovich Rossels

THE doorbell in the hallway sounded timid and jittery, like a brass bird hurtling against walls of brass.

Olga grew pale. She laid down her fork, then her knife. Her husband glanced at his watch and said irritably that she was a fool. They never come at 10 o'clock. They come in the middle of the night or at the break of dawn. Every child knows that.

He put his coat on and went to answer the door.

When he got there, he took one deep breath and yanked the door open.

Three women were standing on the threshold. "Let your breath out and relax completely," as your therapist says during the exercises.

"What do you wish?"

"Attorney Sedov? May we see him?"

"Come in, come in. . . ."

Must get rid of that damned doorbell. . . . Anyone has any business here, let him knock. . . . Let them wrestle at the door, as his nanny used to say.

"It's rather late to talk business," he said loudly for the benefit of that fool Olga, to calm her down a bit. "But anyway, come in, come in. This way to my office, please."

This turned out to be an ugly affair. Counter-revolution. In the city of Ensk. Employees of the regional agriculture department—three agronomists and a zootechnician. Dreadful Articles, too—58-7 (harmful activities), 58-11 (counter-revolutionary organization), 58-14 (sabotage), and still others. All four defendants—sentenced to be shot. . . .

"It's like a nightmare," said one of the women, the youngest one, who looked like a Komsomol girl from a propaganda poster. "It's just madness. . . ."

"Katya!" scolded the other woman angrily, her *pince-nez* gleaming sharply.

Katya, the girl with the short-cropped hair, said humbly: "In some cases it happens. . . ." But instantly she was up in arms again. "What do you think I am, a NEPist fawning on the Soviet authorities? Of course, it's a nightmare. My darling Vitek, a sterling Party man, and they. . . ."

Then she burst out crying, just like a little girl. The other two women—both the stern one and the flustered one—also began to cry, shaking with hysteria.

Why should this have come to him, Sedov, a Muscovite, up to his ears in work? There is no dearth of good lawyers in Ensk; that is, excuse me, attorneys for the defense. Excellent trial lawyers, such as Dobrolyubov, or Hasenzweig. . . .

"They have all refused. They cannot appeal. They cannot come to the assistance of the unmasked and exposed enemies of the people."

"And Hasenzweig?"

"He's got a conscience, that one. He said: 'I can't, they'll hound me to death; my own brother, Semyon Yulevich, who used to work in a pharmacy, has been denounced as an enemy of the people. Go to Moscow, see Sedov, there's a truly noble man for you. . . .' And he gave me your address. . . ."

"But, you see, the truth of the matter is that I have just now. . . ."

"But they'll kill them!" the stern looking woman screamed. She used the word "kill," not "execute," and it stabbed him to the quick.

Olga stood in the door. Ramrod-straight and cold, she looked the way she always did whenever something had to be negotiated with her mother-in-law.

"Can you come here a minute, Vlodechek?" she said in a voice that sounded like a playback of an old record.

The three women looked at her, fearful and imploring. Her look promised them nothing.

"You must be mad!" she whispered fiercely. "Such a dreadful affair! And in Ensk, to boot! Why should you go there?" Her voice rose. "I am not an unfeeling monster. But there are limits. I could understand it if you were assigned. . . . But to butt in of your own free will!"

Collected and matter-of-fact, he returned to his office. The women saw at a glance that all was lost.

"You have no right to refuse!" shrieked Katya. "If you do, you are not a Soviet man, but a coward!"

Slowly and clumsily, the stern looking woman with the *pince-nez* fell to her knees before him. The flustered one did the same. Katya also knelt down and looked up at him with hatred.

"I'll go," he said sadly. "Of course, I'll go. . . ."

* * *

The head of the legal consultation office, Ivan Pryakhin, called "Workers' Pigeon" behind his back, was a man from the "social advance." He was generally respected and considered a "good guy" by everybody, even by those old fossils among the lawyers to whom Kerensky was simply Aleksandr Fyodorich and who were unable to forgive "those new ones" either their barbarian style or their crazy acronyms, such as MKCH, or Narkomyust, or that same MCD (member of the College of Defenders) which had replaced the noble word *advokat*.

"No, Vladimir Nikolaevich," said Workers' Pigeon sadly. "Do what you wish, but I will not sign your directive." Then he lowered his voice: "Just think what a nasty thing you're getting yourself into!"

"I'm within the law," Sedov said.

He said this especially loudly, in an irritated tone of voice, because he despised himself. Way down deep he knew he was whining hideously, begging Pryakhin to be firm and not to sign the necessary papers. If only he would refuse, as was his right, in a manner admitting of no recourse, Sedov would not have to go.

"Well, that's true, of course," said Workers' Pigeon. "You're absolutely within the law."

"When is the trial coming up? Thursday?" Lenya Savitsky's voice cooed cordially. "Too bad I'm tied up on Thursday. What a pity! Why don't you ask our colleagues? Perhaps one of them will be able to. . . ."

No one spoke up. Obviously Savitsky was squirming out of something nasty. Many were doing that. . . .

Pryakhin looked carefully, first at Lenya, then at some old woman whose tearstained face bobbed up in torment in front of the attorney's desk. Then he turned to Sedov, sighed, and wrote the usual formula: Legal Consultation Office number such and such directs attorney such and such to conduct the defense in a criminal, social (*cross out when not applicable*) trial. . . ."

"Be careful," he said in a very low whisper.

And then he signed: "Ivan Pryakhin."

All at once Sedov felt a tremendous relief. It was the same kind of feeling he himself had noticed, once the sentence was pronounced, in the defendants he represented. Any sentence, even the harshest one, produced the same effect. Everything was decided, signed, there was no sense fretting any more.

He now felt a different kind of tension mounting within him. He had to hustle to the station to get his ticket. And, before that, to the prosecutor's office; and afterward to Ossoavyachim to say goodbye to Olga (who knows what might happen; one must take one's leave properly).

Sedov picked up his briefcase, bowed formally to his colleagues. Ivan gave him a friendly smile. Caesar Matveevich waved him off with some ancient Roman gesture, as if he were a departing gladiator. Lenya Savitsky patted his sleeve. Others—and there were only twenty of them left in that huge, clownish hall with ornate stucco work on the ceiling, once the seat of the insurance company "Salamander"—the others did not even lift their heads.

"The riders never noticed that one slid off his horse, And they rode on singing Yablochko to the end"—wrote a Komsomol poet. Olga loved poetry and Sedov willy-nilly remembered many stanzas.

Still they did notice. Kostek Zvavich caught up with Sedov on the corner of Pyatnitska street. Catching his breath, he said "what-do-you-know" and, since Sedov had no time to slow down, they ran on together carrying on a conversation as weird as many other things happening at that time.

"Cut off your nose to spite your face," said Kostek. He said it nonchalantly, almost gaily. But there was a twinge of pain on his face; he was like a little boy wronged.

"Four death sentences," said Sedov.

"A drop in the ocean. And it's no use. It's simply too late. Before you get there, they may already . . . they may have. . . . When was this sentence pronounced? Day before yesterday? A special tribunal? That means this is a final sentence and cannot be appealed. So what do you think? Do you think they'll dawdle for two whole days?"

"I'm going to. . . ." He mentioned the name of the Great Prosecutor. "I'll ask him for the postponment of the execution."

"So you're going as one lawyer to another? Presenting your arguments? You, blockhead!" shouted Kostek, the noble, white-haired child, the stouthearted friend. "Sure, go on, go on, present your arguments! It's easy to argue with him. You'll give him a paragraph. And he'll give you a deportation order." Kostek sighed. "Or hard labor. . . ."

"Quiet," Sedov begged him. "Everyone's looking."

Kostek did not really have any hope, nor did he want to persuade Sedov to change his mind. He just needed to talk it out, to scream it out, to unload his burden. Who knows . . . he also may have been thinking that Vlodek Sedov, too, will be there no longer and there'll be not a soul one could open his heart to at all.

"Whom are we really defending? The accused? No! Ourselves. 'I am inclined to agree with the prosecutor that my client's crime deserves the harshest punishment; one's blood runs cold at the very thought of the abysmal enormity of the deed. . . . However, taking into account the great humanitarian aspects of our Constitution, I beg you, if it is possible at all. . . .' That's all, even though you know damn well they are trying an innocent man. Because you know. . . ."

He broke off just as unexpectedly as he had started.

"Aw, all right. Come back soon, safe and sound. Here. . . . Here's something for you to read on your trip."

He stuffed two rolled issues of some magazine (*Socialist Rule of Law*, it seemed) into Sedov's pocket, and shook Sedov's hand, holding it so tight it hurt.

"No, Kostek," said Sedov. "We have no right to spare ourselves. It's disgusting. And, anyway, you're really exaggerating. . . ."

* * *

One could enter the prosecutor's office without any pass, just walk in from the street, even though in other offices, some of them a thousand times less important than this one, there were stringent regulations governing comings and goings. But in this case the wide-open gates conveyed a very specific message: any Soviet worker who would have as much as an inkling of suspicion about someone—be it espionage, diversion, obstructionism, supporting the kulaks, consorting with the enemies of the people, or whatever—could come here at any time of day or night to sound a warning.

Inside the building, weird human derelicts with the eyes of madmen roamed endless corridors. A tiny old man, dressed in a worn out coat of a railroad man, told Sedov sternly:

"One cannot delay any longer. *They* are preparing a coup. . . ."

In the waiting room of the Great Prosecutor, a young assistant, a deathly weary Armenian with a pale, intelligent face and red, swollen eyelids, rose to greet Sedov. Sedov knew him slightly: in 1934 or 1935 they had both participated in a debate on the subject of Pashukanis's book, and they found themselves in agreement.

"What is the sentence?" asked the assistant, gently giving Sedov to understand that one should not presume to knock on the Great Prosecutor's door except in cases of utmost importance.

"It's that affair in the Ensk agricultural region," said Sedov.

Of course, they should know. Cases of that kind are always reported instantly. Marked "top priority," these special reports bring detailed information about counter-revolutionary groups, and about all and sundry kulak doings revealed in particularly shocking ways (terrorism, diversion, harmful activities, and so forth). The Ensk affair belonged precisely in this category. Four death sentences were pronounced!

But the assistant, unfortunately, could not recall the case. With a childlike smile he spread out his hands, indicating that, really, swamped as he was with work, he could not possibly be expected to remember details. However, because this was a matter of four death sentences, he thought it might be all right perhaps if he announced Sedov's presence.

Always and everywhere there is a price list, Sedov thought. If this were a case of two death sentences, the man might not have bestirred himself, but because there were four—well, that's something else again, that made it all right.

The assistant came back almost instantly and announced in a well-modulated baritone which betrayed his well-to-do family origin:

". . . very sorry . . . he can't possibly see you now. . . ." Then he added confidentially: "You have no idea how busy he is just now. . . ."

"But the sentence has already become final. We must send them a wire. Can't you wire them to hold off the execution of the sentence?"

"Just leave this to us," the assistant smiled his elegant smile and stretched out his effeminate white hand. "Good luck!"

Sedov thought that in all likelihood the man was indeed going to find a way, do everything he could . . . he had such a kind face. . . . But there should be no delay.

"Because otherwise they'll kill them!" It was as if some stranger's voice shouted within him. He did not shout "execute," as a lawyer would; he shouted "they'll kill them. . . ."

He got to Olga's office half an hour before train time. They had no time to talk. They hugged and kissed. Then they looked at one another and once more they clung together in a long, desperate kiss, only to grab a hat and run immediately afterward. But for five more long minutes they stood there, hands tightly clasped, in the middle of a large room crowded with desks. And the activists sitting all around them, colored badges in their lapels, the young Voroshilov sharpshooters, ever ready for the anti-aircraft, anti-chemical warfare, and sanitary defense, looked at them earnestly and with respect.

* * *

Sedov was traveling in the "soft seat" car, while Marya Antonovna (the woman with the *pince-nez*) was in the "combined, no reserved seats." Naturally, he asked her to join him.

They were alone in the compartment, because Sedov's fellow travelers went to join some friends at the other end of the car. Occasionally they could hear gales of laughter, exuberant shouts, and songs, lively and vigorous for the most part. They sang most often a new song which Sedov liked very much: "Swelling with mighty power, never conquered. . . ."

"I'm an agronomist myself, don't you see?" Marya Antonovna was saying softly. "I could swear to it: there's some tragic error there . . . or some unfortunate combination of circumstances. . . . Good Lord, if only their trial had been open, if only I could have appeared there, ask two or three questions, I am sure that the entire accusation would fall apart. You know, all that time all I wanted was this one thing: that the trial be open to the public. . . ."

"Article 111 of the Constitution does provide for certain departures from the principle of open trial," said Sedov cautiously, and he felt himself blush. "But, of course . . . Mirabeau was supposed to have said once: 'Give me whatever judge you want—let him be partial, greedy, let him even be my enemy, but let him judge me in an open court.' "

"Beautifully said!" sighed Marya Antonovna. "People have had such a clear concept of these things for such a long time already. How come then . . . how come that even today. . . ."

"I wish you wouldn't generalize," said Sedov severely. "This analogy is totally out of place. . . ."

Good Lord! Whatever happened to him? Was it really he, Vlodek Sedov, life of the party, a graying epicurean, a noted wit whom Mikhail Efimovich Koltsov once described on some occasion or other as "the man with whom one would not be bored even while cruising through the stratosphere"?

Marya Antonovna looked him over carefully. A tiny bitter smile crossed her lips. But right away she grew afraid that he had observed and understood that little smile.

"No, of course not," she said quickly. "Of course, you are quite right."

Sedov told her that the case was especially difficult. The usual practice, he told her, was as follows: the NKVD passed on to the courts those cases that were quite open and shut. Whenever there was anything unclear or doubtful, such cases were directed through other channels. Thus he was not sure at all whether the case could be won on its own merits. Hence his anxiety. . . .

Marya Antonovna seemed suddenly deflated and in a hurry to get back to her own compartment. It was high time she went back, she said. She had left her luggage unattended. Sedov had no intention to detain her, though he knew full well she had no luggage—neither a suitcase, nor a basket, nor even a purse such as women do carry to hold a comb, a mirror, or a handkerchief.

His head propped up on a rough, dusty bolster, Sedov stretched out on the seat. With a case of this kind it would be stupid and foolhardy to get all worked up "betimes" as his nanny used to say.

The memory of the good woman somehow beset him all too often of late. Perhaps that was because she had been so intimately bound with the most serene years of his life.

He pulled out of his coat pocket the magazines Kostek had given him for the trip. *The Socialist Rule of Law* and the latest newspapers. Best thing to read when one is in this kind of mood. . . . Let's see now. . . . Poems by some little girl (grade VI-b): "Vile vipers, triple cursed, you dared to bring treason into our Soviet land! The pitiless court will stomp you out in disgust; there can only be one sentence: Death to the rabid dogs!" An article on "The Tasks of the Prosecutor's Office in the Light of the Constitution" . . . Comrade Vyshinsky's speech. And then there was an account of the meeting last September of the Moscow College of Defenders.

Sedov settled himself more comfortably. Let's see . . . "Improvement of the material conditions . . . at least 70 per cent of the income of the College should be earmarked for the earnings fund . . ." Let's see . . . "With a fervor devoid of all rational content . . ." Poor Aleksandrov. "Balderdash, drivel, trivial and harmful notions . . ." The style was vigorous, no doubt about that!

At the time of the meeting Sedov was on vacation, in Kislovodsk, and thus he never attended. Caesar Matveevich later bent his ear recounting in a subdued whisper all manner of dreadful happenings. But the old man was dotty and liked to color his tales. Sedov could have asked someone else, but he has long since adopted the principle of never asking anyone about anything.

Let's see . . . "When Comrade Kudryavtsev spoke of the possibility that there might be spies, diversionaries, obstructionists, and other enemies of the people hiding among the lawyers, some in the audience reacted noisily to his words."

Of course, it was rather childish to react that way to a political speech. And, of course, where there is no fire, there is no smoke. Some hostile activities, obstructionism, spying, all this must be going on, no doubt about that, it's bound to be! It is quite possible that the Ensk affair has indeed been exaggerated and, out of pure fear, fashioned to fit the pattern of the "propaganda campaign." Is there really anything extraordinary in the fact that he, a Soviet lawyer (pardon, an attorney for the defense!), is going there to clarify the matter in accordance with Soviet law?

Loud voices sounded in the corridor outside. The door squealed open, like a noisy piglet, and three young men, Sedov's long lost travel companions, entered the compartment.

They were all dressed with "technological elegance"—in blue leather jackets; one of them had the end of a bright yellow tape measure protruding from his pocket. They were all engineers, going from the construction site at Chirchik to the electrostation at Kemerovo, but—for some strange reason—traveling through Moscow and Yaroslavl. In some complicated way or other they were all connected with both Narkomtazprom and Narkomvod. And they were all trying to outdo one another in telling jokes about both these institutions.

"Just imagine," they roared at Sedov. "Our Mishka Leskov fulfilled the norm eleven times over. Still they did not want to send him to the Stakhanovite convention. They said he was on a transport list to go to Stalino for some other meeting. Can you imagine that? What bureaucracy!"

"Or perhaps that was merely the work of some harmful elements," snickered another. "Do you think that there aren't any in our administration? They haven't caught them all yet, not by a long shot."

And they all started cursing the administration, people's commissariats, and that same Mishka Leskov, who could have made the norm twenty times over were it not for the gay life he was leading.

Sedov agreed: but yes, of course. . . . He was thinking regretfully that a glass wall, tight and unbreakable, separated him from those strong young men. They could be plunged into his anxious and threatening world at any moment, but he could never again enter their carefree world.

* * *

From the railroad station they went directly to the District Court.

"I'll wait downstairs," said Marya Antonovna. "It'll be easier for you that way."

Sedov agreed readily. She was right: it would be less embarrassing.

"Will you do me a favor?" she asked. "When you get there, go to the window at once . . . and give me a sign. Just wave your hand if they . . . if they had not yet been . . ."

Only the court secretary was there, an elderly, colorless individual dressed in a peasant shirt. A typical minor Soviet functionary, he had been ridiculed a hundred times by Valentin Kataev, Zorich, and Arkadi Bukhov.

"You've come in connection with this case?" He was so amazed that he rose from his chair. "Surely, you must have been mislead. This is a special case."

Sedov declared that he was well briefed about all aspects of the case, but that nonetheless he would like to familiarize himself with the court records . . . Where are they?

The secretary replied that he could not give any information regarding such subjects, and that Sedov would have to wait until the deputy chairman came (the chairman himself was ill). But, most likely, the deputy chairman would not want to talk to him, either. . . .

"No, no you must have been mislead. You do not realize that. . . ."

"Where are the records?"

The secretary hesitated briefly, and his eyes wandered to a closet door flush with the wall.

"What difference does it make?"

Sedov sighed with relief. He went over to the window, nodded his head, then waved his hand a few times, nodded again. . . .

The secretary watched him suspiciously. Then he said:

"Have a seat. Comrade Konukhov might be late. He didn't leave his office till 4 A.M. last night. . . ."

The deputy chairman of the District Court was a handsome man of military bearing in a greenish Stalinist tunic adorned with the Order of the Red Star.

"You're too late," he told Sedov, without offering him a chair. "It's out of our hands now."

"The court records are still here," said Sedov. His voice was very firm, he hoped.

"It would be interesting to know where you got this information."

What should he do now? Implicate the court secretary? That would be terrible, a betrayal! But then, what else? After all, they are not going to shoot him for that; at worst, he'll get fired.

"I heard a word here and there," he said lightly. "And the secretary here confirmed it."

"Popov! Come here!"

The secretary had the look of a kicked dog, his hands trembled.

"What's the matter? That a f f a i r isn't done with yet?"

"No." The secretary swallowed loudly. "Not at all. . . ."

The deputy chairman glanced sharply at Sedov.

"Does this not seem strange to you, comrade defense attorney? Our local attorneys, who were here all the while, who probed all that filth and blood, attended the trial. . . ." Here he raised his voice, "and not one of them was willing to write the complaint. Their revolutionary conscience would not let them do that. And you? Without even being thoroughly familiar with the case, you drop everything and run here from Moscow. And why? To try to save enemies of the people? Is that it?"

Then he said slowly and clearly, as if he dictated a memorandum:

"Of course, we shall make it our business to learn all the aspects of this affair. To clarify your po-li-ti-cal attitude. And your mo-ti-va-tion. . . ."

"That's your business, to clarify matters," said Sedov unpleasantly, in the kind of tone Karenin often used. "I haven't come here to save anyone but simply to fulfill a professional obligation. In line with the provisions of Soviet law. . . ."

He took a deep breath.

"You can refuse me. In writing. But in that case I shall be forced to advise . . . (here he mentioned the name of the Great Prosecutor) . . . whom I have already informed about this case."

Good Lord! What sort of language did he have to use: "I shall be forced to advise . . ." Brrrr! . . .

"That's the way the pedagogical aspects of court proceedings get diluted till they don't mean a thing," said the deputy chairman with unfeigned bitterness. "Postponements, cassations, supercassations. . . ." Then he added wearily: "Please wait in the waiting room."

The door did not shut tight and thus Sedov heard snatches of the telephone conversation (obviously, the ailing chairman was called):

"He really turned the screws . . . Looks like the Federal Prosecutor's office got into the act. . . . Those law-abiding sons of bitches. . . . All right. . . . I get it. . . ."

* * *

Five huge, cardboard bound volumes. Wearisomely uniform handwriting of a secretary who had obviously studied calligraphy in the old type school where, unlike today, they really taught you how to write a legible hand.

An experienced lawyer always begins reading the records backward, beginning with the sentence. First things first.

"The rightist-Trotskyite, spying, diversionary, sabotaging group. . . ." Everything in good order: depositions of witnesses, confessions, evidence. . . . And yet, a very peculiar case!

Improper seed was used for sowing? But this region, as well as the two adjoining ones, had a bad harvest that year because of the drought. They infected the cattle on purpose? But there was an epidemic of epizooty throughout the entire country. "A base attempt on the life of Olga Dubyak, an agrarian woman Stakhanovite, a participant in the All-Union Convention of kolkhoz Stakhanovites, who came close to being attacked by the bull named Gloomy (from the 'Bright Road' kolkhoz), the animal being temporarily deranged as a result of the poisonous injections administered with a malicious intent by the former zootechnician Rostovtsev. . . ." "The former head of the regional administration, Osmolovsky, gave 250 rubles to the kulak henchman Sorogin, with the despicable purpose in mind to get him to remove the magneto from the Fordson tractor in order to disrupt the sowing effort. . . ." "Hidden sabotage in the application of the sowing methods. . . ."

Sedov leafed through the pages of all five volumes time and time again. Not once did he see a mention of some expert testimony. How was it possible? A truly cavalier disregard of the law!

Still there was some expertise . . . Sedov came upon the prosecutor's summation (contained, for some strange reason, in the envelope marked "Personal Papers, of the Convicted"). The prosecutor's conclusions were peculiar: "It proved difficult to establish the facts . . ."; "One should presume the possibility of premeditation . . ."; "The probable ability of the saboteurs to obliterate all traces of their despicable crimes made it impossible to establish. . . ." These were supposed to be legal documents?!

Sedov was not allowed to take notes. Making notes was considered a serious offense. He had to rely on his memory. Fortunately, his memory was excellent. Take, for example, a passage from Comrade Vyshinsky's speech, the one he had read in the *Socialist Rule of Law*. Quote:

"One must adopt the principle of behaving toward everyone in such a way as to make it impossible for them to ever take advantage of the acquaintance if they should turn out to be the enemies. . . ."

This was probably correct under the conditions of capitalist encirclement. But what did he mean by "everyone"?

Toward the end of the day, the court secretary came to see Sedov, closeted in a corner room on the third floor.

"Forgive me," said Sedov, who felt guilty toward the pitiful little clerk.

"For what?" the other asked sadly. Sedov could not very well say: "Because I got you into a mess." He said something else: "Because I occupied someone's office so unceremoniously. It is probably needed for someone else."

"No," said the secretary. "He doesn't need it any longer."

Sedov realized that there were scratches and holes on the white-painted door of the office; obviously, the name plate had been torn off hurriedly, wood and all.

"I wanted to talk about something else. . . . I think it's bad that you're holding up this case," said the secretary, and immediately he began waving his hands, afraid that Sedov did not understand what he was trying to say. "I'm not speaking from the official point of view . . . It's just that they are there, waiting for . . . death . . . Just think how they must feel. It's better to get it over with. I know them all. . . . This is a small town. . . ."

He was about to say something else, but swallowed the words and fell silent. For some strange reason Sedov felt sure the secretary was about to say: "They are good, decent men. . . ."

* * *

The next day Sedov again had a talk with the deputy chairman. He needed permission to see the prisoners. Again he met with a refusal. And again, in Karenin's voice, Sedov said:

"In that case, may I have this in writing, please, and I shall advise. . . ."

"Cut out that namedropping, will you?" said the deputy chairman disgustedly. "All I want is for you to try to understand this whole thing. Here we are, right smack in the middle of a deadly battle and you pen pushers poke a paragraph in the spokes of our wheels. What is all this? A bourgeois deviation or something worse?"

"Don't you see that it could conceivably come to light that they are innocent? Or not as guilty as they were made out to be? It is my duty to start with this premise."

The man in a green Stalinist tunic gazed at Sedov sadly, gravely, almost compassionately.

"It cannot possibly come to light that they are innocent, it simply cannot. When a battle like this one is going on . . . It just can't be that they are spotless clean. That's the whole logic of this struggle."

Despite all this, Sedov got his permission. He was to see three prisoners—Kuzim, Khrenovskykh, and Osmolovsky. He had no legal grounds to see the fourth defendant, Ryazantsev. He had been approached by the wives of the first three only. The wife of the fourth defendant, Sedov learned in town, bundled up her twins right after the sentencing and left for parts unknown.

Ryazantsev's family and relatives—and especially his brother, chairman of the Regional Trading Association—denounced him. They realized that those four were contemptible scoundrels who had lost all semblance of humanity, villains . . . those four precisely whom the comrade from Moscow was trying to defend with an obstinacy worthy of a better cause.

* * *

The train bringing workers to K-sk arrived at ten minutes after eleven. Because we are living in a motorized age, the old droshkys have been liquidated, but there were no taxicabs as yet. It took Sedov fully twenty minutes to drag his weary feet from the railroad station to the prison.

There was a lamp over the prison gate. Not a floodlight, nor a lantern, but simply a lamp. Its light was so bright that somehow the freshly painted green gate and the door leading to the control post (and upholstered in shiny oilcloth) looked startlingly gay.

Sedov tried the door—it was bolted. He knocked once, then again, much louder. The bolt clicked lazily, a small window opened. In it a blue-banded cap appeared, apple red cheeks, and small eyes.

"What is it?"

"I am an attorney, here to represent the defendants. I have permission to see them."

"A defender at this time of night? At night everybody is a defendant!"

The window snapped shut. There seemed nothing to do but to go away. Yet somehow Sedov did not go; on the contrary, he began hammering against the door with his hands and feet, just as he used to when he was a small boy and his mother would lock him up. But heavy tufting underneath the ice-covered oilcloth muffled all sound.

When he finally bullied his way into the guardhouse, Sedov managed to obtain precious little. The guard called his superior, who announced that he was merely the commandant of the guard, while the prison commandant was asleep and could not possibly be awakened; the executed (he kept referring to the sentenced prisoners as "the executed") may not be seen without the express permission of the prison commandant.

Out of sheer force of habit Sedov threatened them with the Great Prosecutor and some other high authorities, but they were merely surprised at that. The Prosecutor could go fly a kite.

Somehow, the commandant awakened on his own, or so it seemed. Anyway, he came over in his tall riding boots, cavalry trousers, and a lavender nightshirt with white linen buttons, lugging a military drill under his arm. He was young, curlyhaired, and swarthy like a Gypsy. Hammer and sickle, and a star, were tattooed on his forearm.

The prison commandant declared that the permission from the District Court ran counter to the existing regulations, and that he had his own instruction along the line of the NKVD directives. It said clearly who could and who could not visit the sentenced prisoners, and there was not a word there about any defense attorneys. Besides, he added, Sedov probably did not know what hardened and obdurate enemies of the people these particular defendants from the regional trial were.

At this point Sedov assured him fervently that he was in possession of new information indicating that in all likelihood they were faced with a miscarriage of justice and a court error. Was he to believe that the commandant would refuse him and choose to take the lives of innocent men upon his conscience? All he wanted was to be able to talk to the defendants in order to get at the truth, nothing more. Was the commandant, after all, a human being, or wasn't he?

Finally the Gypsy pulled the drill over his broad shoulders and said angrily that yes, he was a human being, although in his kind of work the devil alone knew when a man turned into an animal. Comrade defense attorney probably had no idea whatsoever how many counter-revolutionary vipers there were and what dreadful misdeeds they were guilty of. And how clever they were at working both sides of the fence! One just couldn't figure them out. One spy, the most hardened one of them all, worked for four different secret services; yet, when he was being taken down to the cellar by the commandant and the boys . . . obviously, that's the end of the line, don't you see? . . . still he shouted: Long live the Party! Long live Stalin! Even at the last moment that reptile wanted to fool everyone.

He himself, supposedly in command here, has managed to wreck his nerves in the eight months he's been there. One night, a short time before, he managed to break away and spend an evening with the boys over at the car pool, and—would you believe?—they laughed at him; they said: Loshka, you're getting gray; you can apply for membership in the association of the old political ex-convicts.

Then, all of a sudden, the commandant became matter of fact again and asked Sedov why he was going to see only three prisoners when there were four involved in the case. Sedov explained.

"That's not good enough for me," announced the curlyhaired commandant. "Suppose that fourth one is also one of us. . . . What would my conscience say if I failed to check on that? What do you think?"

Suddenly Sedov grew afraid. The young man sounded all too naive, considering his job and that little phrase about "boys taking him down to the cellar." Sedov had no more doubts. The commandant was simply pretending, trying to trip him. Small wonder he got his permission from the District Court so easily. They must have called the commandant, of course, and told him to set the trap.

"The law does not empower me to do such a thing," he said firmly. "I've got to stick to the letter of the law."

"Law, law!" the commandant exploded. "According to the law we could have bumped them off three days ago already. And now you tell me they are our kind of people. . . . So what shall we do about our conscience now, eh? . . . Oh, all right, I'll decide myself."

* * *

When they entered the room together, each man looked like death itself. It took a long time before they could understand what this was all about.

"I am here to defend you," Sedov kept repeating. "I came from Moscow to write a complaint."

The prison commandant had come into their cell in the middle of the night and, out of sheer lack of experience, had led them all out together, all four men condemned to die. What were they to think and to expect?

"Can we also complain?" asked timidly a man with tired, slightly squinty eyes. "You see, both I and Comrade Ryazantsev have confessed everything, that is, of course, that we have been engaged in harmful activities."

The gloomy giant with the wise face of a monkey turned out to be Marya Antonovna's husband. He was the first to collect his wits and tell his tale. Unbelievable, all those outlandish accusations! Take that money he was supposed to have given in order to have the tractor destroyed. . . . True, he gave 25 rubles to Vanka Serogin, the head of the administrative and supply department. That money was for the felt snowboots for Masha. Vanka's father-in-law makes them.

"And then—just imagine that, if you please!—that same Vanka comes before the court and testifies that yes, Osmolovsky did tell him to remove the magneto from the tractor and promised, besides money, to smuggle him across the border to Poland. Devil knows why to Poland, of all places! Just because my name ends with a 'sky,' I suppose. And everybody believed him. When I told them at the trial about the snowboots, they all burst out laughing. And the prosecutor rubbed it in at least five times: 'That's the kind of felt boots *Mister* Osmolovsky is concerned with. . . .' "

Vitalka Khrenovskykh, Katya's husband, bore an amazing resemblance to the prison commandant. They looked like two brothers. The same Gypsy face, the same youth, and the same crazy, flaming eyes. They even spoke alike.

"What's going on here, Comrade Defender?" he called out loudly. "One Party comrade against another? What is all this?"

Ryazantsev, a brown-haired young man with an emaciated face dominated by huge eyes, said quietly:

"Obviously some hostile organization is at work here. They slandered us, specialists in our fields, in order to sabotage the kolkhoz work. Not one agronomist, not one zootechnician left in the region! Do you realize what a diabolical, destructive plan this is? I have written the NKVD about this. Three times. No answer. It is possible that there are some saboteurs there, too? . . . Some of Yagoda's posthumous bastards. . . ."

The fourth man, Kuzin, remained silent throughout the night (they talked for five hours). He spoke only three sentences:

"I am not guilty. . . . Four children. . . . How could I possibly agree to it? . . ."

* * *

For some strange reason Sedov felt embarrassed as he looked at the pleasant, tired face of the assistant in the Great Prosecutor's office. The man failed to send a wire to Ensk, of course. But he kept up his nice and friendly manner as if nothing had happened at all.

"Now I really must see . . ." here he mentioned the Great Prosecutor's first name and patronymic. "As it turned out, this whole affairs is pure fabrication from beginning to end. This is a breach of Socialist rule of law that cries for redress. . . . I am willing to assume full responsibility for this statement."

Dumbfounded, the assistant stared at Sedov. Obviously it had been a long time since he heard anyone voicing such a strong opinion. He even said: "Ho-ho. . . ." Then he went to report the new developments.

The Great Prosecutor got up from behind his desk and walked forward, hand outstretched, to greet Sedov.

"Aaa. . . . Here is our fighting attorney . . ." he said gaily, his eyeglasses gleaming. "I must confess that I do recall our little encounter with some pleasure. This way please. . . ."

This was a sporting gesture; some five years before Sedov and the Great Prosecutor had had an opportunity to cross swords in a celebrated economic trial pertaining to inadequate productivity. Their polemic on this occasion had been sharp and not without its brilliant moments.

At that trial, they represented the two sides. They were—or so it seemed, at least—on a footing of equality. But now Sedov felt his knees weaken.

He had come determined to behave as he had during that trial five years before, to speak coldly and logically. Yet nothing came of it. He grew emotional, he vituperated, shouted slogans. Chaotically, plaintively, he was recounting the story of the felt snowboots, and the bull Gloomy, and the magneto.

The Great Prosecutor listened to all this in disgust. (Possibly, it occurred to Sedov suddenly, this was the disgust of a good technician faced with a bungled job.) He wrote something quickly in his notebook, tapped his pencil on the glass table top, again wrote something down. Sedov's voice rose even higher.

"This is our common daily bread! Our sacred task! To make sure that no unjust sentence, not even one, is passed in the name of the Republic! To make sure that our laws. . . ."

Here again it seemed to Sedov that the Great Prosecutor fixed him with a glance full of kindly pity, such as in Sedov's native Kineshma was reserved for the village idiot Pasha, the possessed one.

"I promise you that I shall investigate this case thoroughly," said the Great Prosecutor solemnly and pompously, perhaps even overdoing it a bit. "*Sine ira et studio*," he said.

* * *

Three months later the Great Prosecutor recalled the case when he appeared before a meeting of the employees of the investigative services of the Republic.

"Just a short while ago," he said, "we came across a case of brutal violation of our Socialist rule of law. Regional agricultural specialists in Ensk were convicted on the basis of Articles 58–7, 58–11, and 58–14. These men had been accused of some absolutely fantastic deeds, such as 'an attempt on the life of a Stakhanovite by means of a bull named Gloomy.' (Laughter.) This simply unbelievable affair could have happened only in the conditions created by the harmful activities of the following men, who have already met with a well-deserved punishment: district prosecutor Nikishin; his deputy Salzman; chairman of the District Court, Kalinin; his deputy Konukhov; also, the following heads of the regional committee and the regional executive committee, who have already been executed in this connection . . . (here followed a long list of names). Comrades, we must take a closer look to discover the roots of this affair, to see whether at the bottom of all this we shall not find a clever, well camouflaged Japanese spy, lying low, together with his family. . . ."

And indeed, a week later it came to light that there was a spy in Ensk. A Japanese. With a family. . . .

Those other four men were released for lack of evidence that would permit establishing the fact that a crime had indeed been committed. Sedov did not get locked up, either. That is, not at that time. . . .

He did get locked up considerably later, in 1952, in connection with a totally insignificant case of a certain Nosov who had stolen 20 pounds of pears from the kolkhoz orchard. In the course of the trial Sedov proved that despite the well-known abundance in our country, the defendant, a man saddled with a large family, had nothing to give his children to eat. The regional prosecutor wrote to the proper authorities, providing a serious political evaluation of attorney Sedov's antics and recalling to mind a thing or two from Sedov's past as well.

However, Vladimir Nikolaevich did not stay in jail long at all: one year, three months, and seven days. He is presently a very respected member of the Moscow College of Defenders (that is, attorneys). And as far as those other four—once sentenced to death—are concerned, they are all alive and doing well. They are all grandfathers by now. And one of them is even a member of VASKHNIL, the Lenin All-Soviet Academy of Agricultural Sciences.

Translated by Marta Erdman

Iosif Brodsky

A Prophecy

We'll go and live together by the shore;
huge dams will wall us from the continent.
A home-made lamp will hurl its warming glow
across the roundness of our centered space.
We shall wage war at cards, and cock an ear
to catch the crashing of the maddened surf.
We'll gently cough, or sigh a soundless sigh,
whenever the wind soars too raucously.

I shall be old, and you will still be young.
But, as the youngsters say, we'll count the time
that's left us till the new age breaks, in days,
not years. In our own private Netherland
we'll plant a kitchen-garden, you and I;
and we shall sizzle oysters by the door,
and feed on sunny octopus, and bathe
our bodies in the octopodal sun.

Let summer rains crash on the cucumbers;
we'll warm ourselves like Eskimos, and you
will gently run your fingers down their green,
untouched, and virgin stripes. I shall inspect
my collar-bone beyond the looking-glass,
glimpsing a giant wave behind my back,
and an old Geiger counter, cased in tin,
that dangles from a faded, sweat-soaked strap.

When winter comes, unpitying, it will
unmake our thatched and rural roof. And if
we have a child, we'll call the boy Andrei,

the girl Anna, so that our Russian speech,
grafted onto its wrinkled little face,
may never be forgotten. The first sound
of the first letter of our alphabet
is but a lengthened breathing-out, and thus
may be asserted for all future time.

We shall wage war at cards until the tide's
retreating sinuosity draws us
as well, with all our trumps, down and away.
Our child will gaze in silence at a moth,
not fathoming its urgent moth-motives
for beating at our lamp. But then the time
will come when he must make his way back through
the dam that walls us from the continent.

1965

Two Hours Down by the Reservoir

"Demon, I am bored . . ."
—Pushkin

I

I am an anti-fascist anti-Faust.
Ich liebe life, but chaos I adore.
Ich bin prepared, *Genosse Offizieren*,
dem Zeit zum Faust quite briefly to *spazieren.*

II

In old Kraków he mourned his *Vaterland*,
not being swayed by Polish propaganda,
and sought the bright stone of philosophers,
doubting the depth of his abilities.
He snatched up the floored scarves of blushing girls.
He warmed to questions of sexology.
He starred on the department's polo team.

He studied the card-player's catechism
and crunched the candy of Cartesianism.
And then he crawled down the artesian well
of ego-centrism. But Klausewitz's
sly craft of soldiering remained somehow
beyond his ken—perhaps because his own
dear *Vater's* craft was cabinet-making.
Zum Beispiel, cholera, glaucoma, plague,
und auch tuberculosis, roared and raged.
He tried to save himself by puffing *schwarze*
Zigaretten. Moors and gypsies drew him.
He was annointed Bachelor of Arts,
then won his laurels as Licentiate,
and sang in seminar of dinosaurs.

The man was German; German was in his mind,
And what is more, *cogito ergo sum.*
And *über alles* Germany, of course.
(Well-known Vienna waltzes fill our ears.)
He bade farewell to Kraków without tears
and in his *drozhky* quickly drove away
to take his Chair and lift a stein of beer.

III

A new moon glimmers in the ragged clouds.
A man stoops over an enormous folio.
A crease deepens between his bushy brows.
His eyes show demon glints of arabesque.
A black slate-pencil trembles in his hand.
The Arab delegate, Meph-ibn-Stophel,
peers from a corner at his Faustian brow.

Candles flare up. Beneath a chest a mouse
makes scratching sounds. "*Herr Doktor*, it's midnight."
"*Jawohl, muss schlafen, schlafen.*" Two black mouths
say "Miau." A *Jüdisch' Frau* slips silently
from the dark kitchen with an omelet
that sizzles in salt-fat. The *Herr Doktor*
writes on an envelope: "*Gott strafe* England, London,
Francis Bacon."

Enter and *exeunt:* devils and thoughts.
Enter and *exeunt:* years and visitors.
The costume-changes, weather-changes, change
of words, can't be kept track of. Thus the years
roll by unnoticed. He knew Arabic
but not Sanskrit. And he discovered late
in life *ein kleines Fräulein,* Margareta.

Faust sent an urgent message off to Cairo,
refused to give his soul up to the devil.
Meph came non-stoph, and Faust put on a new
costume, and, glancing in the mirror, was
convinced that he had been made young at last,
to last forever. He left with fresh flowers
for her boudoir. *Und veni, vidi, vici.*

IV

Ich liebe clearness. *Ja. Ich liebe* neatness.
Ich bin to beg you not to call it weakness.
You vill opserve dat he lufft flower-girlss.
Day untershtant dat *das ist ganze* urgent.
But this arrangement *macht der grosse* minus.
Die teutschne Sprache, macht der grosse cosine:
one's heart can *nein gehabt* to be consumed at home.

There's no point in expecting *alles* to come
from men: "Oh, moment, stay, thou art so fair."
The devil walks among us hour by hour
and waits, each moment, for this fatal phrase.
But men, *mein' liebe Herren,* insofar
as they're uncertain as to their strong feelings,
will lie like troopers, conscientiously,
But Goethe-like, they'll let no chance slip by.

Und grosser Dichter Goethe made mistakes
which make his theme *ganz* problematical.
And Thomas Mann betrayed his signature,
and *cher* Gounod embarrassed his *artiste.*
For art is art is art is art is art . . .

Better to sing in Heaven than to lie
in concert halls. *Die Kunst gehabt* needs feeling's truth.

Faust may, in the end, have been afraid to die.
He knew exactly where the devils dwell.
He had devoured the works of Avicenna
and Galen. He could dry up water on the knee
and tell a tree's age from its cross-section.
He knew just where the distant star-tracks lead.
But Dr. Faust knew less than *nichts* of God.

V

There is a mystic lore. And there is faith.
And the Lord God. And differences among
the three, but points of unity as well.
The flesh saves some men; others it destroys.
Not to believe is to be blind. And sometimes swinish.

God, then, looks down. And men look up. But each
has a substantial interest of his own.
God then is limited? He is. And men?
Men, I dare say, are also limited.

Men have a ceiling of their own, although
its place and shape are not securely fixed.
The flatterer finds a corner in men's hearts;
men see the devil, but are blind to life.

Such then was Dr. Faust. And such again
were Marlowe, Goethe, Thomas Mann, the mob
of bards and intellectuals, alas,
und readers drawn from a quite different class.

A single torrent wipes their traces out,
dissolves their test-tubes—*Donnerwetter!*—and
their wild ideas. May God grant them time
to ask "Where are we heading?" and to heed the shouting Muse.

An honest German will not wait to take
der Weg zurück, even when he is invited.

He takes a *Walter* from his warm trousers
and goes for good into the *Walter*-closet.
"*Fräulein*, pray tell, *was ist das Inkubus?*"
Inkubus, das ist ein kleiner Globus.
Noch grosser Dichter Goethe framed a rebus.
Und, hocus-pocus, huge malicious herons
flap up out of the Weimar fog to seize
the key from his deep pocket. Eckermann's
sharp eye was not enough to save us then.
And now, *Matrosen*, we have run aground.

Some tasks are truly our own spirit's tasks.
All mystic lore's a sign of unsuccess
in our attempt to deal with them. *Ich bin*
is otherwise not worth an explanation.
Zum Beispiel, ceilings are a prelude to
their roofs. Greater as poem, lesser far
as man, I recollect a Virgin, niched,
and breakfast copiously served in bed.

September's here again. I'm bored. The moon
is full. A gray witch purrs against my legs,
I've tucked a hatchet under my pillow. . . .
Now let us have some *Schnapps* . . . so . . . *abegemacht!*
Jawohl. September. Dispositions sour.
A grinding tractor skids on the mud field.
Ich liebe life and the *Völkisch' Beobachter.*
Gut' Nacht, mein' liebe Herren. Ja, gut' Nacht.

September 1965

Translated from the Russian by George L. Kline

Leo Lipski

Day and Night

(for the opening of the Volga-Don Canal)

> . . . Blessed be the name of Comrade Jesus Christ!
> from a letter of a Polish miner in France to the Consulate General of the city of X.

LEAVE me alone, all of you. You with your rages and your madnesses. Let me lean, slowly, as though over a stream that flows along. It will reflect my changing image, together with phantoms of many years ago. Let me look at them, if for a moment only.

No, we did not build the Volgostroy. At any rate, it was not our fault that in the spring, together with the melting of the ice, the cement dock disintegrated and floated away. We were not the ones who constructed it. Really. Still, we did suffer terrible hardships. Especially in winter.

Hundred-watt light bulbs burned in the latrines, but they gave no heat. Mornings, when we were awakened, it was still dark. And incredibly cold outside the barracks. To go out into the cold hungry is a terrible trial. And undressed. But, of course, you are quite familiar with this sort of thing, and in a minute it will make you vomit. But wait.

Once, I remember, before the war, several policemen led a man and beat him over the head and across the face. I could not take my eyes from the sight. A small crowd was following behind them. And I had to look. Maybe you too will one day find something at which you will *have* to look.

I was a doctor's aid and sometimes received a salary: fifty rubles. It wasn't little. I finished my night shift. I telephoned the camp saying I would be coming back in fifteen minutes. The kitchens had no telephones. I could not call to say I'd soon be over to taste the food. To check, supposedly, whether it was good. The nightmarish chance that one of the women may decide at night to go into labor slowly diminished. I didn't know the first thing about it. Grisha had said to me:

"You just go there. They manage alone."

I knew they managed alone, but that was something else.

The power plant gleamed white. The Uzbeks called it "Faro"—meaning pharaoh.

And they were afraid. Hung all over with jointers, from a distance it looked like a large diamond. Two turbines were in operation, though this we could not hear. Hundred-watt light bulbs, electrical appliances in the kitchens. . . . The fog was lifting slowly and HE—quadrangular, gigantic, windowless, one of HIS arms stretched over the Volga—rose and fell, electrical jointers glittering. The Uzbeks whispered:

"Faro."

Then they said so softly that you could think you had imagined it:

"HE."

From the camp we had to walk. Sixty kilometers daily. Through our oppressive, overwhelming exhaustion we felt sparks of curiosity: there was uninterrupted thunder, nearer and nearer. Illusion resulting from fatigue? We came to a town where you had to shout whenever you wanted to say something. The town's inhabitants were quite used to it. They communicated in sign language. Working in an invisible underground factory, they built airplane engines. At all times they were testing 700. Dear Jesus!

Double-flash signal. A quarrel in the kitchen. Three soups on the floor. Noisy as a beehive at takeoff. A little man, a tailor from K., sat on my bunk. And stared into space, mumbling to himself. Grisha was ill. He would not come in until the afternoon when there was more work to do. I wasn't going to get any sleep during the day. As well as at night. For many reasons. Three-flash signal. The little tailor sat on my bunk. He was afraid of the cold. Even the bravest of them wept going to work. Though their tears did not fall. They froze instantly. But this little man never wept. Yet he was afraid to go outside. The guard had to chase him out. Some of the men still slept as they walked around. Trying to prolong sleep until the last moment. It won't help you, little brothers, believe me. The Volga wind I had talked with the night before will wake you up. You will awaken with frost over your eyelashes. And woe to those who had not eaten the soup.

I could make the main camp in fifteen minutes. A kilometer's run. Some spiritual adjustment. As if something tightening inside me. Hardening, but becoming more sensitive.

"How many?" I asked.

"Seventy-six men." I had seen almost all of them yesterday, the day before, and so on. They stood lined up in the hall, against the wall, at ease. The camp chief:

"You'll look them over."

"Where?"

"In the cell."

I nodded agreement.

In fifteen minutes I had to examine them all and determine their condition. One month in the Special Column equaled a year of camp. Or so they said. And you had to watch out not to get into trouble yourself. It was not simple, considering they were all weaklings. I felt tense. But then suddenly a terrible calm came over me. I no longer heard what the chief was saying, he moved his lips, like a fish, I saw and heard nothing but the 76. Nothing.

"Now then, children? Talk."

I went to the first face, a peasant face, bearably pale;

the second: no, too obviously shrewd;

the third, the first shouted "I have a fever," I measured the pulse —no, at the same time I saw the sixth pulling down his pants, phlegmon: "step out, dismissed";

fourth, fifth, seventh;

the seventh: "wait till I get my hands on you!"

eighth;

the first, hysterically: "I have a fever," I stuck in the thermometer;

ninth;

the seventh said: "I have just three days left";

tenth, eleventh, twelfth, thirteenth, fourteenth;

fifteenth: "a knife isn't always the best answer" I smiled charmingly;

the first was making curious movements with the thermometer, I let him know I saw him;

sixteenth;

seventeenth, convincing, the ass naked, a narrow stream of dried-up blood; well-known hemorrhoid patient;

eighteenth, nineteenth;

twentieth, let him go, the boy was white, pluse —130: "dismissed";

suddenly the seventeenth, "turn around, that's it, open your mouth," internal hemorrhage, tuberculosis, the stomach, that must be it, "why did you show me your ass . . ." "because . . . because . . ." I called the hospital, "go lie down";

twenty-first, twenty-second;

Twenty-third: a big gash in the leg, a most un-typical spot, he must've been rubbing it all night, "step out";

the first, I take his thermometer, normal;

twenty-fourth;

twenty-fifth, a Moscow thief, I never did like him, he stood there silent, had been running a temperature in the morning, "dismissed, YES YOU . . .";

seventeenth, hemorrhaging all night, though I could be wrong, the fresh blood may have thrown me off;

twenty-sixth, twenty-seventh, twenty-eighth, twenty-ninth;

thirtieth, thirty-first: all doubled up, faking, "lie down," hard stomach, better not, "step out";

thirty-second, thirty-third;

thirty-fourth, stood silent, but it was pellagra, an advanced stage, this he couldn't fake, certainly . . . "step out";

With some uneasiness I noted how many I'd already dismissed;

thirty-fifth, thirty-sixth;

thirty-seventh: "my belly," he groaned, "lie down," I touched the belly, hard, I tried a trick, tickling, the belly softened, a grin appeared on his face, he was going to work that day;

thirty-eighth, thirty-ninth;

careful, careful;

fortieth, forty-first;

forty-second: huge, a long tunic, he threw himself on top of me, bit my heel, probably a fake of some kind, I picked myself up;

forty-third;

forty-fourth; I encountered motionless pupils, I looked again, motionless, I covered them with my hand, uncovered—motionless, "step out";

forty-fifth, forty-sixth;

forty-seventh: legs swollen, like dough, higher up as well, "step out";

Finally, seventy-four.

One, I knew, was in bed.

"And the other?"

He was sitting in his bunk. His penis had been hammered on to the wooden boards with a heavy nail. He did not pretend to be in pain. There was no blood. I went to a telephone.

"Grisha, you'll have to get up. The main camp. A guy has nailed his you-know-what to the bunk boards."

I signed the papers. The men I had dismissed went to the doctor's office in a convoy. The one in the long tunic, to the psychiatric ward. The electrically operated oak doors opened. At that moment— four-flash signal. To work.

Ten minutes to go. I collapsed on the snow. Exhaustion gripped at me like a mad dog, crushed me down. I felt completely helpless, emptied out. They would've had me dismiss the whole camp, 70 thousand people. They would've liked to see me in the Special Column. No. They would like to have everyone dismissed, as though through some miracle. At least for that day. No matter what happened after. I picked myself up from the snow. Here it was untouched, shiny as silk. A hundred meters farther there were barbed-wire fences and watch towers. In the distance I heard a band playing. In this weather! Well, well. I bundled up, walked for a kilometer and then a half.

A parade. We stood on the podium, I, the chief's deputy, and someone from accounting, whatever his name. The band was playing, over by the wide entrance. The columns lined up in formation of fours. It was seven o'clock. Strong lights illuminated the band-stand. It began.

I had borrowed a pair of felt boots from Vanya, to keep my feet from freezing. Thirty thousand people marching by, that, I knew, would last. They walked on and on. Stakhanovites, weaklings, cheats, frauds. The columns fell in formation in the dark, crawled out into the bright lights of the band-stand, then disappeared in the fog and the mist. It began to snow. Coats full of holes, shoes made of rubber tires, of felt. Shouting, calling. Unit chiefs. Back up, then: Forward. Fingers wrapped in rags. Poor things, they would go numb anyway. One cheek was frost-bitten. Forty below zero . . . Wind, snow. That cheek had been turned to the Volga. I rubbed it hard. The men's eyes were watering. Even the bravest of them. With the exception of the little tailor. They walked against the wind, ice formed over their faces, frost over their eyelids; they breathed heavily.

No guards were necessary. There was a large circle of wire fences and watchtowers. Tens of kilometers long. They wouldn't run away. Where? Even if they knew Russia like the palm of their hand. They wouldn't. This was so obvious that they didn't even try. Unless they were mad. Not even the hospital food administrator. And he had quite a fortune stashed away on the outside. He walked around like a king. But he wouldn't either.

One face broke away from a labor unit and was coming toward me. In these final moments I still had the power to grant dismissal. The face was almost completely covered, bandaged all the way up to the eyes, only the eyes glistened. He stopped. But said nothing. The eyes glistened. I took his hand. The weather was too cold to feel the pulse. I could see a young forehead, yellow. A Chinaman? I pulled down the lower eyelid: jaundice? That was it. Tiny veins fluttering beneath the skin, very rapidly, disappearing, very rapidly. "Stay." He sat down on the podium, legs hanging limply.

"Did you see somebody yesterday?"

"Aleksander Aleksandrovich," he said softly.

At that time my little tailor had come in to see me. Before the receiving hours Aleksander Aleksandrovich was saying:

"I only dismiss every second man who's sick. That's the best I can do."

"Too many for the hospital."

"That's not my worry."

Aleksander Aleksandrovich—the jaundice patient said to me—had told him:

"Well, little brother, it looks like pneumonia. But what can I do? The man before you had a broken leg. Come back tomorrow."

And he prescribed camphor. So I said to the patient:

"Go to Olga Petrovna."

Olga—the twenty-year-old youngster. She was the boss around there. Anyway.

The parade. More Stakhanovites. If they ever did own felt boots, they traded them in for food; now they wore footclouts. Footclouts were a wonderful invention.

When I used to go with the labor units to cut wood in the forest camp, footclouts were lifesavers. Eight kilometers march each way. For two months I didn't know what the bunk I slept in looked like. I left before daybreak, returned at night. Groping in darkness. Gradually we accumulated saws, axes, bowls, little lamps. It was summer then and blueberries ripened in profusion. About mushrooms I knew little. Sometimes I found raspberries. Before the saws arrived we had glorious peace. I would find myself a clearing in the woods and lie in the grass. I would toss leaves into a stream. Serenity. One could forget. Grasshoppers. Gentle buzzing above the grasses. Then the forest, slowly darkening. Tinder. I would light a fire and toast bread. And one day the saws arrived. And axes. And noise.

A unit of Uzbeks passed in front of us. They had been dying *en masse*. Of various kinds of tuberculosis. A whole sector of invalids within the camp. Just going there a man could earn a living. Nothing but homos.—Oooo, *salute* Dzafer. Don't cry. Yes, it was you. I bandaged your wounds and you kissed me. You wanted it.—They passed, disappeared in the blizzard. The band was playing. I couldn't understand how . . . their fingers . . .

The power plant was barely visible through the haze and the snow. Sometimes it vanished completely. The columns continued to pass. By now you could not see the people, only snow and a quivering human mass. I was cold, cold. My thoughts froze. I stood and stood. And stood. More columns of men. And still more. They came straight at me, through me. I saw only their unshaven, sunken faces. I tried to stop them. But they took no notice of me. They walked on as if I did not exist. Yet I could see them, they were dying.

The huge doors closed. I escaped to the kitchen. The first kitchen I could find. I was unable to breathe for five minutes. I was dripping wet. Then I proceeded to taste. That too was part of my duties. I tasted—first caldron, second, Stakhanovite, fourth. I signed papers that the food agreed with the standards specified by the rules. Then the second kitchen, the fourth, at the fifth I could only look.

There they had once given me some cans of food. Thinking I was a dog, thinking I might cause trouble. But later they never gave me anything more, since I was not a dog. I was a sucker. They just gave me bread, sometimes. Who knows—they thought. I went to get a shave.

The barber was stocked very well. I recognized supplies from the hospital: Vaseline, tonics. Ten barbershop chairs. Freshly painted. White tunics. Bottles full of sweet-smelling fluids. Mirrors. The barber copied, made an effort. For me, there was cologne, good soap.

Anybody could go to the barbershop. But very few had the strength, or the desire. The invalids, who would have liked to come all the time, because it was a pleasant place, had special visiting hours, not many. Total relaxation. The men that worked there were just like their counterparts outside. Talkers. How they could talk: that so-and-so would show up, because he had a boil on his bottom. For a special visit. The head barber would say he needed lanolin for his better clients. Especially for the camp's police chief. A former Moscow prosecutor. I was to meet him that day. I didn't like him. That four drivers had been crushed against the nets and that for three days they had tried to save them, but finally gave up. They'd have to shut down the power plant. Then, that the new machines for thawing earth had arrived, but hadn't been unloaded. They were left standing on the tracks, rusting away. Oh yes, because the connecting wiring, or some other such thing, was missing. And that the cement blocks for the canal were about to be delivered. And so on, and so on.

I tried to sleep. But the cologne woke me up. I hurried to the clinic. The receiving hours were from nine-thirty. The secretary sat at his post. His name was Buehler and he spoke in German. He was young, moved with the strange charm of a victim of coronary disease, and had beautiful hands. I asked for Grisha. He was with our chief, the twenty-year old girl. I reported the matter of the nailed-down penis.

Grisha was forty and came from a collective farm. He had committed a fraud of some kind. They gave him three years. He returned—committed fraud again. They gave him five years. He had learned fraud here, at the camp. At any rate, during the war he had been a sanitation officer. He knew a lot. The best remedy for baldness—shave the head and then apply iodine. This, allegedly, helped.

So, about that penis. Olga Petrovna walked in, with Grisha behind her. Olga had blue, slanting eyes, a rather ugly nose. A good figure. Nice legs and knees. She was tactful and composed. Excellent at selecting her people. Decisive and wise. And—good.

When she said: no, it was the same as when someone else said: yes.

It had not been easy for me to get into the clinic. I needed the approval of the camp director. Somehow she had taken a liking to me. I knew I'd be accepted. She was smiling a little when she examined me. She stared at me, intently, she didn't take her blue, slanting eyes off my face. She sat in a leather chair, I sat facing her. We were separated by the desk. And by the fact that she was "free" . . . Dosage for this or that drug. Symptoms of TB and so on. Then, with a slightly different inflection:

"Will you whistle for me some of your hit tunes." I stiffened, like an insect. "Whistle, go ahead, don't be afraid, the walls are soundproof."

I whistled "The Albatross," "Blue Skies." I went on whistling for some fifteen minutes.

"Do you dance?"

"No."

"Why?"

I then became less interesting to her, but she smiled and said:

"Well, now you may go and start working."

She gave me her hand. How well I remember it, even today. Where are you after all these years, Olga?

From then on I became a highly privileged person. Even the camp director could not dismiss me easily.

But now she walked in, Grisha behind her. Grisha was grunting, coughing, his face was red. So I too blushed, thinking that they were going over to see that penis. I said to myself:

Lucky I won't be there. But she turned to me:

"Why don't you come along. You've done the camp? Right. Let's go."

She was wearing high felt boots. It looked very pretty. We walked towards the snow that shone like silk. She asked:

"Is it true that you'd dismissed a drunk from work?"

"It's true. But he was from the police. The chief's deputy."

"You must be very careful."

"How do you mean?"

"Listen, you haven't been here very long. A Soviet man knows, even here, at the camp, how to behave. But you don't. Do you want to continue working at the hospital?"

"I do, but. . . ."

"I know . . . but you cannot always. . . . Yes?"

"Yes."

"Then stay at the dispensary. But don't be an idiot. Lucky they told me about that drunk."

The wind was blowing from the Volga.

"Is it true that free nurse Natasha has fallen for one of the prisoners?"

"Yes. Everyone is talking about it. That they do it on a table at the dispensary. Very uncomfortable. . . ."

"Enough. Let's talk about something else. I'll have to dismiss Buehler."

"Why?"

"Orders from the top, everyone from 58. . . . I liked him. Enough of that."

I looked at her. A young thing in a schoolgirl overcoat. Navy-blue with fur trimming. Her head was covered with a leather cap pulled down over the ears. Slanting, blue eyes.

"By the way, are the sanitation boys working well? On your shift?"

"Yes. Now the . . . is frozen"—I didn't know how to say 'excrement' in Russian—"and they have to chop it with the axe."

"The shit, you meant to say."

"Yes."

"I haven't time to look over the latrines. I am counting on you. And barracks 132 and 133, have they been fumigated?"

"Yes. The invalids had to crowd in together."

"Of course they did. But are they at least using the bathhouses?"

"Some aren't too eager to, not in winter. The Uzbeks freeze terribly."

"Let them freeze. Tell the others, too."

"They often come down with pneumonia after a bath."

"Never mind. I will not have lice in my sector, or bedbugs."

Invalids freezing naked in the bathhouses. . . . Waiting for their clothing to come back from fumigation. . . . She felt I had certain reservations.

"Do you think no one checks up on me? And this is how it should be. I talk to you like this because you are a Westerner."

We approached the gate to the main camp, which opened electrically. The guard:

"I wish to report that Akhmatov has refused to go to work and has nailed his. . . ."

She pushed him aside:

"Take me there."

A gloomy cell, with one hanging light bulb. Akhmatov, a bearded giant; huge and thin.

"Now then, Akhmatov, what in the world have you done?"

Akhmatov sat silent, shaking his head to and fro like a pendulum. Only his throat moved. This one was not a faker, oh no.

"Akhmatov, Comrade Doctor is speaking to you. . . ."

Olga interrupted the guard. Clearly Akhmatov was still dazed from thinking. Clearly he had thought all night. And many other nights. And then he nailed himself to the bunk boards. Threats would be useless. He would let himself be cut into small pieces. His eyes opened and closed. She hopped on to the bunk, second tier. She sat down next to him. She turned to the guard:

"Leave us!"

Then she took his huge head in her hands. He stopped shaking; he was now wide awake. He looked at her almost consciously. She said:

"Aren't you ashamed?"

He covered his member with his hand.

"What are you in for?"

"I stole a slice of bread. I didn't want to go out to work."

"Now then, go on and pull out that nail."

He knew that as soon as he did, everything would begin all over again. Guessing his thought, she asked:

"For how long?"

"Three years. Kulak, kulak. . . ."

"How long have you been in?"

"Two years."

"You fool, you'll be out in a year."

But he was filled with peasant stubbornness. She added:

"I'll make sure of it personally."

He seized the bunk with his hands and started roaring. Not from pain. The bunk boards cracked in his hands. He roared like a bull. While she was pulling out the nail. She examined the wound to see how bad it was. Then she hopped off the bunk. To me she said:

"You may bandage it up."

He was still roaring so that the whole building shook. So many months of his slow rebellion gone to waste. . . . Pointless rebellion, in fact. Olga shouted:

"Akhmatov! Quiet!"

For the first time Akhmatov looked at her with sane eyes. His gaze softened. He began crying soundlessly. She said:

"And next time I'll let the militia help you, Akhmatov."

"Remember!"

And she left the cell. No, she was returning.

"Put some iodine on my hand. . . ."

Three of her fingers were bleeding heavily. Akhmatov had seen to it that the nail was well hammered in. I bandaged her fingers and prepared to go. She said to the guard:

"The militia . . . tell them I'll handle this myself. . . ."

Then we went outside. She knitted her brow in a childish squint:

"Take him some sulfa."

She seemed still interested in the sanitation men. Do they get milk? Even divers did not get milk. There was a herd of cows in our town-camp. The power plant again vanished in the fog. It was nine already.

At nine-thirty we had receiving hours for the dismissed and the labor units working at night. We walked past the Stakhanovite barracks. Was it possible? A gramophone. Mendelssohn's scherzo. I decided to return here as soon as I had time. But I never did have time. So I never found out what it was. A hallucination? . . . Another storm, so heavy you couldn't see more than two meters in front of you. She arrived at the dispensary looking like a doll: cheeks pink from the frost, skin white, lips unbelievably red. She went back to her office, where she had once examined me, and she asked to see Buehler. Next day he was no longer around. He was transferred to join those from 58, those to be sent away.

We had five general practitioners and one venerologist. Also a dentist. Vanya, Petya and two others prepared dressings. I and Grishka No. 2 took care of medicines. The dentist put in gold teeth, mostly; this was the latest fashion that had come from Moscow. And all the camp dignitaries had their front teeth capped in gold. The hospital food chief, for example. A woman with a child came in for some cotton. Or someone from the barbershop, to get vaseline. And some alcohol, which was rather scarce. Pure alcohol, of course. An orderly came from the hospital for codeine.

He was a drug addict and afterward became very nice. He performed minor operations himself. Even uncomplicated appendicitis. The patient was up on his feet after three days. All of a sudden, a messenger from Olga. Sending for me. She was sitting buried in some statistics. Without lifting her head she said:

"There's been a call from point 126. Something's happened over where the Poles work. It would be best if you went."

I knew point 126. They had a cozy, warm hut and the orderly always served you tea. Sometimes bread as well.

"But hurry," added Olga.

The orderly took bread for dismissing men from work. That was his privilege. So I hurried over to point 126, situated across the Volga. Over where they had been digging the canal and preparing the flood gates. Quite a distance away. There were railroad tracks everywhere, intertwining like human fingers. Farther along, a tractor. Dragging a huge tree. Then more tracks. Many tracks. With trains standing over them. I was running and I was thinking that today I'd be too late to see the camp director. I'd have to wait another week, and every day was so full of tension. Finally I reached the shores of the Volga. Here began the air-rail lift that transported gravel. I was in a hurry, so I asked the local orderly for a ride. Noisily the little carts rolled in. Tumbled over. Emptied the gravel. One of them was for me. They put me inside. Rrrr. A sudden jolt. Everything looked tiny, as from an airplane. At last I found myself over the Volga. The carts moved along rapidly. They were not intended for people. What's more, they wobbled. I held on to the walls and the sides. Overhead there was a strong wind. I hadn't returned Vanya's felt boots. I was passing above the power plant, very high. If it hadn't been for the storm, I would have had something to look at. But I was enveloped by fog. Suddenly the cart stopped. If serious repairs are necessary, this may last for hours—I thought to myself. I was hanging above the middle of the Volga. I felt I had to move, but the cart was too small. You traveled in an embryo position. At best. It was windy up above. I thought I might freeze. I rubbed my cheeks. And ears. And nose. Finally it started up again. So suddenly that I almost fell. It made a zzzz sound and stopped at the depot. I could not get out. They had to help me. I felt somewhat dizzy. They took me to point 126. Then I saw what was going on.

These men had not gotten shovels. Or spades. They lit a bon-fire. In front it was too hot, in the rear too cold. They were jumping around like monkeys. A large bonfire. The air was turning colder and colder. You felt like crawling in the fire. My little tailor did just that. First he began dancing around the edges. Then he went inside. And his clothes caught fire. He continued dancing. And burning. The power plant was barely visible, as if sketched in pencil. Against its background he danced his fire dance. The little village tailor. Then they poured water over him. And he froze over, like Lot's wife. He couldn't make a move. But there was a fire. Encrusted in ice, burning, like a saint. He promenaded around and around. Then the whole labor unit went wild and clustered around him. Dancing a dance. Boom, boom, boom, African fashion. I walked into the fire and grabbed hold of the tailor. I started smoldering a little myself. . . . The tailor who never wept. And he was not weeping then, either. He seemed concentrated, as if searching for something inside the bon-fire. 126. I was given some tea, my tailor started eating snow. Some preferred it as a thirst quencher. I messed up Vanya's felt boots with the coals and the gravel. I put the tailor in the care of the 126 medical assistant and left. The poor little fellow had to stay in bed. He would keep warm. And the labor unit was still dancing around the bon-fire. Once more I climbed inside the little air cart and arrived with a loud hiss at the lower depot. I flipped out of the cart, like gravel. I did not move. I felt very sleepy and would have liked to remain motionless. But they lifted me up. I saw the thawing machines. It was nine-thirty. I had to sleep. I saw women at work. Cooking. It was becoming a little lighter. The power plant now seemed to be outlined in pastel. The queen of life and death. The canal would not be ready before spring. And the huge concrete slabs. They filled the entire car on which it was printed: twelve tons. Who could lift that? Maybe the American construction elevator. I went, stumbling along from fatigue, to the dispensary. To give my report to Olga. But they'd already telephoned, so it was not necessary. Olga dismissed me for two hours. Back to the barracks. There the general was talking about the Germans. He was ill. Many of the dismissed gathered around him. He did not try to hide his hatred for Russia. He felt he had "the truth." God knows where from. He trusted the Germans. They were our only hope. He left for surgery. To prepare strategic plans. I fell asleep immediately. That day I had to see a great many people. Already sleeping, I was thinking that the following day the general would no longer be there.

People met at the camp, like meteors. People of all kinds, like sand pebbles. Today he was there. Tomorrow he was not. At the camp you were more free than in the free world. A little bit more. You didn't have to think that. And how many years you still had to go was almost immaterial. Although to us, only this was important. To us—Europeans.

I got up after half an hour. I had to. I crawled down from my high bunk and splashed my eyes with cold water. It was rather warm at the barracks. They were built of wooden boards with sand or clay between them. Warm and dark. A lighted bulb hung from the ceiling, making you aware of the nearness of the power plant. I tried to make myself look presentable. I was going to the women's sector. I brushed my teeth with soap. My hair had grown out a little. I had a Polish military overcoat. I put it on. I pushed back my earflaps. Vanya's felt boots, it turned out, could be scrubbed clean. I took along a gift: methylic blueing, a beautiful methylic blue dye.

Women were allowed to nurse a child for two months. Then they went to work. Also during pregnancy they had certain privileges. Some tried to become pregnant. Some poisoned themselves with iodine. Some induced miscarriages by taking quinine. Or by jumping up and down, or God knows what else. The one I was to visit had just miscarried. The women's barracks were surrounded by a high barbed-wire fence. The guard let me pass without difficulty.

I walked inside the barracks. First impression: tropical birds in cages. Separated with blankets. Triple-tier bunks. And what a wealth of colors, of ornaments and trinkets! Like a Christmas tree. I took a deep breath. A world all of its own. An amazing new world, so close by. I hadn't seen such a display of color for a long time. Each woman had her own little showcase. Made of paper, of colorful rags. It was so warm that some of them sat practically naked. I had been away for so long. A woman's world.

Somehow, I was not very good at living among men. I generally had no friends. Women were much easier to talk with. You could get a story from any of them. Even the most stupid. But suddenly nothing, nothing but men. And they touched you. You had to develop a defense mechanism—a dulling of the senses.

"Natasha, Natasha!" The one I had come to see.

Natasha leaned out of one of the second-story cages and asked: "What?"

She was wearing a short little green negligée. Nothing else. She was still rather weak. She slid down to the floor slowly, and smiled.

She had been a dishwasher at the dispensary. Vanya was with her. In a tiny room, at night. In a room large enough only for a bed. Nothing more.

So she slid down cautiously. How long had it been since I'd seen a woman's back, and thighs? No, this was not desire. Well then, well then. . . ? I knew. I regained the precarious balance: Renoir. Dégas.

She was twenty-two, had a boyish hair style and astonished lips. I handed her the gift. Actually, I didn't know why I had come.

"Vanya told me to bring you his greetings. And to visit you. And ask you if you still liked him."

"Like . . . who's to tell a heart what to do? I am quite happy without him. I thank God for that. Do you know we're getting new gowns? I'll dye mine a pretty blue. . . ."

"You'll lend me some for my scarf, won't you?" a head popped out from one of the cages. A rather young head.

"Vanya will be very sad. What should I tell him?"

"That . . . that it all ended by itself."

"You don't want to come back to us?"

"No. . . . The work was all right. . . . But no. You see, everything would start all over. No, anyway, I'm going to be working in the kitchen."

A shoemaker from Poland was behind it all. An influential man, the shoemaker. People traveled two hundred kilometers to see him.

"So?"

I didn't feel like leaving.

"Stay a bit longer."

Pink air. Ruffles in the windows. And women—looking at themselves in the glass panes. And women, washing themselves in small buckets. Heads popped out from behind paper curtains, delicate ruffles, yellow, blue, green, and red—the color hardest to find. And ribbons. Like a Persian market. Nothing but women. Washing. Changing. Waiting for their lovers, their powerful lovers, who dismissed them from work. I shut my eyes. Then opened them slowly. Like a sponge, I absorbed the mood around me. With every pore.

"What kind of coat is this?"

"A Polish military coat."

"You brought it from back there?"

"Yes."

It always stirred considerable interest.

"Well children, I must be going."

I left. On the way out I gave the guard a slice of bread. He was an invalid and a Kalmuk. But he had different interests. Not women. I walked through a gray world. Colorless and hollow. I tried not to think of the tropical birds.

I returned to the dispensary. Grisha was running a temperature. Bandages lay strewn all over the place. Disorder. No one around. Except Aleksevna Petrovna. A doctor. Grisha was a fellow who always had his wits about him. I sat down at his side. He was stretched out on the sofa used for patients.

"How goes it?"

"As soon as I eat a little something, I'll feel better. You go to cook No. 9, the one-eyed guy, and tell him that I, Grisha, am ill. You'll get something. Go, my friend. Otherwise I'll die here like a dog. Food is the only thing that helps."

Kitchen No. 9 was near by. I went in, looking for the chef. There he was. Staring at me with his one eye. Made me feel uneasy. He stared some more. I said:

"Grisha is sick. . . ."

"What?" He pretended to be deaf. It gave him pleasure. I walked over closer.

"Grisha is sick. . . ."

"Very fishy, very fishy."

I became even more uneasy.

"Very fishy, very. . . ."

He lifted his white cap, uncovering a huge bald head. Then he sat down and proceeded turning his palm, first to the outside, then the inside. In this way he was expressing doubt. I tried the third time:

"Grisha's sick, maybe some food. . . ."

He pushed me away.

"I'm not deaf. I can hear you. I did hear you. We'll see what can be done."

And he gave me a can of beef. And then had some noodles warmed up.

"Here. I hope Grisha feels better."

He winked.

A pan full of noodles—one meter wide. I could feel the can of meat inside my pocket. The noodles were plump, golden-brown. Grisha jumped to his feet. He started opening the can with a surgical knife. A whole frying pan! He grunted, like a bear. Snorted. Coughed. Then grunted some more. After he finished half of the noodles, he stopped, lost in thought:

"Yes, yes. . . ."

With a pained expression he started eating again. This meant to say there would be nothing left for me. I boiled some potatoes in a sterilizer. Poured cod-liver oil over them. Salt I always carried with me. Then I ate. Grisha looked up at me and mumbled:

"Ah, yes. However. . . ."

He finished eating and I had to take the frying pan back. Grisha turned to the wall and slept. The orderlies were cleaning up. Washing the floor. Picking up the bandages. They closed the boxes, screwed tight the jars. One of them, looking straight at me, drank f e r r u m p o m a t u m.

"Good. Sweet. Like wine," he said. Grisha stirred in his sleep.

"Enough, pig," I said.

He stopped and looked at me.

"On the outside, I'm an electrician," he told me.

He scrubbed the floor.

"On the outside, I'm an electri. . . ."

"So what?"

He burst out laughing.

"Guess how many years they gave me. Guess. For two-and-a-half meters of wire."

Besides, he was rolling his eyes.

"Want to know how many meters I really stole?"

He counted, counted.

"Three kilometers, maybe four. Something like that."

And he continued scrubbing the floor.

Gradually I started to prepare bandages, medicines. On various shapes of cotton I placed stereotype ointments. This we did by the thousands. Petya came. His work was the same as mine. Then Vanya. He prepared the enemas, tubes for blood testing, sterilized syringes. For morphology. Urinalysis. The doctors arrived. Four women. It was becoming noisy. The doctors wrote prescriptions on slips of paper. Then the patient came to me. I administered this or that. I had learned to make a dressing fast, yet so that it stayed on. 300, 400 dressings in one evening. That was something. Vanya's work was sloppy. The floors had been scrubbed. We all had on white coats. Like torreadors. But in the waiting room—noise, arguments, fighting. Grisha slept.

"Well," I said, "you better get up."

Olga walked across the waiting room. It calmed down, like an ocean. Then it erupted again. I went to see Anna, the doctor, to get one of the men dismissed. To send him to a hospital. He, allegedly, had the hives.

"All right," she said.

She was small and young. Just graduated from the medical academy, one month before. She didn't know too much. But was full of the best intentions. I noticed she wore a pair of lovely little felt boots.

"I must be on my way," I said.

I went back. Then Olga walked in.

"Everything ready?"

"Yes, yes. Open up the doors."

The mob poured in. Like a herd of bulls. Grisha:

"Have your cards ready . . . your cards ready."

Now we began working with great rapidity. A bandage in the groin. *Adonis vernalis*. Mercuric ointment against swelling. Digitalis, just for the bed patients. Bandages of all sizes. *Ung.Hydr.Prec.Albi.* Instead of iodine, gruen. Sometimes sulfa. Seldom the hospital. Frost bites. Rotting fingers, noses. The enema. Injections. "Go on, pull your pants down!" meanwhile, two dressings. The medical assistants were boiling the syringes. Careful, an intravenous shot. Lucky he had a vein. I could find it easily. Bandage up a head. The bodies stink. Sweat. Again an enema. That one over there thought it was oral medicine. "Down with your pants!" He looked at me astonished. Wondering what I'd do to him. Simultaneously I put a dressing on an elbow. An elbow and a knee. It had to stay on. Throughout the whole working day. That one for the enema had to be taught the right position—on his side, knees bent. Slow pulse. I wound up the clock. A woman rushed in, screaming. Clutching her belly. With Vanya behind her. The woman continued screaming. I bandaged a foot. There were many sore feet. Still screaming. Vanya wanted cotton. I said—"Wait." But no, Vanya wanted it now. Bismal for diarrhea. Nothing helped. I recognized the handwriting of Anna—the doctor. She dismissed men readily. I gave him rivanol. *Ferrum pomatum.* The favorite drink of the sick and the healthy. By now we were walking over dirty bandages. Everything stank of puss, more and more. I took a suppository out of a carbuncle. *Parametritis.* I sent him to the venerologist. Toward the end you wound up feeling somewhat drugged. The carbuncle was large, the size of a man's palm. I poured in iodine. He jumped up and down, hissing. But the behind was bandaged beautifully. Next. The visibility was growing worse and worse, and so was the stench. Grisha vomited. And thus it went for three, four, five hours.

Meanwhile I spotted an elderly gentleman, dressed with utmost care. He was waiting. He wondered if he could have some suppositories and if I would like to come and visit him. Today. Barracks No. 226. He spoke Russian a little differently than the rest. Probably better. As he was leaving:

"I do hope you will have tea with me later today. I assure you it is good tea."

He picked up his immaculately clean little pan. He bowed. What an extraordinary thing to do! But then a needy behind covered him from my view. I made a note not to forget him. The lamps were switched on. I felt my hands making complicated movements. Precise movements. The dispensary was filled with fumes and terrible smells. I could have lain down on top of the bandages and slept. Ah, to sleep. I had no strength left, not even for those who were covered with sores, swollen, stinking. Not even for their torn, yellow bodies. Another, and another, and still another. Finally Vanya shut the door and said:

"Enough."

Grisha threw himself on the couch. I said:

"Move over."

But I could not sleep. I was thinking. Of how it used to be in the forest camp. Incomparably worse than here. And yet. . . . Men would go behind the latrines to pick up herring heads. And suck them. You could not enter the little hospital. The six with phlegmon stank so much. There was no sulfa. Men looked like barrels, with their arms and legs swollen up. Like elephantiasis. And yet. . . . Especially in the autumn. I fell into a hole in the marshy forest.

The dogs found me. I had lost my direction. Almost drowned in mud. Then the cold weather came. I picked the fruit of wild roses. It was sweet. I worried that I may forget my name. I wrote it down on a piece of birch tree bark. But first I asked several men who knew me: "What is my name?" Their answers agreed. All except one. I carried the piece of bark around with me. People were drinking salt water by the litres. They swelled up and were dismissed from work. But they died often. From acute inflammation of the kidneys. Now again it was time to get up. I went over to barracks 226. The little man lived upstairs. He saw me.

"One moment. I cannot see you just yet. I have to put on my dark suit."

And he proceeded to change, from a gray suit, held together with string, into a dark suit. The dark suit was very old. The little man looked about sixty and in his behavior you could sense a certain originality. He introduced himself:

"I am Igor Aleksandrovich Yasenin."

Then he invited me to join him on the upper bunk. He had prepared biscuits with cheese. He hurried down for some hot water. He made tea. Then he began hunting through the pockets of his dark suit (which turned out to be a tuxedo) and came up with a little photo:

"This is my mother."

"Where is she living?"

"In Leningrad."

"She is still living?"

A shocked expression—the terrible thought that she could be dead.

"Oh yes, yes, praised be the good Lord."

Then a sudden switch:

"I never had a woman in all my life. I've read *Death in Venice*. That's the last book I was able to obtain. Vasily, the young fellow from the hospital, had betrayed me. Yes, I remember . . . I remember, we were in the bathhouse together. What a beautiful body. He wasn't a doctor's assistant then. Only later, with my help. An intelligent boy. A school graduate."

"In what language did you read. . . ."

"In German. I also know French. We talk in German."

"What do you do around here?"

"I get food at the hospital, in the summer I tend to the garden.

Nothing else. But now there's to be a new camp director. That means there'll be hard times for me. Because he doesn't know me."

A pause.

"Listen, my boy. . . . Could . . . could you find me someone? Maybe yourself?"

I shook my head.

"How about the others?"

"I'll try."

"Please, please do. I never had a woman in all my life."

Then he began telling stories about the First World War, receptions at Countess Cherkalskaya's. . . . It seemed that there was a young boy there who played the piano, the Countess's son.

"He played in Poland too, I think. . . ."

"Yes??"

He became lost in thought.

"Well, I must be going," I said. "I am on nightshift. By the way, do you think it would be possible to deform the situation in Russia?"

He thought a moment.

"No."

Another pause.

"No. No. I know what you have in mind. Something, like Kafka. I cannot imagine it. This is a make-believe country. You can deform only that which exists. What is make-believe cannot be deformed."

"And do you exist?"

"From a scientific point of view—no. From a point of view of 'common sense'—not much, no more than an outline of a shadow. All these people," he made a sweeping gesture with his hand, "do not realize how little they exist. . . ."

A pause.

"And why do you ask?"

"Some day, when I'm free. . . ."

He shrugged his shoulders.

"I'll tell you a story. I used to work up north, preparing statistics. I would receive telephone calls: that such and such section of the railroad has been completed. I prepared reports, and on the basis of these reports we would obtain building supplies. Once, an inspection team arrived from Moscow. They checked the camps. It was discovered that, at twenty different points, for one year nothing at all had been done. That there was no railroad, just tundra, and in the tundra—camps with people who had been sleeping the entire year. . . ."

"I really must be going."

"Good night, then. Please remember my request."

I slipped down off the bunk. On the lower bunk sat a man to whom Igor Aleksandrovich, leaning down, said: "Good evening, sir."

I left the barracks.

* * *

Evening. The wind again was blowing from the Volga. Maybe it would quiet down the next day. People were running in all directions. You could not see their faces. They huddled. They fought against the cold. A losing battle. On the run, they rubbed their noses, cheeks. Stuffed rags all over themselves. Except over the eyes, for fear they might fall.

The closer came the hour of leaving for work, the more alone you became. Locked in with your own destiny. Face to face. You walked outside, as though in a glass ball. If you fell, no one would help you. You too would not help anyone. You had no strength to spare.

I stopped at the latrines. Living men steamed. They were trying to keep their bottoms from freezing. Not always successfully. Shoemakers worked day and night. Tailors too. Laborers stood at roll-call. In formation of fours. Wrong count. They stood from two to three hours. Finally the sick man who had fallen down in the latrine was being carried out. The invalids sold oranges for a slice of bread. The Uzbeks. They received packages. Everyone walked rapidly. From one barrack to another. As rapidly as possible. Some made occasional stops. A labor unit was going to the bathhouse. I decided not to see the police chief that day. He had his own room where he brought women. I was to give him a pair of civilian pants. Brought over from Poland. Then I gave up meeting with the camp director. The barracks were swaying before my eyes. I could see the bright lights of the dispensary. That night I had to work.

Grisha was asleep, Vanya was asleep, Petya was asleep. I too wanted to sleep, even for a quarter of an hour. The orderlies were cleaning up and swallowing vitamin pills. I paid no attention. Olga had gone home. Buehler was still there. The venerologist was still examining the women. I dropped off for a few minutes into a nervous sleep. Then a patient walked in—he had a fever. I dismissed him from work. But first I wrote it down in a book. I added a few degrees, to make it look better. Another man walked in. Fever. A third, a fourth, twentieth, sixty-first—all had a slight fever. Finally I told them to strip naked. I stuck thermometers in, at random: the mouth, the armpit, the anus. Some were faking. A local inflammation of the mouth, and there's fever. Or the anus. Or the armpit. I examined the spots. These men had friends at the hospital: milk injections. A sore, smelling of kerosene. A sore that never healed. I dismissed 167 patients. As never before. It was almost eight o'clock. I locked the doors. Only emergency cases. My book went to Buehler. All was well. At eleven Vanya, Grisha, and Petya woke up. The orderlies had gone to bed.

Vanya stretched himself and said:

"How about a little something to drink? Petya?"

"Yes, but what?"

"Denatured alcohol, naturally. Only we must drain it a little."

"Start draining."

"Right away."

But he didn't move.

"And how about a little snack to push it down with?"

"A good idea."

"Well then? . . ."

"Grisha, off to the kitchen with you!"

"I have fever."

"Don't give me that, pal. Go on. And you, Petya, start draining. We should fix five drains. Though, I can drink mine undrained."

No one was moving.

He screamed:

"I'm going to knock your teeth out, you sons of bitches, I'll have you hanged. . . ."

This was no laughing matter. Petya started working on the drains. Grisha hurried to the kitchen.

"And you—you come here to me."

This was spoken in my direction. His voice had quite a different tone, it was almost caressing:

"What's the news from Natya?"

"Nothing much. She sends her greetings. And she says she'll not be coming here any more."

A moment's silence. Total silence. I said:

"Here are your felt boots."

"I won't be needing them. But your coat, the blue one, will you lend it to me?"

"Yes."

"Yes."

"That's fine then."

He closed his eyes. Making believe he was sleeping. One minute, two, three. Finally:

"What a whore."

He no longer pretended. He was staring at the ceiling. Petya silently drained the alcohol. Through five drains. Time dragged. Grisha came back.

"It'll be ready in half an hour."

The alcohol made a drip, drip sound. No one was saying anything. Vanya stared at the ceiling. As if trying to find something up there. Vanya:

"How much?"

From the other room:

"Almost three quarts."

Again silence. Grisha came in. Carrying potato cakes and canned meats. We all jumped up. Raised our glasses. Proceeded to eat out of the frying pan. To drink the pure alcohol. You had to know how to drink pure alcohol. It wasn't easy. Before swallowing you had to take a deep breath. Vanya drank, something terrible. Straight from the glass. And stuffed himself with food. The rest of us also stuffed ourselves. Vanya turned to me:

"What a pity you're a Jew."

Then he continued eating.

"Aleksey, a non-Jew, is a pig. Stepan, a non-Jew, is a son-of-a-bitch, Seroza, a non-Jew, also a pig, Kossovsky, a non-Jew, another pig, so many, many pigs."

He went on eating. Vanya, drunkenly affectionate:

"And you are a Jew. A Jew, think of it, my God. . . ."

He shook his head to and fro and sighed. Petya, too, felt frank as a result of the alcohol:

"Once I finished off a Kike Yid. . . ."

"Shut up. You know he's a Jew, a little bit. Anyway, who cares. Will you lend me your blue coat?"

"Yes, I told you."

"I'm going over to the women's section. . . ."

"It's closed at night," said Grisha.

"I don't care, I'll climb over the fence."

"It's very high."

"I can do it. Anyway, it's none of your business!"

He went on eating, washing it down with alcohol. Vanya:

"Let me have some ether, man. Not from valerian, pure ether."

Grisha got up, handed him a large bottle. Vanya inhaled with pleasure. Then he drank some more. Suddenly he stood up.

"Am I walking all right?"

"Just fine. But the militia'll lock you up, no question about it."

"I'm putting the blue coat on, and I'm off. Going straight for that fence."

Aside, Grisha showed us with his finger that Vanya had gone mad. Vanya went on mumbling to himself:

"I'll tell her, I'll talk to her, I'll cuddle her up."

A smile was fluttering across his broad face. He put my coat on. Repeating the last words:

". . . I'll cuddle her up. . . ."

He disappeared. I said:

"That's it. Now, off to sleep, children."

* * *

Two o'clock, three, four. At four Olga walked in, together with the head regional doctor and two men from the NKVD. Olga turned to me:

"How many people have you dismissed from work?"

"One hundred and sixty seven."

"You didn't know about the typhoid shots?"

"No."

Olga was saying something to the NKVD men. One of them:

"Let's see, then."

Consequently I had to shuffle along to all the barracks where the dismissed men slept. Olga brought several thermometers. The men's temperature was much higher now. This was what saved me. . . . And Olga, too. The second man, the quiet one, mumbled something about sabotage. Then they went into Olga's office. They sent for some alcohol. I thought to myself: All's well.

The head regional doctor said, turning to me:

"A fever after typhoid shots is not an illness. You had no right to dismiss them."

And he left. Olga also went to bed. But before she went she was a bit difficult. I had to wake up Petya and ask him to take over. I ended up whistling pop tunes in her soundproof office, striking up the rhythm with my palms, my fingers. Then she was no longer difficult. She said:

"They almost got me. And they'd have been right. And it would've been because of you. Now, go away."

She lay down on top of her desk and fell asleep. But I did not sleep. I was lying on the floor, like Vanya, with my eyes wide open. And I was thinking. I thought, among other things, about how I would visit Olga in the women's sector of the camp. And about Vanya going there, over the barbed wire fence. And so on.

* * *

I did not find Vanya during my visit at the jail. Perhaps he had fallen asleep somewhere, in his drunken stupor. Perhaps Natya had cuddled him up. Or perhaps he went up to heaven, since he really existed so very little.

A parade in the dark. Some electrical connections had broken. You could see nothing but the marchers' silhouettes. They seemed to rise as they moved away from the gate. The power plant glittered brightly. It possessed all the attributes of the divine. It even drowned 50,000 people when the dam broke. Pray for us! Forgive us! Forgive us, as we do not forgive our trespassers! The hour of death is very near. Huuu!

Translated by Barbara Vedder

Józef Mackiewicz

Contra

THERE are two truths. The first circles the earth and faithfully reflects in the water clouds floating overhead. It sends back an echo in a canyon. It records accurately the rustling of trees and reeds by the lakeshore. It knows where to place every stone in a shallow brook and why it sounds like a perpetual splash. That truth hears the tiniest buzz of an insect and the flimsiest of human words. But it never smiles, not even when shining sun rays through apple blossoms in the spring. Neither does it scowl with anger when it rolls up thunderclouds and drives them over flat fields announcing a storm. It displays neither love nor hatred. It does not mock anything, for nothing on this earth strikes it as funny. It does not beat its breast over anything, for it deems nothing worthy of it. It neither changes nor reforms anything. Whoever killed a fly did so. Whoever killed a man did so. It is completely indifferent, because it is completely objective. It is total truth, the natural one.

Its only supernatural feature might be discarded in a mystery, yet unsolved: How, and above all why, did it give birth, in the same woods and prairies, cities and fields, on earth, water, and in the air, to the second truth?

The second truth appears to consist only of good and evil. But to take its word for it might be misleading. Its good and evil are relative values. This truth is never at rest, so that it seldom offers a clear reflection of things. That is why it smiles or scowls so often. Constantly on the move, it can hardly keep up with the rush of human words and gestures. It claims to record them as accurately as the first truth, but it actually only tries to adjust them to its relative aims, changing many things in its haste. One might think that it is like the morning mist that will be dispelled by the first rays of the sun or by a breath of breeze. But it is not so. It stays on the surface, desperately clutching at scraps of the first truth. Spreading over the land, it swears its oath on the same woods, fields, and springs; it calls for witness a bird's song, a speared cat's scream, or man's blood, skilfully pleading before the court of human imagination; yet always to the exclusion of other witnesses. . . . That second truth performs, lifts its arms to heaven, curses the rain and the wind. It promises the sky. It seldom keeps its pledge.

The first of the two truths is silent, the second persuasive. The first is calm, the other passionate. Knowing itself not alone, it loudly claims to be the only one, therefore binding and valid. And it is to some extent right there, because it is an official truth, dependent on the regime under which it operates. It might be briefly described as the truth of partisan interpretation of facts.

* * *

In the last century, at a time when the matter began to be widely discussed in Western Europe, that is, between the years 1823 and 1877, the tsarist Russian government deported to Siberia over a period of 55 years 598,000 persons.

* * *

After the overthrow of the tsarist government, the Council of People's Commissars, acting under the personal instructions of Lenin, promulgated on December 20, 1917 the decree establishing the *Special Committee Against Counter-Revolution and Speculation*, commonly known by the abbreviation CHEKA.

On April 15, 1919, the All-Russia Central Executive Committee published the first decree on the establishment of *Camps of Forced Labor*, further elaborated in detail by the decree of May 17, 1919, signed by the chairman of the All-Russia Executive, Avanesov. Ninety-seven concentration camps were set up at first.

On February 6, 1922, at the Ninth Session of the Supreme Soviet, the CHEKA was renamed *Special State Political Office*, abbreviation OGPU.

Under the decree of July 10, 1934, the OGPU (under the name of *Chief Office of State Security*), became a part of the Commissariat of Internal Affairs—NKVD. At the same time, as a means of assisting the campaign against counter-revolution, the government created the *Osoboye Soveshchannye* (sentencing teams), empowered to hand down administrative verdicts. In the period before the Second World War, these "O.S." teams sentenced to death or to concentration camp over twenty-two million people.

The number of concentration camps passed 200, with many of them divided into sub-camps, called *Lagpunkt*. That number included such giants as Kolyma, with about three million convicts.

In the course of the twenty-two years between the Revolution and the Second World War about forty million persons lost their lives in the Civil War, by execution, by starvation during the forced collectivization, or as inmates of concentration camps.

* * *

The rotting roofs of the huts in *Lagpunkt 244/16/9* and the guard towers at the corners, with their soldiers, were bathed in warm sunshine. It glittered on the rusty barbed wire, tawny like the stems of dried up weeds in the fall. The western slopes of the Urals were swept by a dry wind, swaying the tufted peaks of the pine trees and the sharp spires of the firs. But the sky was still deep blue and the wind brought no clouds. It only sang in the treetops. Mountain rocks gleamed with granite sparkle.

Other waves were also coming from the west, invisible radio waves. Viacheslav Mikhailovich Molotov, People's Commissar for Foreign Affairs of the Soviet Union was speaking. He announced the outbreak of the war. The wall calendar in the camp office read: June 22, 1941.

For how long was the news awaited? Was it from the first complications after September 1, 1939? Or from the entry of the western powers into the war? From the time of the war in Finland? Or from which of the futile, silly rumors born every day, every week, every month? Or perhaps always over the past twenty-four years?

Nothing is lost in nature. Forces accumulated over years of silent waiting now broke out with redoubled energy. It was something the camp authorities never expected: among the most crushed, beaten, corrupted, depraved men—in that mass of barely staggering informers, ever ready to sell one another for a can of mouldy cabbage soup or a crust of clay-like bread—there was stirring. Slogans were scrawled on walls and fences: "Hitler will save us!" "The Germans will finish the Bolshevik regime!" "Don't oppose the war!"

It is hard; it is very difficult to grasp it today, after so many years of cursing war and branding as criminal anyone advocating it. . . . Oh, how difficult it is to recall the truth of the boundless joy that the word "War!" evoked over the vast spaces of the Union of Soviet Socialist Republics, from the Niemen to the mouth of the Amur, from Murmansk to Mount Ararat!—War! Have you heard: war! What incredible luck! Not only in prisons, camps, solitary cells, and dungeons. In cities and kolkhozes people stood staring westward at the approaching war, as though expecting from it a miracle. After twenty-four years of slavery they waited for liberation. After twenty-four years of bolshevism they waited for its end. It did not matter who did it: good or bad, from the left or the right. It could be Hitler or Churchill, so long as he was the first to say the magic word: "War."

Some built triumphal arches. They picked flowers in the fields. They greeted the victors with bread and salt. Not Germans, Englishmen, Frenchmen, Japanese, or Negroes. . . . They greeted war!

On the very next day, on June 23, walls were covered with words scribbled with chalk or charcoal: "Down with Soviet rule!" "Death to Stalin!" "Long live freedom!" The authorities responded immediately. Officers of the Third operating department of the KGB arrested everyone found in possession of a piece of chalk, charcoal, or pencil. Later everyone on whose clothes they could find the slightest trace of chalk, charcoal, or lime. There were mass executions in the camps, as in 1937 and 1938. But these measures and the piles of informers' reports in the security offices did not change anything. Scrawled slogans continued to appear. At the same time about one out of three prisoners submitted a petition for his release, on the ground that: "his greatest desire is to go to the front, to fight for the Party, for Russia and our beloved leader Stalin." But already in August 1941 a circular instruction prohibited further releases for military service, as it was found that the prisoners took the first opportunity for passing over to the enemy.

That was what experienced NKVD and NKGB officials had expected from the beginning. That is why, on the very first day of the war, an order was issued to "liquidate" the prisoners in those camps in western Russia which could not be evacuated in time. That is why in June and July 1941 prisoners in Provenishki in Lithuania, in Budslav, Vileyka, Lvov, Minsk, Kiev, and many other places were massacred.

* * *

Scrawls on fences, crude leaflets, and appeals for the overthrow of the Bolshevik regime appeared all over the country. Most of them were not printed, but written by hand in large numbers.

In the meantime the German armies pushed ahead and in October they took Mozhaysk. On October 16, riots broke out in Moscow. Mobs ran wild in the streets, breaking into state shops and factories. The special store for privileged senior officials, the *Select* on Sadova street was looted, and then the *Prodmag* store for ordinary citizens. Storefronts and doors were broken on Tverska, Myasnitska, Pokrovtse, Maroseyka streets. Cobblestones and bricks were flying. Some fires broke out. Black smoke mixed with clouds of dust hovered between the houses over the aroused crowd.

—*Gromi! Gromiii! Uraaa!* . . .

Cars with escaping dignitaries, high party officials, and their goods were stopped on the outskirts of the city. Everything that they tried to take away was looted. Such checkpoints were nicknamed "Get off and give" stations.

"Get out! You've fattened up enough on our blood!—and the party bosses, omnipotent until now, meekly climbed out, glad to escape with their lives.

Party and Komsomol members remaining in the city hastily burned their identity cards, tore up documents, and tossed Marxist literature out of the windows. The wind carried the papers over the streets. People trod over covers with pictures of Lenin and Stalin. Official posters were torn down, official portraits trampled.

But it was a revolution without organization and without a leader. General Silinov, commander of the Moscow garrison, was summoned personally by Stalin and ordered to crush the riots at any price. He threw into the city special NKVD units with automatic weapons. On October 17, they wiped out any opposition. On October 18, order was restored in Moscow. Workers swept with big brooms piles of Communist literature, torn and mixed with broken glass, and party card covers trampled in the mud.

It was a revolution without a leader and without organization. The Red armies, fighting resolutely in some sectors, did not display on the whole much resistance or spirit. The number of men taken prisoner grew with amazing speed. On October 10, in the Bialystok-Minsk trap alone, 323,898 were taken. By the end of the month the total reached 895,000. At the beginning of August 600,000 surrendered near Human. By the end of the battle of the Ukraine

665,000 were prisoners of war. In October, in the battle of Azov, the Germans took 100,000 men. The operation concluded on October 17, in the Vyazma-Bryansk region, resulted in the surrender of 67 Soviet infantry divisions, 6 cavalry divisions, as well as 7 armored divisions and 6 brigades. These were figures without parallel in the history of war, for such a short period.

There appeared a special type of Soviet soldier, nicknamed *nurik* (diver) just after a few weeks of the war. He dived by throwing down his arms, submerging in the Russian space and crowd, to emerge only after the Germans occupied the area, with the thought of waiting out the war—until the destruction of the Bolshevik system. Such an inactive mass is a psychologically normal occurrence in upheavals lacking any leadership, or any definite purpose or idea. This does not mean that anti-Soviet attitudes were not strong at the time, but simply that they were amorphous in character.

The anti-Soviet counter-revolution in the years 1941–44 was a typically grass roots movement. The revolution of 1917 was planned by the Russian intelligentsia, and the Bolshevik take-over was achieved by Lenin's organizing talent and iron will, following the pattern of all revolutions inspired from the top by an intellectual élite and then imposed on the masses. The wartime counter-revolution in Russia did not follow that pattern.

It was an authentic revolt of the masses, without the pictures and biographies of leaders to be inserted in future textbooks. Paradoxically, the anti-Bolshevik counter-revolution of these years conformed to the Marxist philosophy of history, according to which mass movements start at the bottom. Its history was simply the story of countless thousands of small people.

Even at that time it was said: "If only Hitler produced some constructive, positive political idea. . . ." But he did not even need to do that to overthrow the Bolshevik regime. Not stifling every budding attempt at the organization of a movement, and not using methods and a policy that deprived it of any hope of success would have sufficed.

* * *

Bishop Polikarp of Włodzimierz in Volhynia, and the orthodox archbishops and bishops of Lithuania, Kiev, Narva, and Mitau addressed a letter to Hitler in which they assured him that they would pray to the Almighty asking him to grant victory to those who took up the heroic struggle against the Bolsheviks.

General von Manstein, the conqueror of the Crimea, received a delegation of Tartars, who presented to him gifts of precious tapestries for "our liberator, Adolf Effendi."

The Caucasian tribes of Kabardins and Balkars handed to the former German consul, Captain Brautigam, a finely chiselled set of horse reins encrusted with solid gold, asking him to transmit their gift to Hitler as a token of their gratitude for liberation.

And so on, and so on. . . .

* * *

Shortly before the start of the campaign against Russia, on April 24, 1941, Hitler summoned his minister Alfred Rosenberg and told him: "Goering is preparing a four-year plan for the territories we are to conquer in the East. All the raw materials will be immediately supplied to Germany. As to the police side, I leave it to Himmler, who has a strong hand."

On May 9, 1941, Hitler said: "I am not interested in these wild Caucasian nations. All I care about is their oil." On June 22, 1941, the secretary of state at the Ministry of Food in Berlin, Mr. Backe, is reported to have said: "The kolkhozes will be kept. If they had not been invented by the Soviets, we would have had to invent them for exploiting the East."

On September 1, 1941, the newly appointed Reichs Commissioner for the Ukraine, Erich Koch, stated: "The Ukrainians are the original Slavs. I will rule them with vodka, tobacco, and the whip."

According to unofficial reports from the Soviet prisoner of war camp near Częstochowa, only two thousand out of the thirty thousand Turkmens survived. The rest were machine-gunned by the S.D. Einsatzkommando as "superfluous Asians."

The reign of the Commissioner for the Ukraine Koch, who reported directly to Hitler, soon became so favorable to Soviet interests that the following story gained currency in German military circles: "When Stalin was handing out decorations at the Kremlin in the winter of 1942–43, he put the first medal aside and said: I cannot give this highest decoration today, because it has been earned by Reichs Commissioner Erich Koch, who is now performing his duties in the service of the Soviet Union in the Ukraine."

As a result the Ukrainians, in accordance with a previous resolution of their organization OUN, took up a struggle on two fronts: against the Germans as well as the Bolsheviks. It grew in intensity in 1942 and 1943, and the camps of Sachsenhausen and Auschwitz, the prisons of Lvov, Cracow, Berlin, and Vienna saw an increasing number of Ukrainian inmates.

A soldiers' newspaper published in the field in the sector of General von Bock's command, *Der Durchbruch*, had in its issue of July, 1941, a story called "The Well," in which we read: "Thirsty, we seek out a well. People beyond the Bug river greet us as if we were their allies. They don't understand that we do not need their alliance. All we need is their well."

Adolf Hitler extended his "Untermensch" theory to all people living east of the Warta and Niemen rivers. He had a particular aversion to Slavs. All the eastern territories were eventually to become German colonies, and the natives were to be treated no better than Negroes in Africa.

That is why whenever local German commanders formed anti-Soviet units they did so on their own initiative and mostly without the knowledge of the headquarters. This restriction made it impossible to carry out any broader recruiting among the population.

Among the various ethnic groups and anti-Soviet émigrés there were, of course, many individuals or cliques of opportunists who tried—as they always do in the midst of wars and upheavals—to turn the situation to their advantage by organizing various national fascist movements, by outdoing each other in anti-Semitism, and by seeking favor in every way through accommodations with the Nazi program. All such attempts, treated by the Germans with condescension or open contempt, produced no more than minor puppet agencies, and achieved no significant results.

Thus, while in the earlier stages the majority of Soviet citizens waited for a rallying signal to start a joint battle against the Communist regime, later they became deeply divided by a split among the peoples under the rule of Moscow. Some were compelled by Hitler's policies to take up guerrilla warfare against the Germans, others fought against the Red armies. Partisans confronted anti-partisans. The vast area occupied by the invaders, from the gulf of

Finland to the Caucasian peaks, became the theatre of a second civil war.

It differed from the first civil war in having a unified command and an organization only on one side—the Communist one. If any leader had appeared on the other side, he would soon have found himself in Dachau or liquidated on Hitler's order.

It may never be possible to establish accurately the date of the formation of the first anti-Soviet armed units of the local population in the vast spaces of Russia during the Second World War. One of the earliest might have been the volunteer battalion near Bryansk. The six Cossack "sotnias" mustered in Mohylev under the command of the former Red Army major, Kononov, might claim priority. All over the area at the rear of the German armies, in the regions where parachutists dropped at the order of Moscow organized guerrilla warfare, anti-Communist bands were formed spontaneously by the local people.

On both banks of the Don, Cossacks suddenly appeared, as if rising from the steppes, men who had been in hiding to avoid the Red Army draft. Some old weapons and even old uniforms were dug up from ancient caches. Whole units of Cossack cavalry passed from the Soviet to the German side. Some aging veterans of the Civil War emerged from their hideouts. Clergymen of all denominations donned the vestments of their creed, and solemn services were held in all the churches. The former Cossack ataman Kulakov and the hero of the Civil War, General Shkuro, surfaced amongst the Cossacks. A provisional staging camp was formed in Voyenstroy-Seleshchina and Cossacks flocked there—singly, in groups, and in whole armed formations. A political organization was established under the name of the Cossack National Liberation Command.

The Kalmuks formed sixteen autonomous cavalry squadrons. Stavropol, Terek, and Kuban Cossacks, Circassians, Karachays, Balkars, Osetynians, Dagestanians, Karabdynians, Ingusians, Chechens, Azerbedjanians, and Georgians took up arms, waiting for some proclamation, some Great Charter, calling them to a holy war against the Bolsheviks.

But no Great Charter was forthcoming. No one posted any proclamations in the towns, the villages, the kolkhozes, hamlets, and scattered settlements of the steppes.

All they got was some lukewarm promises from embarrassed local German commanders. Some officers, acting on their own authority, tried timidly to establish some sort of military organization in their respective areas, but that was all.

No one knew which way to turn, what to expect.

* * *

In 1944 the German front was breaking and crumbling. Pierced simultaneously in several places, it folded back and retreated, despite Hitler's maniacal and repeated orders to hold the ground to the last man. The impact of these reverses caused many changes. One of them was a change of views on the "Untermensch" theory of its former enthusiastic proponent, the second most powerful man in the country, Heinrich Himmler. As a result, some military circles, hitherto fruitlessly trying to revise Hitler's eastern policy, were permitted to institute at least some half measures. These included the activation of the Vlasov movement. But it all came much too late....

On March 31, 1944, cavalry general Kostring signed an order permitting the establishment of a Chief Headquarters of Cossack Forces. General Pyotr Krasnov was appointed its commander. Members of his staff included General Naumenko, Colonel Pavlov, and Colonel Kulakov. The Cossacks were placed under the direct orders of these headquarters.

On June 17, ataman Pavlov was shot dead while carrying out a night inspection of his outposts, either by his own overeager guards, or by Soviet partisans. General Krasnov replaced him with Colonel Domanov, later promoted general major. It was he who led the Cossacks from the Niemen region, in which they had camped for several months.

There was only one way left: it was the only still open road of the migration of eastern tribes to the West.

* * *

On February 8 of the same year, 1945, in a Crimean palace which used to belong to Nicholas II, a cousin of His Britannic Majesty, Emperor of India, Defender of the Faith, George VI, His Majesty's First Minister, Winston Churchill, rose to offer this toast:

> It will be no exaggeration or flowery compliment when I say that we regard Stalin's life as most precious for our hopes and our hearts. . . . I devoutly hope that the Marshal will be spared for the Soviet Union's

sake and to help us to march forward toward times better than those we have lived through recently. Personally, I walk with more confidence and faith in the knowledge that I have the friendship of this great man, whose fame spreads to-day not only through Russia, but the entire globe. . . .[1]

* * *

1945. It was springtime. The last spring of the Second World War. It was a different spring, unlike any that the Cossacks ever saw before. There were chestnut trees instead of maples, lilacs instead of scrub pine, slim cypresses instead of willows. It was a spring without melting snow which leaves huge, deep puddles. Spring under southern skies, in mountains where cacti and agavas grew in cracks between the rocks; pelargonias were budding on the walls of the narrow streets. The air was thin and that is perhaps why one missed the heady fragrance of spring in the steppes.

The Italian population had no end of gripes and complaints. Italy has not seen such a strange invasion since the times of the great migrations.

According to a census taken as early as September 1944, 15,590 persons came to the region of Tolmezzo, including 7,155 armed men under ataman Domanov.

Exiles from various Eastern European countries flocked to northern Italy. In Vienna, bombed daily by the Allies, crowded with refugees and a mass of slave workers deported by the Germans, there were smart operators selling forged travel documents. Such a "Cossack" indentity card cost about 3,000 marks and was helpful in escaping across the Alps. According to some estimates, the number of refugees who kept close to the Cossack force in Italy, though they had nothing in common with Cossacks, exceeded 25,000. They all wanted food, shelter, life. Separately from this main concentration, regiments of the 162nd Turkmen-Azerbedjan division were camping along the river Po, mainly in the Riccione-Ravenna sector, later around Rimini. The Russian regiment "Varyag" and other formations were also there.

The Caucasian Corps, under Sultan Kelech Girey, camped in the mountains near Paluzzo. Kuban Cossacks under Colonel Lu-

1 This is not the original wording of Churchill's toast, but rather is a retranslation into English of Mackiewicz's translation into Polish. [Editor's note]

kanienko were settled around Covazzo. The Don Cossacks were quartered in Olesso, changed its name provisionally to "Novocherkask" and even put up some new street signs. Domanov's staff headquarters were in Tolmezzo, where he was joined in February by General Krasnov, with his wife Lydia Fyodorovna. Some regiments were moved southward, to the Adriatic shore. A newspaper called *Kazatskaya Zemlya* (Cossack Land) started publication. But it was not a "Cossack land"! It was an alien land, alien in creed, nationality, temperament, food, and drink, and most of all in current political atmosphere. Most of the Alpine mountain regions were held at the time by Italian partisans, all the way from Genoa and the French Alpes Maritimes, through Torino, Como, and the Dolomites eastward. It was a very bizarre situation, perhaps something of a paradigm of the entire war reflected in a small mirror. The partisans received weapons, ammunition, and military instructors from the British; but their leaflets, political slogans, and agitators were supplied from Russia. The partisans were at least 60 per cent communist; fighting against the Germans, they opposed with equal vigor the fascists of the short-lived republic of Mussolini, as well as the supporters of Italian monarchy. The scarce Italian national flags among the mass of red ones had gaping holes in the middle, where the crest of the House of Savoy had been cut out. There was, however, an alliance between the Communists and the Catholics. The "red shirts" fraternized with the less numerous "blue shirts" of the Catholic organizations. Marshal Timoshenko's son, who escaped from a German prisoners' camp, marched side by side with a "Don Camillo" priest. The slogans scrawled at night on street corners read: "Viva il Papa!" and "Viva Stalin."

The political fashion of the time required of the partisans in the hills admiration for everything connected with communism, with distant Russia, the "victorious East," and Soviet "liberation." In the meantime, strange things were happening: down in the valleys, in the familiar towns and villages, one could see the bearded, Russian-speaking "East," carrying the Orthodox slanted cross and professing hatred for communism in any form or shape.

Both sides stared at each other in utter amazement: "So this is the Christian West, our only bulwark and defense against Bolshevik oppression?" . . . wondered Cossacks and non-Cossacks at the sight of the red-shirted partisans with machine-gun ammunition belts slung over their shoulders in the style of the 1917 revolution.

"So this is the real "East," blessed by the best and most just regime in the world? . . . whispered the men of the partisan general Fenulli and the supporters of the great Ercole-Ercoli.

This was the pseudonym used by the Communist leader Togliatti, who returned from Moscow with instructions not to form separate Communist military units, but to merge them in a general "Comitato di Liberazione Nazionale," in accordance with a "popular front" strategy, calculated to assist a future take-over of the whole country. Propaganda guidelines were also established, to counteract the disillusionment that might result from contact with the anti-Bolshevik East.

The Italians, never very strong in geography, were easily convinced that anyone coming from across the Alps and speaking some foreign language must be "Tedeschi"—German. American tanks crushed in the encounter near Via Aurelia some Turkoman detachments, and the rumor went round that they were Japanese. Russian deserters of Cossacks captured by the partisans naturally swore by everything that is holy that they had been forcibly deported and drafted by the Germans. Anyone would do the same to save his life. Thus the confrontation was more or less patched up, according to a contrived version of the truth. Because no one had any interest in contradicting it at the time, nor any means or opportunity for doing so, it became part of official history.

The Cossacks, on their side, had to find their own answers to some harassing questions. No one believed any more the Nazi propaganda about a "Jewish plutocratic bolshevik conspiracy." There had been too many disappointments, too much bitterness. One generally listened silently to comforting explanations to the effect that these were just temporary Allied tactics, that the West was really opposed to the Bolsheviks. They nodded their heads, trying to believe. Some efforts were made to cover up with an external front the gnawing doubts, the ever-present uncertainty threatening to turn into despair. Every morning the mountain slopes of Covazzo echoed the sounds of fifes and choir: "Oh, Kuban, our own land!" Icons of Saint Nicholas the Miracle Worker and the Madonna of Kuban were placed in a local church.

General Fetisov, who was later the ataman of the Cossack camps, planned sowing Italian fields in the spring and pondered where to get seed. . . . But these plans never matured.

It all started toward the end of April, when British aircraft suddenly bombed Olesso—"Novocherkask."

* * *

On April 9 the British Eighth Army opened the offensive, joined on April 14 by the U.S. Fifth Army. They threw the enemy back along the entire front and took Bologna. On the 21st the German defense collapsed all down the line. On the 28th Mussolini was murdered in Dongo on Lake Como. On the same day SS Obergruppenführer Karl Wolff, who had been negotiating secretly for a long time with Allen Dulles, the OSS chief in Switzerland, went to the Allied headquarters in Caserta. On the following day he signed the act of surrender of all the German forces in Italy, with the authorization of the commander-in-chief of the Group C of German forces, General Baron von Vietinghoff.

On the same day, at 9 A.M., General Pyotr Krasnov came with a heavy step into ataman Domanov's room in his Tolmezzo headquarters and told him he wanted to speak to him in private.

* * *

The 8th Battalion, Argyll and Sutherland Highlanders, had a long and distinguished record in the last war, notably in the battle of Tunis. In March 1945 the 78th division, which belonged to the 8th Army, was charged with the difficult task of crossing the river Senio, fortified and firmly held by the enemy, and then the Santerno; then it was to press on toward Ferrara and the river Po. The commanding officer of the 8th Battalion, Lt. Col. Malcolm, went on leave to England about that time, leaving in command Major Leask, a tough and efficient soldier. After crossing the Senio, he reached within twelve days, in the second half of April, the ford of Po-di-Volano near Ferrara, losing about a hundred men in the fighting. It was there that he handed the command back to Colonel Malcolm, who had returned in the meantime, and it was there that they both heard the news of the capitulation of the German forces in Italy.

A few days later the 78th division was ordered to disarm any German formations in its sector that had not yet laid down their arms. A special task was reserved for the 8th Battalion, which had a long established tradition of carrying out without a murmur even the most arduous and least pleasant assignments.

In this case the officers were informed that there lay across their path a "division"—the word was given a sarcastic ring—or rather a horde of opponents of the present Russian regime, who passed to the enemy side and became German mercenaries. Since surrender would mean for them return to Russia and inevitable death, they might not lay down arms voluntarily and might offer resistance.

"I see"—said Colonel Malcolm after receiving his orders. On May 7, the 8th Battalion, Argyll and Sutherland Highlanders, left Tolmezzo and proceeded northward in tactical formation. The rain had stopped. Clouds were still drifting by, but the patches of blue promised a beautiful day. Everything that was green scrambled hurriedly up, climbing as if to make sure of catching a glimpse of spring. Droplets of water glittered on the leaves of the broad-shouldered elms spreading their branches over the road. The leaves of roadside oleanders gleamed with a freshly-scrubbed polish. Hamlets of stone houses clung to the rocks like nests, each with a belfry reaching for the sky in prayer and thanks to God for creating a country so beautiful. Lower down, mountain streams chattered on their way over stones.

Colonel Malcolm was with the advanced patrol, two hours' march ahead of the battalion. No enemy and no trace of resistance was encountered. Black-haired signorinas waved welcome with their kerchiefs, and partisans loaded with ammunition belts, with red scarves around their necks, descended from the hills and took up picturesque poses, giving a salute with their clenched fists, in accordance with communist fashion.

Before they went over the pass, the advance guard received a visit of Brigadier Musson, commanding the 36th infantry brigade. He outlined the situation and described the exact location of the Cossack "division," instructing the 8th Battalion to enter the small town of Lienz on the other side of the Austrian Dolomites. He also gave orders for the disarming of these men: it was a special problem, requiring an appropriate approach and method of operation . . .

"Yes, sir."

"It's a beautiful day, Colonel. I hope you had no trouble."

"Yes, sir. Thank you, sir."

* * *

In the evening of the same day the emissaries sent by ataman Domanov returned to Kotschach and reported the accomplishment of their mission. They contacted a British brigadier general, who told them that the Cossacks were to come down from the mountains into the valley of the Drava, toward the town of Lienz. He could not inform them about the details of their future, but he assured them that they would not be delivered to the Soviets under any circumstances.

* * *

On May 28, 1945, the following numbers of Cossack officers left Lenz for the announced conference with higher British authorities: 35 generals, 167 colonels, 283 lieutenant colonels, 375 esauls, 460 under-esauls, 526 sotniks, 756 standard bearers, 124 military officials, 15 medical staff, 2 photographers, 5 liaison officers with the R.O.A., and 2 clergymen—a total of 2,750 persons.

It was not until they were in the trucks that some of them felt a premonition. The trucks were very uncomfortable. Some of the officers had to stand. Despite the warm weather tarpaulins were drawn over the top. Soldiers with sub-machine guns sat next to the drivers. After driving for 12 kilometers the column stopped and was joined by light tanks, which accompanied it on its further journey along the Drava river, through Greifenburg, Steinfeld, Sachsenburg, Mollbrücke. . . .

After Mollbrücke, still following the Drava, the road turned sharply to the south-east, reaching town of Spittal 13 kilometers farther. The trucks entered the gates of a camp encircled with a triple barbed wire fence. There were sentries all along the wire. The unloading started. Even then, some men, stretching their legs after the ride, looked around and asked: "So this is where they are holding the conference?"

The officers were segregated according to rank, and a hut was assigned to each group. The huts were dirty and dilapidated; old straw covered the floor.

A British officer had the interpreter announce: "Will the generals Pyotr Krasnov, Domanov, and Tichocki step this way." He was told that General Krasnov was not well.

"In that case two will be enough."

Domanov and Tichocki stepped forward. The representative of the British Army told them in icy tones: "Please advise all the officers that, in accordance with the agreement between the military authorities of the United Kingdom and those of the Soviet Union, they will be handed over to the Soviet military command. Departure from Spittal will be tomorrow at 4 A.M."

"When was such an agreement signed?" Domanov asked in an equally icy tone.

"On May 23."

Tichocki fainted and fell down.

* * *

On the following day, May 29, at dawn, two Orthodox priests —Father Alexander and Father Vassily—went into the camp square and started solemn prayers for God's mercy. They were surrounded by a kneeling crowd of Christians and Moslems.

The trucks did not come at 4 A.M. as announced, but at 6 A.M. Ordered to board them, all the men refused. They were surrounded by soldiers with pistols and heavy clubs. The Cossack officers formed a ring, with arms linked in a traditional but not always effective manner. The soldiers started to beat them with clubs, over their linked hands and over the heads. They plucked out the first one and threw him into a truck. He jumped out. He was then beaten again and driven to the truck. He jumped out once more. Then they knocked him down with clubs and rifle butts and kicked him until he lay still in a pool of blood. He was lifted and thrown into the truck like a sack.

Others started to board the trucks. Some of the British clenched their teeth and closed their eyes. It was obvious that the massacre repelled them. But others beat the victims systematically, with relish. There was one who had tears in his eyes. And another, carrying a basket, approached the Cossacks and said, producing some packets of cigarettes from his pockets: Cigarettes for wrist watches!

General Krasnov did not go out into the square. He sat at the window of one of the huts and watched silently. British soldiers noticed him at the last moment and rushed to drag him out. Some Cossack officers pushed the soldiers away and carried their ataman on their shoulders. A British major approached Sultan Kelech-

Girey and said: "I place you in charge and I make you responsible for the behavior of the Caucasian officers."

Sultan Kelech-Girey spat at his feet.

* * *

The invitation to the conference deprived the Cossack mass of soldiers of their leaders. The men walked around restlessly and talked until 2 in the morning, then they went to sleep. On the following day, May 29, a young British officer appeared at 9 A.M. instead of the major and handed to the interpreter a proclamation which he wanted immediately translated to the men. It read: "Cossacks! Your officers were deceiving and misleading you. They have been arrested and will not return. Now, free of their pressure and influence, you will be able to denounce freely their lies and at last give expression to your true wishes. You will all be granted the right to return to your homeland . . ." For all those familiar with the style, it was obvious that the proclamation was of Soviet origin. It concluded with an appeal for strict obedience to British orders.

At 10 A.M. Major Davis declared that the repatriation of the Cossack regiments with their families, ordered by higher authorities, would start on May 31 at 7 in the morning.

It was a sunny, warm day. The news came almost literally like a bolt out of the blue. Panic, weeping, confusion broke out, accompanied by the cries of the children, upset by seeing their parents in a state of nervous collapse. A provisional meeting was called in hut No. 6 of the Peggetz camp. Cadet Kuzma Polunin was selected as *ad hoc* leader of a passive resistance movement. A general hunger strike was proclaimed. To emphasize the reason for it, the men hung out signs in English, reading: "We would rather starve to death than return to the Soviet Union!" Black flags were flown in all the camps and settlements. Provisional altars were erected in camp squares and clergymen started continuous day and night services, hearing confessions and giving holy sacraments. Naturally there was an ample crop of petitions: to the Pope, the King and Queen of England, the Archbishop of Canterbury, to Churchill, to King Peter of Yugoslavia, to General Eisenhower, and to the parliaments of the democratic nations. The British military office accepted the petitions, which were then thrown into the wastepaper basket by Major Davis.

* * *

The sun had only just appeared and the snow of the Alpine peaks was tinged with the pink of dawn. The Cossacks' cows, unmilked in the general confusion, were mooing sadly. Horses and the camels of the Astrakhan units wandered off all over the camp. Mist was still hanging over the Drava river. People whispered to each other the unwritten rule, trying to convince themselves that it would work: "Passive resistance only. Don't touch the British! Active resistance can only harm us, and we would have no chance. The Mother of God will save us!"

They acted accordingly. The prayers continued without interruption, but about 8 A.M. British tanks approached and formed a wide circle a hundred meters from the assembled crowd. Trucks which were to take people to the trains waiting at the station drew up at the huts. The whole camp was surrounded by soldiers with automatic carbines, fixed bayonets, and heavy clubs. People in the crowd started pushing each other. The Cossacks were on the outside, with the women, children, old men, and the priests at their altars inside.

Major Davis drove up in his jeep, looked and drove away. The prayers and the singing of hymns continued. No one really knew what they were praying for. A miracle? . . . Suddenly, at a signal, the soldiers rushed into the crowd, breaking the linked arms and striking the heads bared for prayer with rifle butts and clubs. Panic broke out. People trampled each other amidst screams and cries of pain. Backing under pressure, the crowd pushed against a fence dividing the camp from the surrounding fields, until it collapsed. But tanks were lined up in the fields too. Soldiers fired their weapons, not overhead, but close to the feet of the surrounded people. Beaten, bloody men and women were dragged to the trucks. People ran amuck, tried to run into the woods, jumped into the river. But the river was running high. Horses broke loose and ran away too.

The local inhabitants crossed themselves piously at first, but when someone made a start many rushed to the abandoned tents for loot, catching the horses and cattle. Catholic priests rang the bells in the churches and appealed to their people to stop disgraceful looting. A black flag was flown from the belfry of the church in nearby Dolsach. The British tore it down.

The main mass of Cossacks in Peggetz, retreating from the armed soldiers, attempted to snatch back some of those whom they had already captured. It was then that the first Don Cossack fell down, stabbed with a bayonet. The crowd opened up momentarily and revealed the altars. A priest turned toward the soldiers with a Bible in his hands, but the bayonet of a soldier of the 8th Battalion knocked it out of them to the ground. One of the men shielded himself with an icon of the Virgin, but he was struck on the head and a piece of his scalp hung loose over his ear. Another tried to ward off blows with the banner of St. Nicholas the Miracle Worker. The club tore off the fabric and threw St. Nicholas into the mud, but the Cossack escaped unhurt. At this moment the wife of one of the officers taken away to the "conference," jostled by the crowd, felt labor pains and fell to the ground. Humane British soldiers picked her up and took her to a hospital. She gave birth to twins later in the day.

The improvised chapel, the altars, the holy scriptures, and chalices were all broken and trampled.

It seemed for a moment that the agreed tactic of passive resistance might be abandoned, turning into active opposition, that the Cossacks might attack bayonets and carbines with their bare hands. The mass of defenseless people was ready to charge. . . . But the British soldiers then rushed quickly back to their vehicles, where they efficiently set up machine guns.

* * *

Many of the British soldiers waiting for orders by their tanks displayed compassion. It was later said that one kept saying in broken Russian: "Don't give up. They have no right." A small girl came up to a soldier and handed him a piece of paper on which someone knowing a little English had scrawled: "Kill us, but don't hand us over to the Bolsheviks." The soldier deciphered the message with difficulty and stuffed the paper into his pocket. They say that he wept.

Others told stories about Cossacks who jumped under the tracks of tanks and were crushed to death. A great manhunt for people to be delivered to the Soviets went on along the Drava, from Lenz to Oberdrauburg. People tried to escape into the mountains, but they were shot like chamois. A woman found by a dog in the bushes was accidentally shot. Among the sick and wounded taken to the hospital some jumped out of windows. Many were drowned in the Drava. They jumped into the river not only to get to the woods on the other side, but to find quick death.

At 5 P.M. Major Davis came in his jeep and addressed the remnants of the crowd in Peggetz. The field was strewn with the wounded and the bodies of several beaten to death or stabbed with bayonets. Next to Major Davis's jeep lay the body of a Cossack from Dniepropietrovsk, and nearby a dead woman with a child. The woman had been born in Kuban and the child in Italy.

"Cossacks!"—the interpreter repeated the major's words through a loudspeaker—"I am impressed by your heroic stand, but according to the agreement all those who were Soviet citizens before September 1, 1939, must be repatriated. Anyone who has documents that he was outside the Soviet Union prior to that date should present them."

* * *

About the same time, in the 1946 elections in France, 30.5 per cent of the vote was cast for the Communist Party. In Italy 31 per cent of the population voted communist in the 1948 election.

* * *

AUTHOR'S NOTES

Outside of fragmentary sketches, no objective historical study has attempted to present the entirety of these events. I will confine myself here to a brief outline.

The outbreak of the Second World War—as far as the eastern European nations outside the immediate reach of Germany were concerned—meant a Red Army invasion and Soviet occupation (this included the Baltic countries, the eastern part of Poland with its Belorussian and Ukrainian populations, and Bessarabia). When the Finnish war broke out in the winter of 1939–40, most of the nations occupied or threatened by the Bolsheviks concentrated their hopes on the Mannerheim line and the expected help of the western powers for Finland. The Mannerheim line, however, was broken by the Soviet troops and the western assistance never materialized. 1940 brought a further strengthening of the Soviet

Union, the extension of the territories it occupied, and brutal oppression under the rule of Moscow. A drastic change of attitude then turned the attention of the Eastern European nations to the possibility of conflict between Germany and Russia, while the hopes of liberation found support no longer in the West, but in Germany. These hopes reached their apogee on June 22, 1941, the day of the outbreak of the German-Soviet war.

A somewhat peculiar situation developed in eastern Europe. All the "younger" nations, with a peasant social structure and little democratic tradition, all the way from the Arctic to the Black Sea (Finland, Estonia, Latvia, Lithuania, Belorussia, Ukraine, Slovakia, and Rumania) sympathized rather with the German side.

The hopes placed in Germany met with bitter disappointment, because of the well-known Nazi policies and methods. However, even these methods did not change the basic orientation of the eastern European nations, which continued to look upon the Soviet Union as their enemy number one. This is a fact that merits special attention and study in a new light. After all, if the policies and methods of the Nazis were utterly repellent, this would tend to prove how spontaneous, deep, and genuine was the hatred of these nations toward the Bolshevik system.

The majority of the population within the 1939 boundaries of the Soviet Union adopted a similar attitude, although a progressive division occurred there as a result of the discouraging practices of Nazi terror in the east. D. Karov, using data collected by the Institute of the History and Culture of the USSR in Munich, largely from Soviet sources, reports the following distribution of allegiances in the German-occupied territories, among the basic population of rural character:

In Belorussia—pro-Soviet 20%, neutral 29%, anti-Soviet 51%; in Crimea—pro-Soviet 9%, neutral 30%, anti-Soviet 61%; in the Leningrad region—pro-Soviet 14%, neutral 24%, anti-Soviet 62%; in the Ukraine—pro-Soviet 9%, neutral 10%, anti-Soviet 81%; in Northern Caucasus—pro-Soviet 4%, neutral 20%, anti-Soviet 76%; in the regions of Don and Kuban—pro-Soviet 4%, neutral 9%, anti-Soviet 76%. There were, of course, local variations in the attitudes of different population groups within these regions. For example, the Tartars, some of the Caucasian tribes, and the Volga Kalmuks were almost 100% anti-Soviet.

While accurate figures are lacking as far as the spontaneous anti-Soviet guerilla activities are concerned, the number of Soviet citizens who joined regular formations fighting against Russia on the German side is known. Soviet propaganda dubbed the campaign against Germany the "patriotic war," in an allusion to the war of 1812. Yet already by 1943 the number of Soviet citizens who took up arms, not in the defense of the "Socialist Homeland," but against it, was about one million—twice the strength of Napoleon's Great Army. In 1944 their number, including the R.O.A. (Russian Army of Liberation) of General Vlasov, varied between 1,200,000 and 1,600,000; and this despite the German reverses at the time and the expectation of ultimate German defeat.

During the war, the western powers allied to the Soviet Union naturally avoided publicizing these facts. The Soviet government itself obviously did everything to conceal them. Strangely enough even to-day, many years after the war, the subject is kept under a cloak of silence and remains unknown to public opinion. An important contributing factor is the reluctance of the representatives of the eastern European nations, now in exile in the west, to recall the recent episode of their support of the Nazis against the Bolsheviks, which they view as embarrassing and best forgotten, because of possible adverse reactions of western public opinion.

As a result no one has tried to study the facts objectively. The historical experience of the last war, which displayed profound divisions within the Soviet Empire, is largely ignored and in danger of becoming a non-fact of history, a touchy subject not to be mentioned or discussed.

Translated by Alexander T. Jordan

Adam Czerniawski

for H.K.

View of Delft

1.

there is a view of Delft at the Hague
a panorama of Delft at the Hague
to see Delft
merely climb the stairs
where the Mauritshuis vista is not screened by hills
nor spoilt by spreading chestnut trees

Now the concrete conurbations in steel and glass
have cut off my view of Delft
honest citizens have a roof over their heads
children swing in gardens the ponds teem with fish
but the view of russet Delft brick
the view of Delft's shady canals
the view of Delft's hallowed space
lies beyond a shroud
in the palace of peace in the museum
I stand deprived of those
    boats at anchor
    the ingenious drawbridge
    the high-collared children
    and women in black

2.

He was lucky to have seen Delft
perhaps even today a second-class fare will suffice
but to fix the view not in memory only
there had to be one alive in 1657

who either knew the town since childhood
or having come on business from afar
strolled along the canal's sandy shore
strolled having on his right the towers and walls
strolled when the weather was fine
the previous day the air was sultry
during the night came rain and thunder
now therefore in the cooler air
clouds streak across clear skies
some black carry hail and thunder
on such a day this is the view of Delft
the sun uncertain the walls fitfully dark

3.

Many things I have loved
language moving into verse
and the clavicord's lament
journeys on international trains
vistas of wooden hills and quiet waters
I desired the bright flesh of a girl in Delft
I drank light ale
examined brush strokes through a glass

4.

These are the simplest elements
water and bricks clouds and the light of the sun
groups of women children and men
an allegorical interpretation is not required
there is no need for biographical facts
for the puzzling historical setting
the social system or the economy
I do not know who his wife was
I do not know who taught him to paint
I do not know why he found himself in Delft
on a somewhat cloudy day
was it chance
a sudden summons into distant parts
or was it a prearranged ordeal

a citizen's duty a commission of the goldsmith's guild
and that is not the point

5.

Today a sudden mist
has veiled the town the train was late
it grew dark and I lost my way
no one understood me
the last chance had gone

6.

It is like the perfect sexual act
or Grelling's paradox
that one who never saw the tawny walls
the roof slates now glinting in sunlight
the barges gliding
through a windy day in spring
should get an impression of Delft
not screened behind a complex of high tension wires
nor even behind a factory of luminous faïence

7.

I have seen Delft
        I had waited long
        days passed and years
        I studied learned books
        my daughter read about Babylon
        my son glimpsed the infinity of time
I quarrelled with my wife
I paid my bills
I locked the door
I opened the windows
I ate my lunch I sneezed
but still believed I would see Delft
not in dreams not on postcards not on a screen
that I would see the turrets and forts
        reflected in gently flowing water

I have seen Delft
I beheld Delft
I will describe Delft

8.

Leaves being burnt in the city park
chestnuts veiled in a bluish smoke
into the pond by which children play
dives a duck
the flight arrested by outstretched feet
a flutter of wings
now still
she is borne aloft gently flowing water

Translated by the Author

Adam Czerniawski

Fragment

Wonderful being a particle of the verifiable world
sensuously anticipating distances and shapes
which always change, colors constantly deceive,
a face caught in a glance or thought up at dawn,
hence sorrow, a longing for a sign or a scent
now vanished.

What then is the immortal soul?
If—say the saints—it supersensually floats
like the essential Euclidean form, how is it known?
For not only the smell of wood being sawn,
the cry of gulls upon declining rocks,
but also Newtonian laws and Pythagorean proofs
suddenly coalesce with a summer night:
How imagine soul without eyes or hands?
Who thinking of diagonals could miss
the crown of your hair, could fail to note familiar voices
coming from the terrace at twilight in the asymmetry of stars?

Translated by the Author

Tadeusz Nowakowski

The Liberty Picnic

"How's the wind?" asked Oliphant on the phone.

"Blowing our way!" replied the harassed Sebastian.

Dusk was impatiently awaited. The latest forecast had said the wind would not turn until 10 P.M. Obviously there would be no point in starting the celebrations without the wind blowing in the direction of Prague. The plastic balloons might float to Paris or London or (God forbid!) to Belgrade, instead of in *that* direction.

The invitations, printed on the handmade paper in three languages, had been adorned by the organizers with the emblem of the "Society of Friends of Freedom"—namely, a flaming torch bound with a ribbon bearing the gilt inscription "Libertas." They had something of the charm of a wedding announcement about them, though from the text it looked as though the event would be neither boring nor commonplace. To start with, a press conference was to be held after a speech by Oliphant, director of the "Psychological Warfare" section, at which the newest model radio sets would be demonstrated, shaped like fountain pens, spectacle-cases, or cigarette-cases. After the symbolic inflation of the first balloon, ten thousand propaganda devices, with a million anti-Communist leaflets attached, would be launched. The word "Svoboda" had been inscribed in glowing colors on the balloons. Little parachutes made of transparent, almost invisible material, would automatically become detached at a given altitude. Along with the miniature receivers, leaflets about slave labor in Soviet Russia would begin cascading down from the heavens.

Oliphant had frequently urged his superiors in New York and Washington that a certain amount of coffee, tea, and nylon stockings should also be dropped, but his suggestions were not considered. Very likely Senator Jefferson guessed that Oliphant's father-in-law was the owner of a stocking factory in Cincinnati. The ceremony was to end with a special radio program for the oppressed peoples. Oliphant thought of having a communal prayer set to the music of Bach—Horaček was to write the text—but this idea had not met with the approval of the Central Office, though neither of Oliphant's fathers-in-law was a clergyman.

Not far from the Czech frontier, in a forest clearing between hills, huge hangar-like tents gleamed white. In the largest, a numerous and varied company had assembled, driven up an hour earlier in expensive automobiles. Flags bearing the golden torch waved overhead. Men and women conversed, standing with glasses in their hands, as though attending a garden party or hunting feast. Waiters in impeccable white jackets carried around tiny sandwiches with blobs of salmon and cocktails.

The company was reminiscent of an exhilarated group of municipal clerks who have sneaked out of their stuffy offices for a rare Sunday picnic. How delighted they were with this huge marquee, not to mention the bottles of compressed gas, the mile-long line of trucks with balloons, a power-house on wheels! Grown-up schoolboys playing truant! Director Oliphant's colored balloons wafted them back into a land of delightful memories. Which of them, when young, hadn't flown kites? Which of them, when a child, hadn't stretched out a hand for a New Year's Eve balloon on a stick?

The fluttering ribbons bearing the inscription "Freedom-Liberté-Freiheit" emphasized the festive mood, as did the lively sounds of dance music emerging from the transmitting trucks of the German and American radio networks, "Samba-oh! Conga-oh! Rumba-oh!—oh!—oh!—oh!"

The ladies in particular, smartly dressed in a sporting fashion, strap-handbags slung over the shoulder, slacks, moccasins—a vivacity bordering on excitement. This came not so much from contact with the beautiful landscape and pleasant company as from the unusual nature of the event that had drawn all these people, armed with their field-glasses, cameras, and portable typewriters, to the periphery of Europe.

The proximity of the frontier, generally known to be an iron curtain dividing two worlds, excited even those without any particular political imagination. What, therefore, of subtle and intuitive people, of living seismographs who record the slightest tremors of history, of that international meterological service that ubiquitous and omniscient journalists provide in the world of major and minor politics? In the tent there were quite a few professional congress attenders, with an air of feverish globetrotters and café-gossipers about them; there were airborne defenders of culture, holding diplomatic passports and getting cut rates in hotels; there were activists whose moral sensibilities had not been blunted by the making of speeches and whose brains had not yet been clouded; there were the pale intellectual prophets of catastrophe suffering from ulcers and holding forth in their monthly magazines about Attila and Genghis Khan. Finally, there were the over-sensitive, high-strung, and neurotic émigré refugees: the ex-Ministers, the ex-Ambassadors, ex-Fascists, and ex-Communists, made kin by a shared disillusionment and anxiety. Each of them had written quantities of reports on the topic of the "Iron Curtain," and now here they had it, right under their noses, a few hundred yards away!

Jan Borowczyk, a Polish journalist from London, finding himself in such interesting company for the first time, was asking his colleagues about the main performers of the show:

"Who is that grey-haired man with a furrow between his eyebrows?"

"That's Gutenberg. The author of a famous book about Russia called *Cannibal ante portas*. An interesting book, favorable toward the Communists and toward their opponents. He doesn't say until the last page which is the cannibal: Truman or Stalin. Gutenberg's wife edits a Communist monthly for women."

"In Russia?"

"No, in London."

"And who is the individual with the face of a clergyman?"

"Jean Marron! He traded arms with General Franco and with the Red Republicans. An active worker in an international organization caring for refugees. Three years ago he was encouraging displaced persons to go back to the arms of the "Peoples' Democracies." Today he is opening their eyes to the perils of communism."

"It seems to me I've seen that elderly lady in diamonds at our National Day celebrations at the London 'White Eagle' Club."

"Probably. She is Lady Hopper, a friend of Hungarians and

Poles. She came here to keep an eye on young Szabos. She suspects him of having an affair with Mrs. Karpova, but that's a long story. . . ."

"Have any of you gentlemen seen Barabasz, the editor? I would like to talk with him. . . ."

"He was here a moment ago, but seems to have gone off somewhere."

The representatives of the political refugee organizations seemed to be wearing somewhat uneasy expressions. They formed a separate group, and stood to one side. They eyed the banners and balloons with incredulity, and the journalists with something resembling aversion. Instinctively, they turned their heads toward the thicket beyond which the frontier runs and broke off a conversation half-way through a phrase, became pensive, or spoke rapidly and nervously, or with exaggerated noisiness, to mask their fear.

One of them, a grey-haired man with the face of a poet or artist, kept smoothing down his long hair with one hand, taking off his spectacles and putting them on again, sighing into his glass.

"Horaček, cheer up!" cried his friends. "We're in no danger here. We're backed by American tanks, guns, and aircraft."

"An icy wind is blowing from that direction," a tall girl in horn-rimmed spectacles shuddered. "Don't you all feel it?"

"That depends on your imagination."

"Ten miles beyond this thicket," said Horaček, "lies the little town where I was born. . . ."

"What sentimentality!"

"It was there that I went to school, wrote my first poems."

"My native land is wherever my children go to school: Switzerland today, England, or America tomorrow."

"Would you believe, ladies and gentlemen, that I have at this moment a longing to run out of this tent, scramble through the barbed wire to the other side, and be shot by a frontier guard. . . ."

"Horaček!"

"To be killed in my own country, that isn't so stupid. To lie face downward on that sandy earth, grasp it in my hands, feel it on my chest. . . . Our trees, our meadows in my dying eyes. And our sky overhead. . . ."

"*I beg your pardon!* The sky is the same everywhere. So are the trees and the grass. These are the trimmings of émigré nostalgia, and as for that 'sacred native land,' that's just the great and not at all disinterested exaltation of the right-wing clerical-nationalistic cult of the homeland! What good is his homeland to a dying patriot? A man rests the same in the sands of Libya, Australia, or Patagonia! Don't let's be slaves of a literary imagination," philosophized a young man in a jaunty Tyrolean hat, waving a half-consumed sandwich.

"The reactionists have grown cunning, ha ha!" laughed one of the ladies. "It was they who invented love for one's native land! But perhaps that's merely your suspiciousness?"

"It isn't that complicated at all," explained the young "Tyrolean" fervently. "The wealthy classes have fed a fondness for the trash-can and poverty into the proletariat, in order to get the pariahs away from the migration movements, to fetter them to the soil, to exploit them economically, and—what is more important—to exasperate them into defending their homeland with pitchforks or with rifle in hand, that is, ladies and gentlemen, to defend the great estates. Rich people have no homeland, or rather—they have one everywhere. Particularly wherever their checks are honored. The Lord God was invented for the benefit of the poor, so was the notion of a reward after death in the form of Heaven, and so was poetry about fields and native forests. The wealthy classes, who have created culture over the centuries, knew how to drug the hearts and minds of simple people. . . . This monopoly, ladies and gentlemen. . . ."

"My dear sir, what are you saying? May we know who you are?"

"I am a press photographer," said the "Tyrolean," "but that has nothing to do with it. To go back to the cult of the homeland. . . ."

"I've been afraid of death all my life," said Horaček. "I used to write poetry from the fear of death. Now I am sixty-five, and I don't want to die in Paris, or New York, or Sydney. People in the West don't even know what a blessing it is to be born and to die in the same place."

"Every one of us fears death in his or her own way," said a lady with too much make-up and a Leica slung around her neck. "Some write or paint, others travel incessantly from one place to another, thinking they can conquer time as they conquer space. I hate the oafs who laugh at me because I discard a few years and wear a schoolgirl's beret. Don't they see, damn it all, that I do it only because I'm afraid of death?"

"Well, what do you know!" someone whispered, aside. "A heroic outburst of self-defence by Miss Zverovecova in the face of Providence. Confidentially, Consul, this is the Horaček who. . . ."

"A habitual scribbler, who overacts his role as the first lute player of his nation."

"You should not have come here, Mr. Horaček."

"Mr. Horaček, you talk as though we were not going to return to our homeland. Ladies and gentlemen, I suggest a portion of salmon and a martini!"

Meanwhile, people at the other end of the tent were talking of a more agreeable matter. Broad-shouldered Derek Greenford, the representative of a London newspaper, was informing his fellow-journalists what he had eaten a week earlier on board the S.S. *Batory*, at a reception held to celebrate the opening of a new Southampton-Bombay line.

"I can tell you it was Olympian feeding. Pheasant in bilberries, carp Jewish style, perch in pastry, Astrakhan caviar, vodka, vodka, and still more vodka, and as many cigarettes as you wanted! Filet mignon on toast—finger-licking good, and then—their national speciality: huntsman's stew! Where did these barbarians learn that?"

"The Polish gentry often went to Paris after the harvest had been gathered," put in a youth dressed in the French manner with beret and scarf. "It wasn't until the agrarian reforms in that region of Europe that the closing of many brothels on the Seine was brought about. Too bad, but with the passing of time, that is bound to reflect on cultural links between East and West."

"Gaston, you're impossible," laughed the ladies in fashionable slacks.

Greenford continued his report with the expression of one who has spent half his life eating and drinking.

"The champagne wasn't so good, even for the 'French of the North'! They served us a wretched Bollinger, a sort of warm fluid, and a Veuve Cliquot that tasted like soapy water, but for all that in positively shameless quantities. One might have taken a bath in it."

"I don't know whether you gentlemen realize," put in a certain handsome young man in not very good English, "that it is the Polish peasant and worker who pays for these showy receptions."

By the fiery look which Lady Hopper sent the young man, Borowczyk guessed this was Szabos the Hungarian.

Greenford smiled indulgently:

"I entirely agree with my young Hungarian friend, but let's face it: doesn't the same thing occur in other countries? I don't know any country in which the peasant and worker aren't forced to pay taxes, out of which a certain amount goes to cover representative expenses. This is the way things are in Poland, England, France, the Argentine, wherever you like. The canapés we're eating at this moment, and these drinks (rather too warm for my taste) also come in a sense from the labor of the American farmer and worker. . . ."

"Yes, but . . . but . . . it's a question of something entirely different . . . a question of proportion," the young Hungarian blushed, no one knows whether from shyness or vexation, then unexpectedly he shut up, not finding the appropriate words in his vocabulary. The ladies in pants looked sympathetically at the handsome boy. Charming young fool!

"King Farouk at Monte Carlo or the young Ali Khan at the races spend more than the satellite squanderers," cried Gaston. "And after all, the situation of the Egyptian peasant and worker. . . ."

"My dear!" the ladies groaned, "spare us a lecture. This isn't a London County Council evening course! Tell us something more amusing!"

"I assure you, Greenford," spoke up the Great Gutenberg, "that you didn't eat any better with your Poles than I at the Rumanian embassy in Belgrave Square. They invited us to celebrate the liberation festivities."

"Held on the occasion of the seizure of Rumania by Russia," cried the stubborn Hungarian. "That's no 'liberation.' And you, the author of *Cannibal*, an honorary member of the League of Human Rights—you went there? Impossible!"

"God, what a boring young man," sighed the ladies in slacks. Several journalists looked at the young upstart with dislike, but the socially-polished Gutenberg let the tactless exclamation pass, and calmly pursued:

"After the dreadful Spanish sherry they poured into our throats at Franco's embassy, after the various bleary Amontillados and the cheap wines at the German representatives'—what unpalatable water that Liebfraumilch is!—believe me, ladies and gentlemen, that I drank Rumanian slivovitz as though it were a tonic! I entirely share the expert views of Greenford on culinary matters, though

I differ from him on the subject of nationalizing steel. For eating and drinking, one cannot beat the satellites! They are hospitable and ambitious in matters of cuisine, like all the young and economically backward little countries of the world. . . ."

"Mr. Gutenberg . . . Mr. Greenford. . . . I. . . ."

"My dear friend," Greenford turned in a fatherly manner to the young Hungarian, "with all due respect for your noble indignation, we mustn't lose touch with reality. The Court of St. James, like the White House and the Quai d'Orsay, maintains diplomatic relations with the Kremlin and its satallites. If red cannibals are invited to parties at Buckingham Palace in my country, then, as a Briton loyal to the Crown, I see no reason why I should refuse the pleasure of drinking Polish vodka, or enjoying Russian caviar."

As the excited Hungarian tried desperately to put forward counter arguments, his colleagues whispered to one another with unconcealed dislike:

"Uncouth, arrogant young man! Why does he have to insult influential journalists and a famous writer! He is ruining all our work! He is wrecking valuable press contacts!"

"Don't over-dramatize this," some remarked, aside. "The boy is as handsome as a movie star, and well-built in the bargain. He has full lips, splendid teeth, and skin like a peach. Haven't you noticed, gentlemen, that old Greenford can't keep his eyes off him?"

"Do you think that Greenford . . . ?"

"But of course! He is the king of life, an old Fleet Street jaguar."

"The terror of would-be journalists!"

"But sonny-boy won't agree to it; 'mama' won't let him."

"So it's true that young Szabos is kept by Lady Hopper?"

"The old nymphomaniac won't surrender her maternal rights, for which (so one hears), she pays very dearly."

"*Mon Dieu*, if I had the choice, I'd prefer that unctuous rheumatic from Fleet Street to that doddering old bag dating from the time of Queen Victoria!"

"All that matters, ladies and gentlemen, is which is more useful to the Hungarian cause," someone in a corner joked. "Influential Greenford, friend of a dozen Members of Parliament and *persona gratissima* in the corridors of the Foreign Office, or that silly old creature with a hundred thousand pounds stashed away in savings.

Would you believe that the old bag has yet again confused Budapest and Bucharest in a note she cooked up on her own initiative to the UNO? And when I went to visit her and correct the unfortunate error, her butler brought me a five pound note on a silver tray and a card with the printed inscription 'God save Hungary!' "

"That's nothing new! In 1941 she was living with a latent Nazi, and distributing cards that said 'God save the Great Reich.' "

"That's not all! In 1942 she was looking after a young chauffeur from the Soviet Embassy in London and giving out cards saying 'Pray for Stalingrad.' "

"The basis of all English interests, including political ones, is empirical. The lessons of history, taken so ingeniously by Lady Hopper, reveal all the genius of that wonderful race!"

"How's the wind?"

"Blowing in our direction!"

* * *

Two men were driving from Prague toward the German frontier in a late-model, khaki-colored limousine with military insignia on the mudguards and doors. One was in civilian clothes, the other in uniform. When a flight of aircraft appeared in the sky beyond Pilzno, the man in civilian clothes instinctively hunched up his shoulders, startled, then glanced inquiringly at his companion.

"They are going to shoot down the American balloons with leaflets," the military man explained. "Several Soviet fighter planes are patrolling the frontier. . . ."

"So much the worse for us, eh?"

"How do you mean?"

"The frontier under guard. . . ."

"We'll make it," the man in uniform smiled. "In a few hours you'll be on the other side. As an activist of the Underground, you'll be received with open arms."

"I'm not an activist of the Underground," said the civilian quietly. "They tried to make me say that I was, during the interrogation. But I have stayed away from politics all my life.— What shall we do if they stop the car?"

"Don't think about it."

Anton Hlohovec recalled with difficulty the staggering course of events which, in the course of a few hours, had wrenched him from his domestic privacy and thrown him into the Pankrac jail.

But now they were returning him to life again. He was sitting next to Emil, armed, a friend from schooldays. He gazed at his colonel's insignia, at his leather gloves grasping the wheel, and did not know what to make of it all. He could still hear the gurgle of air in his split ear-drum, felt pain throughout his body. The action of the sinister film, of which he had become the hero, was being worked out too fast and too sensationally for his abilities to reflect.

"Emil, my friend," he said in the car, "is it God who looks after small, helpless people, or does blind Fate throw us around like balls on the ocean wave? Do you think this will come off?"

"It will certainly come off. Two hours more and we shall reach our destination. I have thought out and prepared everything in advance."

"If I hadn't met you, I'd be dying in Pankrac jail at this moment, in a dungeon."

"Cheer up, Hlohovec," Emil smiled without looking away from the tape of the highway. "You've one foot in freedom already."

They drove for several miles, when the man in civilian clothes realized he had not properly thanked his friend for this miraculous liberation.

"Stop talking about gratitude," the colonel interrupted. "A man does so many base things in his life. . . . When the opportunity arises, once in a few years, then why not help a fellow countryman and comrade from one's schooldays? Don't think I am doing this out of sympathy for your political beliefs. I hate the Social Democrats, and as for your attempts at conspiracy, they remind me of the World War I veterans playing world strategists over their mugs of beer."

"Emil, I already told you," said Hlohovec timidly, "that I never took part in any conspiracy. The only passion I have has little to do with politics. I'm a stamp collector."

"I'm not doing this out of sympathy for your stamp collecting," the other laughed.

"I know: our old school, that beloved building in Bratislava!"

"Devil take it! I am doing this in memory of our trips to the 'Palais de Danse' and that cute little——remember?"

"I remember! Marika! They said you later got engaged to her."

"She wasn't fit material for a wife, you know that better than I do."

"Little Marika!" Hlohovec exclaimed. "Who'd have thought it?

God bless her soul. Apparently she's having a great success abroad."

"No. Marika is in this country."

"Have you seen her? At the theatre?"

"No, in the hospital. She's in Košice. I visited her last month. She looks like a ghost, a disease is eating away her lungs. They don't give her more than six months to live. For want of anything else, we talked about you. . . ."

"Me?"

" 'Do you remember timid Hlohovec from Bratislava?' I asked toward the end of my visit. 'Imagine, we arrested him a few weeks ago for a hostile attitude toward the people's authority.' Sure enough, she remembered you very well. She remembered that evening at the Palais. Then we talked about everyone who had been there. I was sorry I brought up this subject. She cried, and in the end she told me to promise to get you out of jail. As you see, I've kept my word. Noble bandits and decent policemen don't appear only in cheap novelettes and films for children. At this moment you are sitting beside a new incarnation of Rinaldo Rinaldini. . . ."

The colonel laughed at the wheel, and Hlohovec could not get over his amazement:

"So it was on her account? Little Marika from our theatre? Admit it, you're in love with her. . . ."

"Don't let's use words that are meaningless. The miraculous intervention of Providence isn't enough for you, you keep on looking for film clichés. Quite simply, I was sorry for her—just pity, that's all. For her and for myself. She reminds me of those times when I was learning to play the violin, and everything was different from now. I don't know whether you remember that as 'little Emil' I once played the Ave Maria solo, in the school chapel when the Bishop came for a visit. It sounds quite cynical, but not long ago I drove that very same bishop to jail, and—this is strange—on the way I had to keep myself from whistling that tune."

"Associations," Hlohovec whispered timidly.

"I was supposed to go on to the Conservatory—but there wasn't enough money. You went to Prague for further studies; I became a policeman. First in our force, then semi-German, and now. . . . That's how it goes with cops and their like. I hope that in due time I'll be helping the American police catch Communist Quislings. What do you think—shall I be of any use?"

The man in civilian clothes was going back in thought to Bratislava.

"How strange this is! Believe me, Emil, that I only saw that girl no more than two or three times in my life. . . ."

"I know that. But it was enough for her that you are from our town, and that you remember times when we were happier than now. . . ."

"We were much younger, the world was different from today, people were better. . . ."

"People are always the same," Emil spat through his window. "We have nothing to get sentimental about. Another hour's drive. Take a nap, brother, take advantage of the opportunity. A long walk and acrobatics await you at the frontier—creeping on your belly between the guards, like in Karl May adventure stories. . . ."

Hlohovec shuddered.

Borowczyk, the editor, looked around the area attentively, and noticed that the representatives of the German authorities had turned up in dark suits, with stiff collars. Taking part in the "Breath of Freedom" afforded them not the slightest gratification. They stayed together. Not entering into conversation with the journalists or the Americans, they were unmistakably steering clear of the refugees. They had wooden and colorless expressions, to stress that they did not intend to enjoy themselves at the festivities, which would not bring them any profit. They pecked at their food reluctantly, wetting their lips with the drinks as though doing someone a favor. One of the icily smiling "Regierungsrats" of whom it was said in the tent that not so long ago he used to condemn his fellow countrymen to death for listening to the BBC from London, was now asking expert questions in a dry matter-of-fact voice.

"What is the risk in picking up leaflets in Warsaw or Prague? How much does it cost to manufacture one balloon? Who was the agent in the deal? How much did he make out of it? How many people have been arrested for owning miniature radio receivers? How many have been shot? Would it be possible to get a few balloons as a present? For my grandchild to play with."

From the other end of the tent came stifled voices, boiling over with suppressed fury: people were quarrelling in Polish:

"Had Dr. Dutkiewicz and I known that we would be so insulted by the organizers, we would not have taken the trouble to come here specially from London and Paris!"

"But, gentlemen, don't raise your voices. For God's sake, there are foreigners everywhere! The good of the cause is at stake. . . ."

"Oh, confound your 'good of the cause'! We know that tune. . . ."

"Forgive me, but. . . ."

"I forgive nothing! We are going to protest to Oliphant. Neither Dr. Dutkiewicz nor I intend to fraternize with Mr. Byclik. Who commissioned him? Whom does Mr. Byclik really represent? Poland and the emigration have had enough of the Mr. Bycliks and their methods!"

"I would recommend to you a sensible compromise. Be things as they may, Byclik's people have taken over key positions in the Society of the Friends of Liberty."

"They must be bitten out, and our people brought in."

"Byclik is no democrat."

"Oh goodness!"

"Forgive me, but. . . ."

"I will not, let's go to Oliphant, and *basta!*"

"We shall make fools of ourselves."

"Byclik is an old criminal."

"Oh goodness!"

"He never robbed anyone yet!"

"Because he never had the chance, but if he had, then he would have!"

"In view of such arguments, I declare to you gentlemen that I no longer feel myself obliged by the resolutions of the last congress. . . ."

"We reserve the right of going to any lengths at the next meeting!"

"Ah? We're being threatened? We're being caught on the hop at three minutes before midnight, are we? Allow me gentlemen, not to name it by name out of respect for Dr. Dutkiewicz, here present."

"Just look out, so I don't tell you in plain, understandable Polish. . . ."

"Colleague Mirecki and I shall go at once to President Byclik. We won't hesitate to warn him that you gentlemen intend to finish him off as far as the Americans are concerned."

"Come, come! This isn't the way, gentlemen, to reach agreement and unity of action. Not this way!"

"Very well, then—a change of front! We'll see who will be first with Oliphant, and with whom the Americans will want to talk—with you, or with us."

"Oh goodness!"

"We'll see, you former mayor of Kalisz, we'll see!"

"Byclik's pipeline! I break off acquaintance with you, Mr. de Napiorowski!"

"To Oliphant!"

"To Oliphant!"

Oliphant, the director, of whom the Polish émigrés were so feverishly talking, was in a separate aquamarine tent, preparing for the start of the "Breath of Freedom." He had flown to Germany that morning with his son. After greeting Sebastiano, the engineer and head of the technical section, he had hastily arranged the final text of his speech with the handsome brunette, Mrs. Karpova, chairman of Czech and Slovak affairs.

"I am just wondering," he wiped the sweat off his forehead, "whether or not to erase this passage: 'Today there is no choice for the free world except to fight for the freedom and justice of all men. It is not true that the fate of our planet depends on solving the dilemma: War or peace. The question we ask is: Freedom or slavery? A life worthy of man—or barbarity?'. . . Who wrote that?"

"Horaček."

"Shall we leave it or cross it out?"

"As you decide, director."

"It would be best," Oliphant pondered, "if it were possible to extend freedom throughout the whole world without infringing peace, eh?"

"Much better," Mrs. Karpova admitted.

"And what do you think of this, Sebastiano?"

"Butcher the Reds wherever they are! I'd say: 'Overturn the Communist governments and create a democratic government just like we have in America! Introduce freedom of the press, religion, and outdoor meetings in your country, disband the secret police!' "

"You don't know anything about politics, Seb," Oliphant laughed. "Just as well that you're filling the balloons with hydrogen, and not making speeches, otherwise you might cause a great deal of harm in the world by your ignorance. Mrs. Karpova, I need a few nice-sounding phrases for the conclusion. You're the most intelligent of us all."

Mrs. Karpova removed an invisible flake of powder from her eyelashes and recited, like a clever schoolgirl:

"A stubborn, invisible struggle is in progress for the souls of enslaved humanity. We believe that by drawing strength from glorious historical traditions and belief in the ultimate triumph of God over the powers of evil and sin, you shall survive until that joyous moment when the sun of freedom will shine through the dark clouds of enslavement. That moment will come!"

Oliphant nodded with admiration:

"That's just what I wanted."

"While I'd say, right out: 'Fight the Red gangsters,' " cried Sebastiano. " 'Wipe them out like vermin, because they took off my younger brother's leg in Korea! Don't stand on ceremony, you sons of a valiant nation! Hang the Communist bosses on the nearest street-lamp! Rebel against dictatorship and tyranny, damn it, and the free world will help you!' "

"Along with Sebastiano the engineer, and his balloons, amen!" Oliphant concluded cheerfully. "Let's elect Seb to the White House, and war will break out on Tuesday morning!"

"Oh, Mr. Oliphant," Sebastiano sighed, "I'd show those scoundrels: an atom bomb on Moscow, another on Peking, a third on Warsaw, a fourth on Prague, fifth on Bucharest, sixth on Budapest, the seventh on Sofia, and the world would sigh with relief. . . ."

. . . "With a breeze from beyond the grave," Mrs. Karpova laughed, and the Grand Vizier clapped the engineer's shoulder. "Terrible child! And to think that Jefferson wanted to make him head of the foreign language broadcasts! We'd have looked well. . . ."

"I'd have refurnished this wretched little world all right, you can be sure of that," the engineer shook his crop of black hair and went off to his balloons.

After a moment, President Byclik reported in order to express his amazement at the presence of Dr. Dutkiewicz and his supporters at the inauguration ceremony.

"These people are known for their anti-democratic beliefs. If we return to a liberated Poland, the nation will reject them. Nor am

I certain, moreover, that Dutkiewicz's party is not secretly financed by the European Movement, which wants to emancipate Western Europe from American influences. Dutkiewicz is notorious for loudly criticizing the Marshall Plan and the Atlantic Treaty in Polish cafés in London. Some people state outright that he is a. . . ."

"A Communist?"

"No: a sodomite."

"I am very sorry indeed," Oliphant spread out his hands, "that a nation that produced Kościuszko, Puławski, and Paderewski, could also produce something like Dutkiewicz. We shall cross his name off the list of candidates for honorary stipends. The new world-order, which will be revealed after the smashing of communism, will erase sodomy once and for all. Is that enough for you?"

"It is, sir."

"The Polish nation is great: sooner or later it will regain independence."

A few minutes later Dutkiewicz appeared:

"If Poles in Poland were to find out that people like Byclik speak up in their name, it would weaken their faith in ultimate victory. I considered it my duty to warn the Society of the Friends of Freedom against Mr. Byclik and his (fortunately) few supporters. Blackening reputations before foreigners and bringing internal problems to foreign attention is not in keeping with our national character, but in the case of Byclik, all public opinion in Poland and the emigration requires that an exception be made. No Polish soldier in the West will take up arms if he finds out that Mr. Byclik, so often compromised in the past, is again dabbling in politics. I need not mention that Byclik is a. . . ."

"A Communist?"

"No: a kleptomaniac."

"I am indeed sorry," Oliphant spread out his hands, "that a nation that produced Kościuszko, Puławski, and Paderewski could also produce someone like Byclik. We shall cross his name off the list of candidates for honorary stipends. The new world-order, which will be revealed after the smashing of communism, will erase kleptomania once and for all. Is that enough for you?"

"It is, sir."

"The Polish nation is great, sooner or later it will regain independence," Oliphant concluded, and he went for a piss.

When he came back, Mrs. Karpova laughed aloud:

"A strange nation, these Poles! But you have a way of dealing with them, Director."

"I learned that little formula by heart, and it hasn't let me down yet. A certain police-chief in New York aptly called them: 'people who celebrate national anniversaries and keep police regulations'."

The field telephone rang. The breathless voice of Sebastiano exclaimed:

"*Hullo, boss!* I've had a great idea. I was reading in the *Herald Tribune* that young people poisoned by communism are denouncing their own parents. Should not your Fred, as a young American, appeal to young Czechs not to do this abominable thing?"

"Fred doesn't speak Czech."

"He could read his appeal from a text in English. Mrs. Karpova would translate into Czech."

"But what will he say to them?"

"What do you mean 'what'? That parents are sacred, that our boys and girls don't denounce their parents. Good idea, eh?"

"Not bad."

"Shall we do it?"

"Yes."

Sunset creeped up to the balloons, tents and automobiles. Some of the guests, tired of waiting, went for a stroll on the nearby hill from which the naked eye could discern frontier guards armed to the teeth. Greenford insisted he could see hidden nests of machine-guns in the ferns, others declared they saw the domes of bunkers and tanks. Monsieur Marron terrified the ladies with tales of bloody frontier incidents. Lady Hopper by mistake directed her field glasses in the wrong direction, and instead of Czech soldiers caught sight of Szabos on the edge of the woods, hand in hand with Karpova.

"I've taken a room in the little hotel on the lake. I'll wait for you at the railroad station at ten tomorrow morning," said Szabos to the pretty Czech girl. "Why are you smiling? Has someone been spreading gossip about me?"

"Do you mean your affair with Lady Hopper?"

"I give you my word there's a lot of exaggeration in that gossip."

"Exaggeration?"

"You've no idea how many enemies I have in our Combat Committee."

"But I thought. . . ."

"It's a completely Platonic friendship. In any case, I'm going to break it off as soon as we get back to London."

"And afterward?"

"Afterward we'll look after our own fate. Why are you smiling? Is it so funny?"

"No, it's not funny at all. I've often thought about it, but. . . ."

"So there is a 'but' between us after all?"

"I don't know whether you understand me."

"Aneczka! I do not understand you!"

"You see. . . . If you, my lad, had more sense and experience, you wouldn't break with Lady Hopper."

"What! How can you . . . you, of all people, say that?"

"I want to ask you something. Do you trust me even a little?"

"Aneczka! How can you ask? I've . . . from the first moment I set eyes on you. . . ."

"Stop laying on the paint so thick!"

"Paint! I can't live without you."

"So you live with Lady Hopper."

"Aneczka, from tomorrow I'll become a decent person."

"No hurry. My husband intends to buy shares in the trading corporation from Lady Hopper. You must help us in this."

"A trading corporation?"

"Trade with the Far East."

"Drugs?"—he asked with distaste.

"No. Old rubbish discarded by the army."

"With whom?"

"The Chinese."

"Chiang Kai-Shek?"

"No. Apparently with Mao Tse-tung."

"That's shameful! And that hypocrite of a woman belongs to the League for Combatting communism!"

"You ought not to speak about Lady Hopper in that way. Ungratitude is the ugliest trait of youth. My husband. . . ."

"Damn your husband! After all, you separated a year ago."

"Darling, I adore you when you're angry! You look perfectly beautiful, like a picture of St. George. I don't believe in the "great thoughts" of old Greenford, who says that morality in business and politics, like virtue in a woman, is an infirmity. However, I see no reason why you should throw thunderbolts on my husband and Lady Hopper! You'd do better to influence your protectress not to hold on to these shares too tightly, and to let them go to Charles. Charles is prepared to pay you two and a half per cent commission on the deal. . . ."

"You're separated from your husband, yet you do business for him," he said with mock indignation.

"I assure you that nothing links us apart from money. I love you only."

"Let's go back to the others."

"Are you afraid of her?"

"I don't like scenes, but I assure you that nothing links me with her apart from money."

"That's fair."

He embraced her gently and kissed her on the mouth.

The two men in the coupé were driving in silence, not looking away from the highway, on which the shadows of trees and telephone poles spread hasty patterns. The motor hummed lullingly, but Hlohovec could not sleep, despite his fatigue. He was trembling inwardly—he had lived through too much in the past few hours. Too many thoughts, images, and recollections surged through his mind.

Only yesterday he had been sitting in that office of the security authorities opposite a man in a leather jacket who smelled of brandy and eau de cologne. Water was rumbling in the radiator. The man in the jacket dissolved into steam. There was a sweetish taste on his cut lip, "Kölnisch Wasser," brandy, the rumbling in the radiator, a growing mushroom of terror in the back of his head —Hlohovec was sitting, terrified, on a stool and could feel dry queasiness mounting within him. The man at the desk was speaking in a tired voice, without impatience or dislike. Then two others entered the room. No, they crept in. He heard the creak of the badly-oiled door and their cat-like tread on the linoleum, right behind him. He felt someone's sour breath on the back of his neck.

Hlohovec shuddered. What had happened next? It was night when Emil came. At first he hadn't recognized him—after all, how many years had passed since his departure from Bratislava to

Prague!—and in any case it was a matter of indifference to him who the man leaning over the stretcher was. He could not ride out of the hell of darkness. Not until morning had he recognized him. By his eyes and friendly smile. Light from the open window was shining over Emil's shoulders. He was amazed to see the walls of a rustic cottage, lace curtains cut from paper, the window without bars. He was free!

The motor was running rhythmically. The wheels bounced on the threshold of a bridge, the springs rocked gently and they plunged into the forest. Hlohovec took the thermos flask from Emil and drank some hot tea. Calmness flowed into him along with the liquid. His body no longer pained, the terror of many days melted away within him. He looked with emotion at the profile of his savior. A few grey hairs at his temples, a vertical line between the brows. The very same concentrated, vigilant look on his face as formerly, in school, over a problem in math. The colonel felt his neighbor's gaze, winked in a friendly way, and smiled.

On the ribbon of the highway, as on a reel of film, Hlohovec saw the young Emil in happy Bratislava. He was then a head shorter. He went around in a tight-fitting jacket, with an athletic club badge in the button-hole. Hair crew-cut. His tie in an exaggeratedly thick knot.

It happened down-town. After the first night of "The Czardas Princess." Four of them were standing in front of the theatre: Emil, Maleček, Kranz, and Hlohovec. With flowers in their hands, they must have looked rather silly. But isn't the lack of self-criticism one of the charms of youth? What came next? Old posters were hanging on the dressing-room walls. Maleček bowed and handed the flowers to the ballet dancer. Marika thanked him and plunged her little powdered nose into the bouquet. Then a long and embarrassed silence fell. Maleček again complimented her on her talent, the girl again thanked him. It was as hot as a steam-bath in the little room. And then Emil burst out with an invitation to supper. Later he protested he'd said it against his own will. Marika laughed approvingly. The bolt had fallen. There was no going back. They all smiled nervously. Little Kranz's lips twitched spasmodically. Two of his front teeth were missing. . . .

Lost in his recollections, Hlohovec smiled despite the pain in his back. He could hear her voice after all these years. He could see her sparkling eyes. He remembered the blue line on her eyelids.

"Turn your backs, boys!" she had said gaily. "And no peeping!"

They turned their backs as one man. The ballet dancer's long legs appeared in the mirror. Her glittering bodice fell to the ground and her small breasts gleamed for an instant. What had happened after that? They went by droshky to the Palais. On the way they smoked cigarettes. Maleček was telling jokes he had read in magazines. Emil watched the meter anxiously. The driver took a long way round on purpose. In the droshky Marika, with a silk kerchief over her curls, promised to dance with each of them in turn, but immediately began complaining that she was hungry. Maleček asked for the menu. He handed it ceremoniously to the girl, as though it were his credentials. Marika—where did the memory of such details come from?—ate a heaped plate of "knedlički" and asked for a Pilzner. Maleček ordered a carafe of vodka. It was gay and sentimental. The band played "In a Persian Market." Emil held up five fingers behind the girl's back as a sign that he only had five crowns. Marika ordered a second carafe, and it was still merrier. And then—the disaster happened! When it came to paying, Kranz took off for the toilet, Emil, pale, gave the waiter his tin watch as a pledge; Maleček asked for the bill to be sent to his father. The waiter called the tough-looking porter. . . .

"What are you thinking about?" the colonel asked. "Of Bratislava, I'll wager."

"Remember? We fought like crazy. . . ."

"Who? With whom?"

"Kranz, Maleček and us two, with that tough porter."

"I remember? But what became of Marika?"

"She escaped through the window."

"And you, the timid Hlohovec, top boy in the class, pushed a drum over the porter's head! The good old bourgeois days!"

"Kranz tried to jump down the stairs and twisted his ankle. Next day they wrote about us in the newspaper. We were summoned before the director."

"And before the police. In those days I was dead afraid of the police. Maybe that's why I became a policeman."

"I can't talk aloud. All my bones hurt. If it hadn't been for you, they'd have smashed me up in Pankrac."

"I can't remember who took Marika home that time," inquired Emil, skilfully passing a peasant cart on the highway. "The police

took me, Kranz twisted his ankle. There were two of us left: Maleček or you?"

"Maleček," Hlohovec lied.

"I don't believe you. Maleček would have trumpeted such an adventure all around Bratislava. Admit it. You slept with the girl in some small hotel. Why such shyness after so many years?"

"Because at the time I was too young and too stupid for that. I was sixteen."

"Marika told me about that incident with emotion. You behaved very gallantly, like a young poet. In the morning you brought her a bunch of violets. Women remember little things like that for many years."

"What are we talking about?" Hlohovec wiped his brow. "We're behaving against all the principles of psychological probability. Danger a step away, but here we are dredging up fond episodes from our memories! It's strange, but while I was in Pankrac I didn't think about death or the possibility of surviving. Yet I was pursued by the details of a certain film I saw twenty years ago!"

"You ought to be thinking instead of what awaits you tomorrow."

"A turkey was thinking about Sunday, but on Saturday they wrang its neck." Hlohovec looked at his friend's nicotine-stained fingers and closed his eyes. For an instant it seemed to him they were stained with blood.

Borowczyk, the editor, was busily looking around. He intended to write a report on the ceremony for the next number of "The Democratic Voice." But first of all he wanted to talk with a colleague by the name of Barabasz about a matter which had been entrusted to him for energetic handling.

Barabasz was neither in the marquee nor anywhere on the hill. Withdrawn from the feverish bustle, he was fishing in a nearby stream with Oliphant junior.

"They rise better in the evening, don't they?"

"Why are you looking at me like that, sir?"

"I had a brother your age," Barabasz replied to the young American. "I used to go fishing with him sometimes, on the Vistula."

"What happened to him?"

"He fell in Warsaw."

"Did they take fifteen-year old boys into your army?"

"They went of their own accord. He had your eyes and the same mop of hair. But he was half a head shorter than you: he didn't eat so well. You won't catch anything with a fly, try a worm."

"Where is it nicer: in Poland or in Germany?"

"In Poland."

"Why don't you go there, sir?"

"I'm waiting for your father to drive the Russians out of Poland!"

"Oh, this organization with the balloons! My father won't ever do it. I wouldn't believe him."

"Don't you trust your father? Why?"

"What sort of a father is he! He's afraid of my mother, and my mother's an evil woman. Before, they used to quarrel all the time, but one day my mother said to him: 'If you go to Florida with Miss Dixon one more time, I'll tell people something about you that nobody knows.' My father got scared, Miss Dixon left Cincinnati for good, and now there's a sort of harmony, but no one knows what will come of it. Awful people—believe me!"

"How can you call your mother 'evil'? That's a sin."

"I have my own reasons," the young fisherman muttered. "It would have been more cheerful at home with Miss Dixon; she's one of the best tennis players in all of Ohio! She serves and cuts like a man! I wish I had her style!"

"Here you are, at last!" Borowczyk's head emerged from the undergrowth. "Over there, they're preparing to take the Iron Curtain by storm, while you go fishing!"

He took Barabasz to one side and began expounding:

"I knew your father. He was the pride of our Party. He never soiled his hands by any dealings with the anti-Democrats. It is with all the greater regret that we have learned that you, the son of the great Barabasz, have taken a position in a weekly newspaper, the political line of which is entirely at variance with the ideals held by your father."

Barabasz, a tiny, bewildered little man with a dazed look, sighed:

"What's to be done?"

"At the last meeting of the CKW," Borowczyk went on in a somewhat harder voice, "your attitude was subjected to severe criticism. I admit that I myself can't find any words to justify what you are doing. Either one is a member of our organization and loyally abids by its resolutions, or else, Mr. Barabasz, one licks the generals' boots. You must decide."

Discomfited, Barabasz sat down on a tree stump and sighed again:

"It worries me too. Don't think, colleague, that I have an easy life in this official newspaper. Every week we print disquisitions as boring as milk and water, and interminable speeches, sometimes recollections of the war. But a man must make a living, mustn't he? Not everyone is suited to carrying loads in a factory. . . ."

"I knew your father. In 1927 when he was offered a very well paid post at the Ministry on condition he stopped attacking the government, your father replied: 'You will not put a golden chain on my lips!' There was a man for you! You will agree with me that today there are increasingly fewer such men in the world. . . ."

"Of course," said Barabasz, who agreed with everyone on principle. "There aren't any such people now. . . ."

"Colleague Barabasz, at the last meeting of the CKW I was instructed to hand you an ultimatum. You must decide. Which is more agreeable to you: a warm little job with hardened reactionaries, or membership in a truly democratic organization? Colonel Kajman, your publisher, is in the tent. You have a splendid opportunity of showing your character and loyalty to the principles that inspired your father. Go, and reject this shameful occupation!"

"Thirty pounds a month," Barabasz sighed. "Where shall I make so much? And there's not much work involved: a few polemics with Byclik's group. . . ."

"What? With Byclik's group? Don't you know that Byclik is our natural ally in the fight against the hegemony of the generals and former ambassadors?"

"But it was different, before! Our movement was fighting him!"

"Yes, but there was a split recently in this connection."

"Incredible! Could you . . ." Barabasz stammered, "could you tell me in which group I was?"

"In the pro-Byclik group."

"And Dr. Dutkiewicz, with whom we worked together?"

"He was unmasked."

"A double-dealer?"

"Yes. His group is playing the role of a periscope for a certain conspiratorial Mafia, in which young anti-Semites joined in with old Jews."

"Damnation!"

"Be that as it may, colleague, go to the colonel and throw the truth in his face! If your father were alive, he'd tell you the same."

"You're right. I'll do it. . . ."

Barabasz took his fishing rod under one arm and wandered off toward the tent, lost in thought.

In the Press tent, the guests had broken into little groups.

"Just listen to a letter I got from Prague, from my only son," Horaček was saying to Szabos. "He writes that he doesn't want to correspond with me any longer. 'You ought to realize,' he writes, 'that you're not only a superfluous man, but also a harmful one. You are our enemy. The mere fact that you live abroad makes it impossible for me to gain a category in the official hierarchy which I have long since merited as an exemplary worker and loyal Party member. You compromise me by your tearful radio broadcasts, where under the cloak of poetry you glorify the past and you obstruct with slime the minds of our working people. Stop playing with politics in your old age, and serving alien interests! . . .' The boy is your age. I used to love him very much, but today, I, the father of this scamp, I tell you—he's nothing but a careerist! Listen to what comes next: 'Your senile, childish obstinacy, for which you assuredly get a generous salary from the Americans and ex-Nazis, makes you belch insults against everything Czech. . . .' It's not true, he's lying! I never said a bad word against my homeland! 'He who attacks our system, attacks our state; he who attacks our state is an enemy of Czechoslovakia. . . .' Do you hear that? These are the words of my son, a man they've turned into a gramophone record! 'Thanks to you, and only you, I am living on starving wages and am regarded by my environment as a suspect person. If, one of these days, something unpleasant happens to me, you'll be able to congratulate yourself: it will be your doing!' A coward, sir, nothing but a cheap, common coward! And that man is my son. . . . I sent him to school, I made him read the classics, I introduced him to the world of music and painting, together we were moved by Bach and Beethoven. I wanted to make a man of him—I failed: I brought him up to be a scoundrel!"

"Aren't you doing him an injustice?" stammered Szabas, embarrassed by this outburst. "At a distance from that system, we cannot imagine the conditions in which our nearest and dearest are living. . . ."

"Oh, Szabos! What's the good of talking? My son has no right to send me such letters."

Horaček thrust the crumpled sheet of paper into his pocket and went off to the other corner of the tent.

When he returned from the river bank, young Oliphant found his father holding a telegram. The bald man was sitting in a wicker chair and pouring over the text of his speech blinking his protuberant eyes:

"I have bad news for you, son."

"Has Miss Dixon lost her singles at Cannes?"

"No. This is a telegram from home. Poor Patricia! We must go back to Cincinnati right away. She's dying."

"There's no hurry, dad."

"She wants to see us at her side."

"Let's wait until Sunday. . . . After all, she's been 'dying' for a year. Don't you know her?"

Young Oliphant closed his eyes and frowned. He had difficulty in concealing his dislike for his mother. An eccentric woman, hysterical, egoistical! He could not forgive her for an absurd scene a month earlier. Thanks to her, on account of a trivial matter such as the damaging of a mudguard, an entire family council had been summoned. A complete dramatic performance! She had lit a candle in the bedroom, taken the crucifix from round her neck and ordered him to swear, before witnesses, in a circle of fat aunts and dried-up uncles from Cleveland that, as long as she was alive, he would not drive at a high speed. "Promise you won't drive over forty miles an hour!" "Fifty!" he had tried to bargain with her. "Forty," the fat aunts and skinny uncles had shrieked. Miss Dixon would never have done anything of the kind, she would have laughed at the whole funereal fraternity! Forty miles an hour! Girls drive at eighty! He had been made the laughing stock of the whole class. He had already been seized by the rebellious temptation not to keep his promise and to step on the gas out of town, at 120. But he saw his mother's wide-opened eyes and the baleful candle flame reflected in the window. He was overcome by a superstitious fear of the vengeance of Heaven, he gripped the wheel and continued to drag along in the humiliating treadmill of his forty miles an hour, and when classmates from Columbus College passed him with laughter and cries, he felt, in his magnificent car, like a cripple in a bathchair. The ribbon of the highway dissolved in his blinking eyes. He drove on and wept.

"Remember two years ago, when the three of us, with Miss Dixon, went to the tournament at Oklahoma City? Then too she sent a telegram to say she was "dying," that she wanted to say goodbye to us. . . . We went back like lunatics without waiting for the tournament to end. We missed the entire finals!"

"You're a bad son," Oliphant frowned. "If it weren't for my official duties, we would go home right away. You know very well that I can't leave all this mess to the mercies of fate. This fool Sebastiano is likely to make a carnival of Nice out of the most important things. In any case, Patricia simply has no idea of what is going on here. We didn't come here for pleasure. Apologize to your father for the stupid things you said about your poor mother. If I stay on here a few days, I shall be doing so only for your sake, you young egoist."

"Horrible creep," Fred thought, but he went to his father and kissed him on the cheek with respect. The Pharisee!—

* * *

Horaček could not stand the smoke and din. He went out of the tent and came across Greenford. In the light of the searchlights which illuminated the entire encampment, the celebrated journalist looked taller and rather like an obelisque. The old Czech barely came up to his chest.

"I don't know if you remember me. Years ago . . . In Geneva, when the League of Nations was still teething . . . And then we were to establish in Lausanne some European federation of liberals. . . ."

"Of course," Greenford lied, "bygone antedeluvian days . . . What can I do for you?"

"I'm looking for someone to whom I can complain aloud. How do you like this floating of wreaths on the river on Midsummer Night? [1] Don't you think that the issuing of a political program that

1 An ancient Polish tradition in rural districts.

would in honest words put forward the question of the liberation of the enslaved peoples from under Russian domination would be a much more effective undertaking in the "psychological war" than the inflation of rubber bladders?"

"I'd be inconsolable," said Greenford, "if you asked me too many questions. Everything I have to say can be found in my newspaper articles."

Horaček caught the fragrant waft of Calvados in his face but did not give up:

"In view of that, I would like to offer you my views on this liberty picnic! . . ."

"I wish you would go to Oliphant. It wasn't my idea."

"I know, but you are a popular journalist, a man who can influence public opinion. I heard your series of talks on the BBC Third Program entitled 'Prospects of Emerging from an Impasse.' There you put forward the suggestion. . . ."

"Maybe we should rejoin the others?"

"Mr. Greenford," the impatient Horaček pointed in the direction of the East, "the people over there, so eagerly written off the inventory of Europe, are waiting for relief. . . ."

With a click, Greenford snapped a flame from his cigarette lighter, lit a cigarette, and said with veiled impatience:

"Yes. It is very distressing. I understand you, sir: you are for a preventive war. The Communists are not far from the truth when they call the émigrés warmongers. Apart from the fact that the era of the Crusades has passed forever—cultural and civilized developments have raised the value of human life—don't you think that plunging millions of people into the abyss of a new conflagration, that the destruction of—let's say—Notre Dame, the Louvre, the treasures of Rome, Milan Cathedral, the British Museum and many other valuable things—would be too high a price to pay for the liberation of the East Europeans? None of us can be sure that it would not lead to general suicide, to the blowing up of our unhappy planet into the air. How can you be sure that East Europeans want freedom? Maybe it's only that you want to go back to your former homeland? . . ."

"Mr. Greenford! . . ."

"My younger brother, who took part in the invasion of Europe, stormed with his patrol into a certain German village near Aachen with a truly Byronic cry: 'We are bringing you freedom!' Do you know what those liberated Germans replied? 'Danke schön, Herr Leutnant, but we don't need your freedom! We lived better in captivity than you in liberty!' Please make a note of the words of our Prime Minister, who said what most of the nation feel: 'We wish to explain to Russia that she is not threatened by any danger of attack from our side. We wish nothing more from her but that she behave towards us like a good neighbor. . . . I believe that with time the power of the human spirit will prove so great for the tyrants behind the Iron Curtain that internal changes will be brought about in these countries. We shall assuredly not alter the relations prevailing there by pressure from the outside. . . .'"

Horaček gazed at him with horror, barely able to draw breath. He felt that an attack of asthma would seize him at any moment. The exasperated journalist gave the impression of a refractory boy telling his elders something out of "spite," so as to upset them.

"Not bad, not bad," the old Czech wheezed. "That's just the kind of aria this comic opera needed!"

"I know your motto! Freedom and independence! What does that mean, my dear sir? Fortunately there is neither freedom nor independence in this world, and all of us are subject to someone or something. If not to God, then to a policeman and his baton. And this is why we aren't drowning in a sea of anarchy. Do you think that my country is an independent country? We are—and I say it without a shadow of regret—satellites of America, just as all of you are the satellites of Russia. . . ."

"Mr. Greenford! . . ."

"What, after all, is political freedom? Does it fill empty bellies or give work to the unemployed? Does it exist at all without full economic sovereignty? I read your new report on the economic exploitation of the satellite states by Russia. Allow me to say that the notion of business is as closely associated with the notion of exploitation as skin and flesh. One must regard these matters cooly, without any nationalistic mysticism. You say that freedom is indivisible. That is not so. History does not confirm it. Free and enslaved countries have existed side by side for many centuries, and —what's worse—it will certainly continue to be so to the world's end. All of you complain that they falsify the elections in your country, that there's no parliamentary democracy behind the Iron Curtain. Allow me to say that anyone who hasn't the money for good propaganda has no chance in any elections. I know of no moment in history when some fictitious "people" or "nation" governed a country by means of tossing an electoral card into the voting box. Always, everywhere, behind the most varied kinds of screens, mafias and cliques govern. Parliamentary democracy? I can give you figures showing in how many countries of the world women are deprived of the right to vote. And did you hear of the electoral tax, which prevents poverty-stricken Negroes from voting in the southern states of America?"

"Mr. Greenford! . . ."

"What is more," the journalist worked himself up, "as a result of the revolutionary development of communications, in the age of aircraft faster than sound, the world will tend towards integration. I am afraid that the smaller nations will have to give up their ambitions and dreams of sovereignty once and for all. There is no return to the *status quo ante*. Politics is not a spiritualistic seance. We must be careful when resurrecting ghosts. The Versailles Treaty and the Wilsonian daydreams of the self-determination of small nations have brought a bloody world war as a result, and everything we are witnessing today. . . ."

Horaček was no longer listening. With a gesture of resignation he went off to the other end of the tent.

* * *

The timid Barabasz, on the way to Kajman, was struggling inwardly with himself. His daughter had not received a scholarship. It would be necessary to pay for the entire half year in advance, from September 1. His father-in-law was demanding the repayment of a hundred pounds before he left for the States. Instalments on the furniture, radio, carpet. The landlord was putting the rent up. His wife had no winter coat. . . . On the other hand, he felt that Borowczyk was right: better poverty than a false moral position.

He sat down on an oxygen container by the wayside and pondered. The one person he had truly loved in his life had been his father. For many years he had been haunted by a heart-breaking recollection from his youth. His father, walking in the direction of a red building, step by step, with his head lowered. There is no cause for pride or satisfaction when a man has to go to prison in his own free country for criticizing the government. He had paused every now and then, sighed, wiped his spectacles. His wife had accompanied him through two streets, the younger children stayed home. It would be bad if the memory of such matters remained in their young minds, but it remained all the same! It was said that their father had gone to Iwonicz, to take the waters. One of their aunts was to send three postcards on purpose, at intervals of a month, from a boarding house in Iwonicz. But the oldest boy had long since guessed why his father did not sleep nights. In a small town everyone knows everyone else. Passers-by stopped, nodded, gripped his hands with sympathy. His father, annoyed, hid his hands in his pockets and muttered. He did not like himself in the role of a martyr. Not far from the red wall his colleagues from the editorial office, a photographer and sympathetic ladies from the Party with flowers in their hands were waiting. The editor became exasperated at the sight of the photographer, told him to go to the devil, then slipped between the half-open prison gate rapidly and furtively. He saw no political sensation in his fate. Some policeman, with long whiskers, pressed his hands sorrowfully, as though trying to justify the faulty system of government in the capital. The days passed slowly, each as like the others as drops of water. In his solitude the editor was devoured by the idea that in England, France, or America he would not have been jailed for his "Press crime," not for a single moment. When he came out to freedom three months later, his oldest son noticed at the prison gate that his father stooped, had grown smaller, and that his temples were covered with grey hair. So many years ago, but how mild in comparison to what had happened later, and what was happening to this very day in those regions! But Barabasz could not rid himself of the thought that it had been men such as Kajman who had thrust his father into prison. Colonel Kajman was a typical representative of that "school." What was even worse, he defended those men, those methods to this very day, in emigration! He does not show a trace of regret or repentance. He knows already now which of his political opponents among the emigration he will put in an isolation camp after returning to his liberated homeland. . . .

Barabasz suddenly got up and made his decision.

The telephone rang again in the tent. Oliphant reluctantly lifted the receiver—he was just writing to Miss Dixon and fixing a meeting in Geneva for the automobile show.

"Hallo, boss," a cheerful voice resounded in the receiver.

"Sebastiano here! I've just had a brain wave! I was reading in *Stars and Stripes* that the Reds are boycotting American dances behind the Iron Curtain. I suggest we broadcast three hours of jazz every day for the oppressed nations. Good, eh?"

"My dear boy," Oliphant sighed with pity. "You're always ready to turn the most serious things into a game for children. How's the wind?"

"In about a half-hour. . . ."

* * *

Young Szabos was feeling terrible. This whole show got on his nerves. He looked with dislike at old foxes like Greenford, Gutenberg, and Marron, and at young know-alls like Gaston or that stranger in the Tyrolean hat, who had argued that patriotism was an invention of the wealthy. The quarrelsome Poles irritated him with their hole-and-corner intrigues, as did his fellow-countrymen paying shameless compliments to foreign journalists. The female international intellectuals (their fringes cut like men's) chattering between sips from their glass about new books published in Paris and London. Cocteau's films, the prices at Majorca hotels, the social scandals and illnesses of their acquaintances—all this repulsed him. The naive Americans in their flowery shirts, hailing one another with loud voices, were also quite alien to him—he loathed sport, haste, the smell of gasoline, the Scout movement, and their noisy, blatant joy of life. But all his dislikes, as he well knew, were only a mask for the true cause of his bad mood: his affair with Lady Hopper was weighing him down like the Biblical millstone around his neck, and his conversation with Mrs. Karpova, worried about the dirty business deals of her ex-husband, filled him with distaste.

Strolling through a little wood, Szabos made the decision to turn a new leaf: he would break away from his present way of life, he would go into a factory and would purify himself by hard labor of the dregs of that old Englishwoman's maternal affection, he would earn five or six pounds a week and burrow into a drab, little room in one of those horrible London housing blocks around Paddington or Kilburn.

He was walking past some ferns—in the light of a searchlight they looked like a weird stage setting—when he caught sight of a small girl in a deck-chair at the entrance of the tent. She must have been about twelve. Covered by a coat, her face upturned to the sky, spectacles on her thin pointed nose, she sat there as though sunning herself on a beach.

Szabos stopped, surprised:

"Young lady! The sun has gone!"

"I'm not sunbathing, sir," the skinny little creature squeaked.

"Then what are you doing, child?"

"My name is Evelyn Greenford."

"Did your daddy bring you here?"

"Yes. Ever since mummy married Milton Warwick, daddy takes me everywhere with him."

"I'm afraid there's nothing of any interest here."

"Oh, no! It's such a noble and beautiful moment. Do you think I don't know what's going on?"

"It's politics, my child. Nothing beautiful."

"But what are you saying! I know all about it."

"Did daddy tell you?"

"No. Daddy thinks I'm still a child. It was Agnes who told me. Agnes is our maid, an Esthonian. Her husband and son are in Russia."

"Poor woman! So it is she who's bringing you up, instead of your mother?"

"Do you think they won't ever come back? We pray for those imprisoned in jails and for those who chop wood in the snow. That ought to help them, oughtn't it?"

Szabos took a bar of chocolate out of his pocket. Lady Hopper packed his pockets with candy, as if he were a small boy. But the little girl with the pointed nose shook her head vigorously:

"I am not eating anything today. Agnes and I fast three times a week. Daddy doesn't like it at all. He even wanted to send Agnes away from our home, but he can't do it. . . ."

"Why not?"

"Because he knows I'd die. It's terrible that the two of us, Agnes and I, can't change anything in the world. I pray. I go to church and I fast, but perhaps that isn't enough."

"It is a great deal. More than others do. But you should not go hungry. You look like a frozen sparrow. If you lose your strength, you will never grow into a strong and healthy person who might be able to change the world"—he heard himself say, solemnly. What a nauseating little scene this was!—he thought to himself.

The sight of little Evelyn remained before Szabos' eyes during the conversation which he privately called "decisive." He looked into Lady Hopper's eyes, lined with folds of yellow skin, and thought of the precocious child, and her yearning to improve the world. He envied her that purity of heart. He listened absent-mindedly to the old woman's voice. He did not deny that he had met Mrs. Karpova and arranged to meet her the next day. He noticed that the whites of her eyes, staring at him, had tiny red filaments reaching almost to the iris, and yellowish blotches in the corners—the sign of sickness. Hard, masculine furrows fell away from her violet-painted lips. The skin of her neck, rubbed with cream and smothered with dark powder, was hanging loose, like that of a turtle. He shut his eyes.

"I don't intend to deny," he said after a moment in a weary voice, "that the situation in which I find myself calls for a firm decision. I should have done it long ago. . . ."

A silence followed, during which Szabos realized that he was afraid of his own boldness.

"Do as you like," she said in an exaggeratedly polite tone. "However, you ought to make quite sure, young man, that you are acting sensibly. . . ."

"I think this will be best. . . ."

"I don't know whether it will be best for you. You're weak and reckless. You need constant protection. You'll be lost on your own."

"I'm not a child."

"You're still a big child, but we won't argue. I planned on taking a trip from Germany to Italy the day after tomorrow, I wanted to take you with me. It was to have been a pleasant surprise for you. However, with things like this—I must know today whether you're coming with me or going back to London. The date for paying the subsidy to your organizational fund falls in a week. I don't want you to misunderstand me, but I can't introduce any confusion into my book-keeping. . . ."

"I understand," he replied, and reddened.

"Have you ever been to Taormina in Sicily? Do you know Naples?"

"I have never been in the south," he stammered, "but I . . . really. . . ."

She reflected for several moments, with a tense expression.

"If it means so much to you," she said dryly, "we can take Karpova with us. Think about it. . . ."

"I'll think about it." He closed his eyes, so as not to see the hated face before him.

"You will have time for important decisions when you get back from Sicily. And now, ungrateful boy, let's join the others. Here you'll meet people who can help not only you personally, but also your unfortunate homeland."

He had the urge to run away, anywhere, but unwittingly gave her his arm. They went into the aquamarine tent, to the kingdom of the Great Gutenberg and his admirers.

"If the Russians are to come and occupy us," the young Frenchman soliloquized—"then let them do it as fast as possible. Nothing is as tormenting as a permanent state of terror. Better a bad certainty than good uncertainty. . . ."

Szabos took a banknote out of his pocket and gave it to a waiter: "A double whisky!"

Hlohovec awakened. He must have dozed off. A sharp pain cut through his shoulders. For a moment he didn't know what was happening to him. Not until he caught the smell of gasoline and felt the warmth flowing from the engine did he remember he was driving in the direction of the frontier.

"They must have smashed me up inside," he complained to Emil.

"You'll recuperate over there. It isn't far now."

The engine rumbled dully—they were climbing through a narrowing landscape at the foot of the mountains. Dusk was falling, but Emil did not switch the headlights on. Crouching over the wheel, the furrow vertical between his brows, he was staring at the highway.

"Won't they have sent a patrol to pursue us?"

"Don't think about that!"

"After all, they must have noticed that we're not there. They'll have got through on the phone to the guard posts on the frontier. We shall fall right into a trap!"

"No one is going to chase us. It's two days now that they've got you marked as dead in the prison register. . . ."

"Dead? But my dead body?"

"Traveling by car," joked Emil.

"Yes, but all this strikes me as too sensational to be true even for a moment!"

"I see you don't trust my professional qualifications. I assure you, old boy, that everything is going according to plan. At the next village we'll stop the car and set off on foot to the forest. I know every track there, every little path. . . ."

"They'll find out that you left in an official car. You ought to escape along with me."

"No. I'm going back to Prague."

"They'll arrest you!"

Hlohovec wanted to exclaim that after crossing the frontier, he would be able to help him, thanks to his contacts in the "Council for Free Czechoslovakia," but he bit it back. He felt in debt to Emil. He was grateful to him for the rescue, but at the same time he regarded his comrade of youth with instinctive fear. That uniform with the colonel's insignia and the red star on his cap disturbed him.

They drove on in silence.

Amidst the guests strolling between the tents and the balloons, a broad-shouldered man attracted attention, rocking at the knees in a manner typical of men who have spent half their lives in the saddle. Colonel Kajman, the hero from the Battle of Węgierska Gorka where—malicious rumor had it—he had captured eight brand-new enemy motorcycles with an outflanking maneuver, losing barely a company of troops. He had come to the balloon show in a bad temper. Dr. Dutkiewicz's group had accused him in front of the Americans of dictatorial efforts. It had been by a veritable miracle, after many humiliating attempts, that he managed to obtain his invitation. Hours of waiting for the wind, the futility of trying to start some sort of conversation with the foreigners, most of whom spoke only English and French, and the presence of his political opponents made him choleric. He ought not to have come here, but he was afraid of proving the truth of the old saying that the absent are wrong. Fortunately, he had bumped into his former subordinate, Sergeant-Major Kula, in the Press tent. In reply to the question "What are you doing here, Kula?" the old rascal smiled: "I'm representing the Free Albanians."

"But you're a Pole!" Kajman was shocked.

"Yes, sir, but because there are thirty Albanian activists in

London, of whom only twelve are experts, I decided to help them. The idea of an Isthmus. You'll ask, Colonel, whether there's living in it? A man has a finger in all sorts of pies. We publish a bulletin called *Albania in Chains*. I write little articles in Polish and my wife, who's Scottish, translates them into French, and a student we know puts the whole job into Albanian, and so we manage somehow!"

The vigilant Borowczyk squeezed his way in between the trucks and asked Kajman point-blank:

"Is it true that Barabasz is giving up his post in your weekly?"

"I know nothing about it. Who told you?"

"I heard someone mention it. But I don't want to repeat gossip!"

Kajman had never liked Barabasz, but because the little man with the dazed look had formerly been writing for extreme-Opposition newspapers and was good with his pen, he had given him the job, bearing in mind the old saying "If you can't cope with a poacher, make him a gamekeeper." Barabasz, although he wore a lamb's skin, still had some bad habits from his long years of poaching. For instance, in the Christmas number he had placed the picture of a general on the fourth page while on the cover he spread out the photograph of the prettiest Polish girl in Manchester. A trifling matter perhaps, but significant.

Borowczyk, seeing Barabasz approaching from the distance, neatly dodged behind the battery of searchlights. Meanwhile, the Colonel angrily drew his breath:

"You're hanging about outside the camp," he said peevishly to Barambaz. "I've heard you go fishing at times like this. . . . What idiocy."

For a moment, Barabasz struggled with his inborn shyness and beating heart, turning alternately pale and crimson:

"Mr. Kajman," he began quietly, "I've been looking for you everywhere, in order to . . ."

"I'm no 'Mr. Kajman'! I have not yet stopped being a colonel! And if it weren't for this miserable exile, I'd be a general!"

"Mr. Kajman," he repeated in a trembling voice, "Please excuse me, but I can't go on any longer. To be sure, I won't have anything to live on . . . My wife, my children . . . But please accept my resignation! I don't want this post any more! Do you hear me? I don't want it, and that's that! The devil take those thirty pounds!"

he was speaking louder and louder. "It's something to do with my father, but you couldn't understand that! No, something even greater is at stake! Faith in oneself and in one's belief! I can no longer fight against Communist totalitarianism in a paper published by men who wouldn't hesitate to introduce into a future Poland a white or a black totalitarianism of their own breeding! White, brown, black and red, overt or concealed, Polish or foreign—this is loathsome to me, Mr. Kajman. That's all! Goodbye!"

"What's the matter with you? Have you gone mad?" Kajman drew back. "What rubbish you talk! Of course, you're free and from this very moment! And you're going to pay me for those words some day, and through the nose! I've long wanted to throw you out on your ear! Go, certainly, go! Be off, you shitass!"

Barabasz, cringing, his heart stuck fast in his gullet, disappeared into the throng of mechanics erecting some scaffolding. He squeezed his way through the din of foreign tongues, his head pulled in between his trembling shoulders. "Good God! What have I done?" Terror seized him. "I've lost my job! I acted like a madman! I ought to go and apologize to him. But it's already too late!" He burrowed into some ferns and hid his burning face in his hands.

Meanwhile Borowczyk, who had been watching this incident, came up to the indignant Colonel and offered him a cigarette:

"He's chucked his job, the son of a bitch," Kajman puffed. "The boor! The beast! But I saw it coming, as soon as that photograph came out on the fourth page . . . The swine! A sewer-rat, sir!"

"You'll find ten to take his place, Colonel. Are there so few capable and willing men among the emigration? But it would be best to keep this incident quiet—that's my advice. If the others found out . . . There would be too much rejoicing in the group of Dutkiewicz *et consortes!*"

"You're right," Kajman blew a cloud of smoke around himself. "I'll find a better man. But this kind of thing hurts me as a Pole. That a fellow countryman in exile should behave in this way to a fellow-countryman . . . It's sheer ingratitude, sir. Boorishness!"

"Allow me to propose a candidate for the vacancy, Colonel.

"Whom?"

"The under-signed. . . ."

"You would . . . You? But you're working for the *Democrat's Voice!*"

"Now and then, Colonel, and at half wages, but what is more important: *à contre coeur!* I am one of those men who are capable of detachment and a broader outlook, a wholesome and positive attitude to a given problem. I admit that my sympathies have always been rather on your side, but *necessitas, dura necessitas.* . . . Besides, I have an idea which might interest your paper, Colonel. I have found out from Americana MP's that some new refugee from Poland is licking his wounds at the hospital in a neighboring village. I could undertake to write down conversations with him. If the man were to declare that the people in Poland have no liking for Messrs. Dutkiewicz and Byclik, whereas . . . Such things are sometimes done in propaganda. You understand me, Colonel?"

"If it's not too obvious, then by all means."

"And—about the job?"

The Colonel beamed and stretched out his hand: "The job is yours, sir! At least here's one advantage from this 'Liberty Circus'! How's the wind blowing, damn it?"

"Apparently it's going to shift at any moment."

Just before the place where Emil had arranged to conceal the automobile, Hlohovec was seized by a fever and began to moan incomprehensibly. He sank into his wretched clothes as into a sleeping-bag. With his eyes closed, he could see everything as clear as day. It might have been the car window. It might have been the screen of a TV set. The banging and whistling made it impossible to catch whole phrases accurately as they whirled in the air, but the view of the streets of his native town was excellent. American and Czech banners were hanging from the windows of the houses. Golden lions and great silver stars.

"Children! Children!" he heard his own voice as though coming from the horn of an old gramophone. "I announce to you that General Eisenhower, by command of President Truman, has appointed me Mayor of liberated Bratislava! As for the shot-down Soviet fighter-planes—kindly present them to my mother as a souvenir!

"Long live my true friend and savior, Emil, general of the united European armies!" . . . "Emil, bow, the bishop is looking." Silver stars were whirling in the air, the shattered bars of the Pankrac jail lay scattered in the street.

"God bless America!"—the bells were ringing above the town.

—"God bless Emil and Hlohovec!" Emil, flourishing the star-spangled banner, and the Eagle of Freedom on his round cap,—marching in front of the Town Hall and following behind—the children—the Social Democrats and the stamp-collectors, murdered in the torture-chambers!—a figure in a leather jacket, in chains, stumbling along . . . "You criminal!" Emil shouted, "you hit my friend Anton Hlohovec, our timid Tony from fourth grade in our High School! We shall hang you for it from the Town Hall tower!" More tanks with Americans were rolling closer . . . "Where are you from, fellows?" "We're from the other side!" "And what happened to the one with the whiskers?" "He's been killed. A bomb got him! He burned to death! He couldn't survive the 3000° C!"

Silver stars were whirling over the roofs of the town, like birds. "Children, Social Democrats, war veterans, Scouts, skittle-players, and stamp-collectors,—the Lord God, the beloved capitalist Lord God has defeated the Red devils with American bombs!" "Long live the Mayor of Bratislava, Anton Hlohovec, whose kidneys and one lung they beat out in Pankrac!" . . . "And now, General, the 'Czardas Princess,' the prima ballerina will appear in sequins, Marika, the fiancée of my friend Emil, who wears the Boxing Club badge in his buttonhole! . . ."

Flowers were flying over the silver town. Carnations, narcissi, violets, lilies of the valley, and roses. Kranz, with his sprained ankle, was moving forward in the second tank and revealing his bad teeth. The porter from the Palais, was riding in the third and playing the "Ave Maria" on a fiddle. The Bishop, in a crown of thorns, was thanking Emil for the liberation. They kissed each other on the cheek! "Turn away, boys, no peeping when I die! . . ." Marika unfastened her blouse and revealed a lung eaten away by TB. "I was trying to escape across the frontier, I was running after the 'Voice of America'!" she sobbed, a bouquet of tiny balloons in her bony hand. "A lifeless droshky-driver was driving me, Mr. Mayor, and he drove me to the cemetery! . . ."

American flags over the rooftops, smoke merrily flying from chimneys into the sky, the sun over Bratislava! The buses, municipal buses, joyfully rearing up on their hind wheels like circus horses . . . Officers in festive uniforms. Can you all hear what they're shouting through the loudspeaker? "Attention, attention, where is Anton Hlohovec?" "Where is your Great National Hero, Anton Hloho-

vec?" . . . "Killed in Panrac. He refused to confess!"—replied the Young Eagles in front of the "Palais de Danse." "My little son, Tony" (is it his mother's voice, in her black shawl?), "I heard you weeping in the night, I got up and hurried to the cellar to bring you a jug of Pilzner and five crowns to pay for Marika's knedlički!"

"Hey lads! Maleček! Emil! Kranz! Let's sing 'In a Persian Market'!" Little Marika's eyes sparkling on the black pillow. Blue lines on her eyelids with a little star in the middle! Cold eyes staring at them from behind the hotel window . . . It was the waiter, a wicked waiter with a red star and sickle on his forehead. "And this necklace, Tony dear, is made of knocked-out human teeth! Emil, my fiance, a colonel in the secret police gave them to me!" "If you had married me and not left for Prague, we'd have had a child, looking like Maleček. Maleček also slept with me in Bratislava, in the 'Crown' Hotel."

"Emil, wipe the nicotine off your gloves, the Bishop has come back to our town!"

Little drops of bloody rain dripping down the screen. "And now, mummy, let's pray to Saint Emil who brought us freedom in an official automobile!" "Saint Marika, patron of the Czech-German frontier, pray for us! . . ."

The banners floated away, the tanks drove past, the bouquet of flowers fluttered off and only the balloons trembled on top of the Town Hall, like tears of joy. "Did you listen to the Czech radio from Munich?" "No, Colonel." "Do you have friends in the Council of Free Czechoslovakia?" "Yes, Your Honor." "Who?" "Colonel Emil with a star in his cap!" "Admit it! . . ." "Strip him naked! . . ."

Hlohovec wiped the copious sweat from his forehead with a sleeve. The sharp pain in his shoulders brought him back to his senses. He gasped for air, his lips open wide, like a fish.

"Emil," he groaned, "I'm scared."

"We're there. Let's go." The Colonel gave him his arm.

The meteorologist's forecast was fulfilled as though by clockwork. The excited Sebastiano shouted into the phone at ten o'clock precisely:

"Mr. Oliphant! Good news! The wind has turned!"

The Grand Vizier gathered his papers from the little table and ran out into the open space:

"Mrs. Karpova! Horaček! Fred, you young rascal! Mr. Greenford and Mr. Gutenberg! Monsieur Marron! Gaston! Herr Regierungstrat! Lady Hopper! Byclik! Dutkiewicz! Szabos! Colonel Kajman! Ladies and gentlemen!"

He ran around the camp, thrilled as a child and set his face to the wind:

"It's coming! It's blowing! It's roaring! Friends, we'll be starting in a moment! Get the film team in place! Microphone ready? Press and guests on the platform! Call the frontier posts. Where's the Congressman who was supposed to arrive at ten o'clock? And the delegates of the Occupation troops? Sebastiano, you fool, set the siren going! Searchlights to the sky!"

The siren ripped the air apart. The triumphant ringing of bells resounded in the amplifiers. Horns hooted from the column of vehicles. The mechanics joyfully banged their tools on the gas containers.

"The wind has turned!" Borowczyk ran into the hangar. "Mr. Barabasz, it's about to begin! I congratulate you on your courageous decision! Let's go, gentlemen!"

Sebastiano stood on the platform and was giving his final instructions through a microphone. Dozens of people came out of the tents and marquees, from the automobiles and neighboring buildings. The crossed arms of the searchlights formed a blazing star in the sky. It was as light as day.

"The records with the national anthems!" the excited Seb directed. "Is the balloon team in place? Have you checked the valves for setting off the leaflets? Where are the sound trucks? Move up the power station! Where's Fred with his speech? Where's Horaček with the prayer? More bells, fellows! When I give the signal—break off,—and music! Full power! Let those devils on the other side hear what's happening! Damn them! For my brother!"

"It's blowing, it's blowing to the east!" cried the guests. The ladies raised their scarfs and wraps, to check the direction of the wind.

"Nearly a gale, damn it!"—now the journalists were also caught by the excitement. "They'll fly to Prague, to Warsaw, maybe even to Russia!"

"Oh, this is thrilling," said Lady Hopper. "Amidst all this excitement I feel younger!"

The delegates of the German authorities, under the influence of the general commotion, also began to shout:

"Nach Osten! Nach Osten!"

Gutenberg's hoarse bass voice was heard above the general uproar:

"I'm worried about possible complications. If those people over there should start firing at the balloons, the bullets will whistle around our ears. If Soviet fighter planes should come our way, then . . . look, ladies and gentlemen—there, on the highway! The American anti-aircraft guns are going to open fire!"

"The hill is swarming with soldiers!" cried Greenford. "This game may cost us dearly!"

Little Evelyn covered her face with her hands and began praying:

"Oh, good Lord God, let these balloons bring them the good news that soon they will be free. Let just one little balloon reach the husband and son of Agnes. And let the prisoners see it through their barred windows. And may no one beat and starve them any more."

Szabos looked at Mrs. Karpova with admiration. Tall, high-breasted, in a fluttering dress, she was standing on the wooden platform, as on a pedestal. In the light of the searchlights, her hair spread in the wind like a banner, she seemed to him the personification of struggle and victory.

"Aneczka!" he cried, enraptured, "you look like the goddess of Freedom, like the Marseillaise brought to life, like Nike of Samothrace! Like Joan of Arc. . . ."

"Remember about the 'Trading Corporation' shares?"

"I'll do anything you want. Let's go to Sicily together! Tell me you love me."

"I love you alone! Nobody else!"

The stupefied and happy young man forgot all his resolutions. He went to Lady Hopper and whispered in her ear:

"An hour ago I behaved like an abominable fool. I withdraw everything I said. I feel better now! As though the wind had blown right through me!"

From under the folds of yellow skin her eyes sparkled full of thankfulness. Her violet lips twisted into a smile. He seized her hands. The hardened skin of her fingers, which had always reminded him of the feel of the bark of a tree, did not repel him in his excitement. He must strike while the iron was hot! When he had expounded to her the matter of letting shares in the 'Trading Corporation' go to Karpova's husband, she sulked and frowned at first, but in the end she yielded. He found himself billing and cooing to her, to put her under his spell until she smoothed back the curls from his brow and said:

"—Shares? At a time like this. How tactless. Like someone sneezing during Holy Mass. But have it your own way, you naughty little brat. It's all under the influence of this marvelously inspiring ceremony. I am so thrilled, I can't even think of my own business interests!"

Leaning on Szabos' arm, Lady Hopper straightened herself and began reciting with youthful enthusiasm:

"I will not cease from mental fight,
Nor shall the sword sleep in my hand—
Till we have built Jerusalem
In England's green and pleasant land! . . ."

"Mr. Oliphant!" the breathless telegraphist ran up at the last moment, "I am very sorry that at such a time. . . . Maybe I ought to wait for the end of the ceremonies?"

"Anything wrong? A radio telegram?"

"Right," the telegraphist wiped the back of his head. "Bad news!"

"From Cannes? Has she lost the singles?"

"No. From Cincinnati."

"I guessed it," he sighed. "Patricia worse again. . . ."

"She's dead," the telegraphist rolled his eyes in sorrow. "An hour ago!"

"Poor Patricia!" Oliphant clutched for support for an instant and shut his protruding eyes. For a fraction of a second he felt something like resentment toward his wife for doing this on purpose, out of inborn malice, just to spoil his stay in Europe. At such a moment! But there was nothing to be done: we can't call off the celebrations! How shall I tell my son? Fred loved her more than life itself. Call the boy here to me!

"Fred, be brave," his father put one hand on his shoulder. "You know that our mother has been gravely ill for a long time. . . ."

"I can guess," his eyes narrowed. "You want to send me home."

"We'll go together."

"To Cannes? To Geneva?"

"No. To Cincinnati. A moment ago. . . ."

"How come? And Miss Dixon?"

"Don't interrupt. I have very bad news for you, my boy. Patricia is dead."

For some time the boy sat in silence and stared at his fingernails. He did not know what to reply. He wanted to cry, if only for the sake of appearances, but he could find no tears under his eyelids. Finally he stroked his father's hand and said,

"Don't worry, dad!"

"Don't worry, Fred!" Oliphant sighed and drew his son to him.

* * *

After the playing of the anthems and unfurling of the banners, Oliphant greeted the Congressman—a venerable old gentleman with his hair parted in the middle, gold-rimmed eye-glasses, a well-cut jacket—and read his speech from his notes. After the closing words "We are confident that this day shall come!" Horaček was supposed to come up to the microphone and make a speech in Czech, but—to the amazement of the entire company—the old man had wandered off somewhere. But thanks to Karpova's presence of mind there was no gap in the program. At the last moment she ran up to the microphone and improvised a graceful five-minute speech. All the same, Horaček's absence began arousing general curiosity.

For five minutes the megaphones summoned Horaček to appear at "headquarters."

"Where's that old Orpheus?" Sebastiano was furious. "After all, he knew he was to speak immediately after Oliphant! He's ruining our time-table. The old fool!"

"Someone must have been the last to see him, after all! He must have been talking to someone. Maybe he's got lost in the neighborhood? It's hardly likely that they've kidnapped him!"

"He isn't here," Karpova reported. "I've searched all the tents. He's disappeared like a stone into water."

"I remember he was talking to me on political matters," Greenford put in. "Then, he went for a stroll in the clearing. . . ."

"He read me a letter from his son," said Szabos. "He was very upset. . . ."

"You're right!" cried a lady. "Remember, he told us in the tent that he meant to throw himself on the live wires at the frontier! I thought it was a poetical metaphor. . . ."

"Impossible. I've known Horaček from childhood. He's an idealist."

"No one has said anything about treachery. We're talking about common hysteria. He was in bad shape lately. He kept talking about death all the time."

"He must have taken offense at something," cried the young Frenchman. "The Slavs are like children. They take offense at any trifle. To the devil with these poets! They parade with their verses like a hen with its egg, and they are convinced they know more about life than dentists or pharmacists."

"Apparently someone saw him walking to the village."

"After him!" cried Oliphant. "He can't have gone more than four miles! It's unheard of for a man in a position of responsibility, a member of the advisory committee, to behave like a little child. I propose we proceed to releasing the balloons. Sebastiano, let's have more religious hymns and bell-ringing!"

"I'll catch him up," Fred jumped into a jeep standing nearby with the agility of an acrobat. Three more people climbed into the vehicle. With an Indian cry of joy, the lad seized the wheel as though it were the fragment of a lifebelt. The car bounced several times over the roots like a frolicsome colt. After several graceful turns, it squeezed through the valley of trucks and almost flew down the highway in a cloud of smoke and dust.

"A hundred miles!" the delirious boy shouted. "A hundred and ten!" A hundred and twenty! A hundred and thirty!

They caught up with Horaček just outside the village. By what miracle he had managed to walk so many miles in such a short time—that was a veritable riddle. He must have been running, not walking.

"Mr. Horaček!" the men from the jeep called to him. "We've been looking for you everywhere, and here you are! Where are you going?"

But the old man did not look round, merely tramped along the highroad, his head hanging, spectacles perched on the end of his nose.

"Get into the car!" cried the telegraphist. "Mr. Oliphant is waiting for you."

"Horaček, what's happened?" someone asked in Czech. "Have you gone deaf?"

"Come sir, get in the car!"—shouted Fred, and he braked the jeep directly in front of the walking man. "My father is asking for you. It's started already!"

Horaček walked on in silence, without paying the slightest attention to their cries. Impatient, the telegraphist jumped out of the car and ran up to the old Czech:

"Hey, you! What's the matter with you? Where are you off to in such a hurry?"

"You were supposed to make a speech. Everyone was waiting for you!"

"Are you getting in or not? Will you please answer me? What are we to tell Mr. Oliphant?"

The telegraphist tried to take him by the arm, but Horaček removed his hand and continued to march on without a word.

"All right! If you don't want to! We won't use force!" the telegraphist drew back, offended. "I ask you politely, that's all. If someone carries on oddly, that's his own business."

"Let him alone," said one of the men in an officer's uniform. "I looked into his face. He won't come back. I know this kind of thing from war-time. That man isn't sick or crazy. He is profoundly unhappy."

Leaning against the automobile, they remained a while on the road, watching the figure of the stooping man as he moved away.

They were crawling through heather. Hlohovec could hear Emil panting behind him. Red spots whirled before his eyes, sweat poured down his face. After a few minutes they reached a clump of trees. Hlohovec lay down on the moss for a rest, and pressed his burning face into the damp earth.

"Get up," the colonel whispered. "It's here. In a moment we'll have to separate. One more spurt, and it's all over. . . ."

Hlohovec raised himself with an effort onto his knees and looked half-consciously at Emil. His cheeks were mud-stained. The blood was throbbing in his head. He could not catch his breath.

"Already? The frontier?"

"Anton," the Colonel lowered his head and wiped away the

sweat with his sleeve, "cross yourself now and run straight ahead as fast as you can. Straight into the blaze of those searchlights. Run three hundred yards and you'll be safe. See you, old boy! Take care of yourself!"

But Hlohovec was seized by an evil presentiment. He stuck his feet into the moss and leaned against the tree:

"Strange . . . Only now do I realize that I don't want to defect at all. I'm afraid of freedom. I . . . I. . . . Why don't you leave me alone! Let me vegetate in my old Bratislava! Emil, let's go home. . . ."

"Man," the Colonel interrupted, "Understand that you MUST defect. . . ."

Hlohovec gazed more attentively at his friend and suddenly his heart jumped.

"You must," Emil repeated. "Get me?"

"I . . . I. . . ." Hlohovec stammered and all his traumatic terrors leaped at his throat. "You want to . . . me? . . ."

"You fool!" shouted Emil, growing impatient. "Don't waste valuable time!"

Suddenly he understood everything. The whole truth of the last two days of deceit dawned on him.

"My friend!" he groaned and convulsively seized hold of the tree. "Is there no other way?"

"None! No help for it!"

"They ordered you to?"

"They ordered me. I am sorry it had to be me. They must have found out that we're friends. I have no choice. It's either you or me!"

"I understand. You want to shoot me down as I cross the frontier. You cheated me. . . ."

"I couldn't do otherwise. Let's not waste time!"

Hlohovec burst quietly into tears:

"Emil, my friend . . . let me go free . . . Have mercy . . . Don't kill me!"

"I can't. I'm only a policeman. There are others over me. It's the system—there's no way out of it."

"You cannot do this. It's impossible!"

"I'm sorry, but it's not my fault. Now run for it!"

Hlohovec let the tree trunk go and staggered:

"Too bad," he groaned. "You could have killed me in the car, when I was asleep. . . ."

"Run for it!" the impatient Colonel repeated. "I'm doing what they ordered me to do!"

"Do it so that it doesn't take too long . . . And so that it doesn't hurt!"

The Colonel nodded. There was a brief silence. The beams of searchlights crossed in the sky. From the distance, beyond the thicket, came the dull rumble of motors and the stifled sound of singing. Something boomed and rang, a crashing sound, like applause.

"I'm afraid, Emil . . . I'm afraid of death and pain!"

"Don't be scared, old man. It only takes a second!"

"Now?"

"Yes, now!"

"Goodbye, Emil!"

"Goodbye, Tony! Run for it, my friend. Don't look round!"

"Emil . . . Emil. . . ." Hlohovec started up with an effort. He tripped on the clumps of heather and ran ahead, weeping. "My friend!" he called, "not at my legs! Not at my shoulders! Aim straight at my head!"

For a moment he disappeared into the darkness, but after he had run a dozen yards a bouquet of pink light burst out from the other side and revealed him crouching, hands pressed over his ears, in clouds of dazzling brightness.

The Colonel took out his revolver and softly went after the defector.

Meanwhile, on the other side of the frontier, several of the journalists did not go out of the tent at all, but were carrying on an argument amidst the ringing of bells and religious music. Opinions were divided. Under the influence of the festive mood, all were shouting at the same time:

"A Hennessy! A Martell!" An Otard!"

"What? Hennessy? A nation of sailors drinks rum!"

"Gin! An ordinary gin with three drops of vermouth!"

"Scotch! Irish whisky! But gin—never!"

"Shut up! 'Curtain Moonlight' is the best!"

"Sulphuric acid! I wouldn't touch it!"

"There's nothing like 'Captain Morgan,' King of Jamaica!"

"Turpentine! There's only one drink: Calvados!"

"I'd give a tubful of Calvados for a half-bottle of my 'Pale Ale'."

"Gentlemen, let's not exaggerate! Men of principle drink pure alcohol. Beer kills the intellect and faith in man!"

The drunk Barabasz, to the mortification of his fellow-countrymen, settled down under the table, compromising the national dignity by his abusive babbling:

"He's crucified Barabasz, that shitass Kajman! Hang him, the scoundrel, on a balloon; Let him float away. . . . My wife won't have a winter coat on account of that bastard! He's crucified Barabasz. . . ."

Several Poles threw themselves on the drunken man and tried to drag him out from under the table. The little man with the dazed look burst into tears, like a child:

"Is this supposed to be your ideal? . . . that a person like Kajman should . . . such injustice . . . on such a great day. . . ."

The ceremony in the open air had reached its climax. Trucks with balloons drove up to the platform. Sebastiano, the master of ceremonies, switched off the mechanical music and a solemn silence fell, as in a church. The Congressman folded his hands over his belly, as if for a graveside speech, and leaned his gray head forward. The officers raised their gloved hands in a salute. The German officials took off their Homburgs.

Oliphant, moved, surrounded by executive members of the Society of the Friends of Freedom, solemnly went up to a gigantic rubber pumpkin. He took the switch in both hands and pulled it towards him. The watchful Sebastiano at that very same instant started a record with the hymn "O Lord, Who art Freedom, bless our labors. . . ."

The balloon set off by Oliphant soared in the blaze of light over the tops of the pine-trees and majestically glided eastward. Shouts and applause drowned the rattle of film cameras. Seized by enthusiasm, the guests went up one by one to the platform, said a few words into the microphone and set off more air vessels into space. The sky, illuminated by orange and silver light, swarmed with balloons. Some flew upward triumphantly, like Biblical doves, while others rose toward the sky slowly and heavily, like huge spiders.

Whole squadrons of inflated birds fluttered across the barbed wires, entanglements and frontier bunkers. Stream after stream, wave after wave, by the dozens, in hundreds they drifted from the illuminated field into the darkness opposite. . . .

Little Evelyn, in a flurry of excitement, clutched her hands convulsively. With tear-filled eyes she followed each balloon to the frontier of visibility—until it became as small as a tear and floated away into the depths of the night.

"Have pity, Lord," she prayed in a whisper, "on us and on them. . . . Have pity . . ." she repeated fervently, "on all men, have pity and hear my prayer. . . ."

Sebastiano pressed another switch. Green light spouted forth from the searchlights, the powerful Psalm of Hope thundered through the loudspeakers.

Translated by John David Welsh

István Örkény

A Prayer

THE policeman drew a big bunch of keys from his pocket. Each key had a small cardboard tag attached with a number penciled on it.

"Please go in," he said, opening the door, after having found the key he was searching for. "No, perhaps you'd better wait a moment. I'll bring a light."

He left us at the open door. Returning to the hall he unscrewed the bulb from one of the lamps and took it into the darkness. While the policeman was busy with the light Miklós came over to me.

"Don't go in, Sari," he begged.

"Don't baby me, Miklós," I said, pushing him aside.

It was a dirty, cold, windowless room. The plaster bulged on its walls. The light sparkled in it coldly, diamond-like, but failed to dispel the accumulated darkness. The discarded desk, pushed against a wall, fled into the dimness with only the faint outlines of a dry inkwell and a dust-covered telephone showing. But the stretcher stood right under the lamp, seeming to multiply its own significance in the harsh light. It was covered with heavy, wrinkled wrapping paper. The policeman had barely touched it but the paper began to crackle and billow as if something under it had moved.

"Please go out, Sarika," implored Miklós.

The policeman let go of the paper. "It might be better," he said hesitantly.

"Leave me alone," I said, losing patience, "I have nothing to be afraid of."

"I wouldn't be so sure," said Miklós.

"The unexpected can always happen," said the policeman.

"You never saw a burned man," said Miklós.

"It's an ugly sight," explained the policeman, "even I don't like to see it."

"Not you, perhaps," I told the policeman, "but I gave him birth; whatever he looks like he's mine."

The policeman was gingerly holding only a corner of the paper.

"He has no face," he said slowly.

"At least step out into the hall," implored Miklós.

"Take off that paper," I ordered the policeman, "it's not my son anyway."

He took it off, neatly squaring the paper like a blanket and placed it at the foot of the stretcher. Silently we peered at the something which no longer resembled anything.

I often think of that moment. How calm I was. How sure of myself. My color did not change; not a muscle in my face moved at the sight. Like trees up to the snow-line our emotions too can only reach to the point where signs of life are still discernible. That which no longer concerns life no longer touches our emotions. This body was past the halfway mark between a living being and dust. I pushed the policeman aside and stepping to the stretcher bent over the body.

"I knew it," I said then.

"Are you sure?" asked the policeman.

"Quite sure."

"Will you sign a statement saying that he is not your child?"

"I will," I said, taking my husband's arm. "Let's go, Miklós dear."

"Wait, just a minute, please," said the policeman, taking out a typed form.

Once we start disliking someone we find more and more faults in them. First the meticulousness of this policeman seemed unbearable, now his politeness was even worse.

"I don't want to keep you, but in view of the investigation I must inform you that when we dug up the grave yesterday a certain Ferenc Palik, Jr., gave a deposition stating that this was your son."

"Who's that Palik?" I asked

"Also a student."

"He lied. I know all Dénes' classmates."

"He did not sound as if he was trying to mislead us," said the policeman.

He was not only punctilious, not only sickeningly polite, but also stubborn.

"One can see that you have no children," I said annoyed. "Such a kid will do anything to be in the limelight."

"He had no reason to lie," he said stubbornly.

"Some lie without reason," I said.

"But he had reason to tell the truth," he said.

"Or else to fool you," I said.

"I'm only doing my duty," he said softly. "Don't be angry with me for that."

Offended, I turned my back on him and he read the deposition to Miklós. It said that Ferenc Palik, now in custody, had recognized the clothes of the corpse which were of the same flecked material as those worn by Dénes Mózes. He remembered so clearly that suit because he had spent almost a week with Dénes Mózes in the cigar store at 3 Ganz Street. He last saw the victim half an hour before his death. He, Ferenc Palik, had just run home to have some lunch when a tank demolished the store. The house was burning by the time he got back.

"That means he was not there when they fired at the cigar store," I said.

"No, he was not there then," said the policeman.

"I knew it," I said. "We can go Miklós dear."

"Yes, Sári," he mumbled without moving. "May I take a look at the deposition?"

"Here you are, Sir," said the policeman.

Worried, I peered at him. I knew this expression. The vein in his temple began pounding, his sunken cheeks were flushed. He spent his entire life in archives. He held the deposition at two corners and unfolded it with such reverence as if it had been one of Petrarch's letters to Cola di Rienzi.

"Where was the grave?" he asked the policeman.

"In Ganz Street."

"Where is that?"

"In Buda, near the Ganz Power Plant."

He examined the document, then looked at the policeman. He was doing research in his own thorough, methodical way.

"How can they dig a grave in the street?"

"In front of the cigar store there's a flower bed bordering the sidewalk," explained the policeman. "They dug a grave under an acacia tree and temporarily buried your son there."

Miklós' glasses flashed as a sign that he was unable to detect a flaw in the logic. Whenever he succeeded in bringing to light a fragment of reality he and his glasses rejoiced together. His main passion was piling up facts. Whether light was shed on Dante's youth, on Petrarch's sojourn in Avignon, or on the disappearance of our son, hardly mattered to him.

"How did my son get to Buda?" he questioned the policeman.

"That I don't know."

"Weren't the bridges closed?"

"Only the Chain bridge."

"Let's go Miklós, dear," I said quietly, "this isn't our son."

"Right away, Sari," he answered obediently. But it was the stretcher that he approached, not me. His glasses shone as if two tiny flashlights were sparkling behind them. I knew exactly what was going on in his mind. The facts were coming to life as he organized them. And the data were stronger than I was.

He glanced at me timidly.

"Have you noticed the material," he murmured hesitantly, "it looks like his suit."

"Do you recognize him?" asked the policeman.

It seems that he has spent most of his time out of doors. The sun has tanned his face but bleached the blue of his eyes. I knew he wasn't responsible for this, yet I hated him for it. I hated him for this and for everything else.

"Please," I asked carefully so that emotion would not tremble in my voice, "what do you want from us?"

"Me?" he stared at me. "Nothing."

"You've probably never bought civilian clothes. But you may have heard something about ready-made suits. When a new material is brought out the factories make of it thousands and thousands of identical suits. . . . I, for example, buy everything in department stores. This too, is a ready-made suit. It costs 870 forints. Please tell me, what does it prove when two suits are alike?"

"It still means something."

"No, it means nothing," I said, "for our son happens to be in America."

For a moment he was speechless.

"And you're only telling me this now?" He gazed at me with

his faded eyes, then turned to Miklós dumfounded. "Why didn't you tell me this right away, over the telephone?"

"Didn't I?" said Miklós, peering at me out of the corner of his eye.

"No, you did not."

"Well, we only suppose that our son is in America."

"No, it is not only a supposition," I said.

"Has he written to you?" asked the policeman.

"He hasn't written," said Miklós.

"Has he sent any word?"

"No."

"Then what on earth makes you think he's in America?"

"Precisely that," I said.

He didn't understand. Either his superior had told him or he had convinced himself that this corpse was Dénes Mózes. Whatever contradicted this, he was unable to accept. I tried to make him comprehend what kind of boy ours was. So typically "now." He wasn't interested in literature; in this respect he was totally different from us. Machines attracted him, and motion and speed, things that are thoroughly alien to us. His most ardent wish was to own a car. For years he had longed to go to America. He would have gladly worked there as a car-wash just so that he could buy his car. . . . This is why he fled when the border was open.

"But he sent you no word," the policeman started all over.

"Because he didn't want to get us into trouble," I said. "My husband is a scientist, while I am a secretary at the Academy of Science. We're not in their good graces anyway and if on top of it our boy escapes. . . . Is all this so hard to understand?"

"All who left have already sent word," he recited his bit like a machine.

In vain I tried to check my voice. I felt an upsurge of emotion and my brain was racing after my words.

"Aren't you ashamed of yourself?" I shouted at him. "You're just a stupid nobody! Why did you call us here? What are you trying to get us into? Isn't there a spark of human feeling in you? It's obvious that you have no children. A mother needs no letter, I don't need to get any messages, I know he's alive. I've got a built-in radar. I even feel whether he's awake or asleep, whether he's well or ill. Right now my system tells me that he's all right, that he has all he needs. He even has his car, a job, an apartment, friends. I too would prefer to have gotten news from him. I was waiting for his letters trembling, but still we were certain that he was alive and happy, and that all his wishes were fulfilled. And now, you order us to come here and, because of a bragging kid's testimony, you want to prove to us that this body is that of our son. . . . You're wasting your breath. We don't believe you. Perhaps you mean no harm. Perhaps one day, when you too will become a father, you'll regret very much what you did to us today. Look at my husband. What has this man done to you? You disgust me, I hate you, I despise you. . . ."

I thought he would be hurt, that he would get angry. I feared he might punish us for my words. But he only stood there, staring ahead of him hesitantly with those faded blue eyes of his. Then he pocketed the letter. Methodically he buttoned his pocket. He shrugged his shoulders, embarrassed. He felt hot, he took off his cap, and combed his hair. On his forehead, above the brim of his cap, his skin was white and he was showing us this white strip between the suntanned face and the black hair, as if to bare to us the only part where even he was not a policeman.

"I don't care," he said after a pause, his voice nervously faltering, "if you wish I can close the proceedings."

"Can you do that?" I asked.

"If the relatives declare that they do not recognize the deceased, then the identity cannot be established."

"We don't recognize him," I said.

"Please," he said, "you may go home."

"Come on, Miklós," I said.

"Right away, Sari," he answered readily.

Yet, he just stood there and looked at the body. Then his glasses lit up again.

"Is this telephone working?" he asked the policeman.

"It is," said the policeman. "First you have to dial O."

"Whom do you want to call, Miklós dear?" I asked.

"Sanyi," he said.

"Why do you want to talk to Sanyi?"

"I want to ask him something."

I remember it was then that I began to be afraid.

"Sanyi is having his office hours now," I said.

"All I want is one single fact."

"Can't it wait, Miklós dear?"

He came over and took my hand.

"Don't be angry, Sari," he said, "I cannot live like this."

"And like *that*, would it be better?"

"May I use the telephone?" he asked the policeman.

"Please go ahead."

"Let's go, Miklós dear."

"In a minute, Sari," he muttered while he was dialing. But first he wiped the dusty receiver clean. "Please, ask Dr. Sándor Tóth to come to the telephone."

I tried not to be afraid. That's the way life is, I told myself. All that lives wants to kill. Only we, the mothers, don't interrogate the telephone, don't wait for the telegram, and a piece of paper slid under the door strikes fear in us. It is not only from evil that one can kill. Goodness, beauty, knowledge can also be the motives. Even to obtain a fact one can kill, although not to know means to hope, but it is only we who do not wish to know the unbearable.

"Excuse me, please, for disturbing you. I'm calling from the police station. I should like to know if our son Dénes has some filling or any other mark of identification in his teeth. I hope it won't be too much trouble for you to look it up.

They have been friends since childhood, and still, how formally they address each other. In imagination they bow after each sentence. Miklós thanked him for the information and sent his regards to Ila. He promised to call again from home and excused himself once more for disturbing him. Then he hung up. He stepped to me.

"Go out into the hall, Sari."

"Why?"

"On his upper left molar he has a crown."

"I want to see it too."

"His teeth will have to be forced open."

"Don't worry about me, Miklós."

"It won't be a nice spectacle," said the policeman.

"Why do you want to stay here?" Miklós asked.

"Please, do step out into the hall," the policeman said.

"I'll join you right away," Miklós promised.

"I want to see it," I said.

"What's that good for?" he implored.

"Because I'll believe only my own eyes."

I noticed that he turned pale.

"All right then," he said, deeply offended.

The teeth were the most intact part of the corpse, the light of the lamp fell on them. I heard the click of the penknife as the policeman opened it. I heard as the blade knocked against the teeth. I went there and pushed the policeman aside. I pushed Miklós away too and leaned over the body. Please, make it that there is no crown on that tooth. Please, make the light go out. Make our eyes go blind. Let me not see and hear. Make me lose speech. God!

A ray of gold sparkled. A tiny sparkle of gold.

"You were right," I told the policeman, "this is the body of my son."

"Do you recognize him?"

"I recognize him."

We went home by streetcar. It was Miklós' job to carry up the fire wood and then I would make the fire. That's how it was on that day too. Everything was as usual. We live very simply. We never go to the movies, and rarely to the theatre, except for the classics. We went to a restaurant only once, on January 17, 1954, when after three years of imposed silence, Miklós' biography on Petrarch was published. I do the cooking; only plain, quick meals.

That night we dined on tea, with two slices of ham and four scrambled eggs. I carried in the tray without any accident. I even ate. I felt no pain. I had no thoughts. It seemed to me that it was not even I who was eating the eggs. We sat silently at the table, but we don't talk much anyway. When I poured the second cup of tea Miklós asked:

"Are you tired?"

"Why?"

"Wouldn't you like to listen to some music?"

"Gladly."

We don't even own a radio. Only the tapping of an old typewriter reveals the arrival of the twentieth century to our home. And, of course, the telephone; but that we banished to the top of the laundry hamper in a corner of the foyer, for neither of us likes it. Miklós went out and called Sanyi.

"They are going to the movies," he announced later, "but they will leave the key under the doormat."

We finished our supper in silence. I still didn't feel anything, except for a little tiredness which sometimes caught my movements unawares. But then, when I had washed, changed, and stepped out into the fresh, cold air, even that vanished.

We usually go there Wednesday to listen to records. It happened before that the Tóths were out, but then Ila always left the light on in the foyer. Now everything was dark in the apartment. We went in and looked for the switch, but could not find it. We were feeling our way around and suddenly we bumped into each other. We burst out laughing. And stopped at the same time. Silence fell. We stood there in the darkness, motionless. I don't know for how long we stood there, perhaps for very long, although in the dark time seems different.

"Where are you?" Miklós asked.

"Here," I said.

"Reach back, maybe the switch is there."

"It isn't," I said.

Silence again. I couldn't orient myself, I forgot which way the door was. I forgot also from which direction Miklós' voice had come. I didn't budge; I even held my breath, as if one could see better when not breathing. Then I couldn't hold it any longer and suddenly I took a big swallow of air.

"What is it? Are you crying?" Miklós asked.

"No, I'm not," I said.

"I can hear it," he said.

"You're wrong."

"It's no shame to cry," he said.

"But, I'm not crying, Miklós."

I was really not crying. I did not even feel anything unusual, no mourning, no grief, no shock. Miklós started out again and turned on the light. His first gaze fell on me, but my expression was calm, my eyes were dry.

"The *REQUIEM?*" he suggested.

"Yes."

"Which one?"

"Whichever you want."

"Will Mozart do?" he asked.

"Fine."

He put on the record. We sat so that we wouldn't have to face each other. He stared at the silk-covered loudspeaker, I watched him. I watched his prominent, sharply contoured chin, his hooked nose, his sunken cheeks. His face, on which age had already begun to work, was still so very familiar, yet already a little strange. He had proposed to me in front of a bed of geraniums in my parent's yard in Kispest. Then he was much more handsome, his face fuller, more attractive, more devoted; now even that has changed. Only one thing remained unchanged: his honesty. He is honest not only with his friends. All he knows about Italian literature, he knows somehow puritanically; he may be sometimes wrong, but he can never be bribed. Seven years ago his critics called him an idealist. Because of that for three years he had to live by teaching Italian, and even I was fired from the Lónyai High School for Girls. But love cannot be robbed entirely. Although time has eroded us, too, his honesty remained intact. This is what I loved in him now, because this is what had remained.

When the *Agnus Dei* played, he said: "One can face even death with hope."

I started. I loved Mozart's *REQUIEM*, but now I barely heard any of it. I didn't even understand what he meant.

"Were you referring to Dénes?" I asked.

He nodded. I was a little ashamed. Throughout the *REQUIEM* I never even thought of our son. I was in a daze, as if under the effect of a strong drug. Only when the Tóths returned did something stir in me.

It wasn't I who had chosen the Tóths. I got them "ready made"; they were my "husband's friends," although Miklós and Sanyi were as different as night and day. The Tóths lived a very different life from ours. We had vocations; they had hobbies. I clothed myself; Ila "dressed." They did not lack for anything, yet they were constantly on a buying spree and it always cost them a few forints more than they had. They went everywhere, to the beach, to soccer games, to night-clubs. Why they're our friends is a mystery to me. True, Sanyi respects Miklós very much, but then everyone respects Miklós.

When they returned home I felt for the first time that something had happened to me. Someone surviving a fire, who had not known what fire was, must feel the same, uncertain way; because that which has no name barely exists. They too were careful not to name the fire. Perhaps it was this caution which made my heart tremble.

We were standing there, all four of us. They were awfully eager. They had bought a Vivaldi record and wanted us to listen to it, or at least they wanted us to dine with them, or if nothing else, then to have a cup of coffee. They had received the coffee from Switzerland, true Nescafé in a Care package. . . . I said: "No, thank you," to everything, "I just want to go home."

"Very well," Sanyi agreed, "today we musn't force Sári." "But then I'll take you home."

"How will you do that?" asked Miklós.

"In my car."

"You have a car?" Miklós was flabbergasted. "Since when?"

"Since today."

"Are you joking?"

"Not at all."

"What on earth made you buy a car?"

He explained as we were going down. By then an inner tension began to build up in me, my saliva turned bitter. He explained that there was no greater pleasure, that man had a hidden yearning to run and this could be satisfied only by an automobile. For thousands of years man could not find a new thrill, but this was it, the thrill of the road. . . .

He was a big man, weighing over 200 pounds, and as he got in the car it moaned in protest. All the street lights were not yet turned on; he switched on his headlights and sped into the white tunnel. There were hardly any people in the streets, though curfew had been lifted for quite some time. We swept silently toward the bridge. I felt that Sanyi was most eager to talk but my presence embarrassed him. Yet pride burst out of him from time to time.

"How do you like that sound, Miklós?"

"Tell me what to say. You know that I don't know a thing about cars."

"That's only a pose," smiled Sanyi. "The great man of letters feels it's his duty to despise the chauffeur specimen. . . . Is that what they call it?"

"Yes."

"Who was the great mind who invented it?"

"Kayserling."

"I can imagine how primitive cars were in his time. . . . Sári dear, do you feel the heat?"

"I do."

I felt sick to my stomach, only the sickness didn't come from my stomach. I swallowed a lot, but all I swallowed were the inarticulate sounds that wanted to pour forth. . . . At the bridge entrance the guards were still standing. We sped by them.

"Let me tell you something," Sanyi started the conversation again, "Why don't you two buy a car?"

"What, a car? I?" Miklós was appalled. "I'm not crazy."

"All you need to put down is twenty thousand. The University would deduct the rest from your salary. You wouldn't even feel that small amount for twenty years."

"But we don't have twenty thousand forints," said Miklós, "and I wouldn't know what to do with a car."

"This, too, is a pose," Sanyi brushed it aside.

And he began to persuade Miklós. So-and-so also bought a car; someone else intends to buy one. The pennypinching misery has ended. Loans are pressed on us. The doctors are already loaded, everyone wants to live again, breathe again, to have fun again. . . . There are more new Moskvich cars around than one would have ever dared to dream. Miklós too wouldn't lose anything if he translated a Goldoni play for the National Theater.

"This is a bad joke," Miklós said.

"An excellent joke," argued Sanyi. "I bet Sári would look very smart at the wheel. . . ."

It was then that I became sick.

"Stop!" I shouted, my hand pressed to my mouth.

Frightened, he stopped. There was a coffee-house on the corner. I ran in. A drum was thundering, some ear-piercing jazz was playing. In the crowded room everybody was staring at me as I raced past the tables with my hands pressed to my mouth. Marble stairs led down to the ladies' room. I locked myself into the lavatory and everything burst from me, moaning, babbling, breaking all dams, everything, everything. The cry of pain, the tears, the shrieks.

It seems the door could be unlocked from the outside too; when I came to, the cleaning woman was supporting me. Slowly my tears ebbed.

The woman brought in her stool, taking off it her tray with the coins on it.

"Rest a little while," she said.

I sat down. I felt that everything had left me, I was totally empty and roaring like an empty seashell. I wiped my face with my handkerchief.

"Don't go yet," she advised.

"They're waiting for me," I said.

"Let them wait," she said, as if she were more familiar with the nature of grief than I. "Now you're the one who's more important."

Obediently, I sat down. Music streamed from upstairs. The cleaning woman asked nothing, nor did she say anything, she didn't even look at me, yet I still felt her presence. This felt good, like a sick person who knows there's no help, yet it calms him to know someone is watching over him.

"Stay a little longer," she said when I reached for my purse. "Close your eyes, they're still quite red."

I closed my eyes. I don't know how long I sat there like this. When I looked up again she was bringing me a glass of water. I drank and thanked her.

"Powder your nose," she said.

"I have no powder."

"I'll give you some of mine."

"Thank you."

She pressed the powder puff into my hand, and when she saw how inexperienced I was, she powdered my nose.

"You may go now," she said.

"Thank you for all your kindness," I said.

"There's nothing to thank me for," she replied, "I've seen a lot of the same."

"May I tip you?" I asked.

"Some other time," she smiled.

I blushed.

"What I meant, this is your job and one ought to be paid for one's job."

"Not in cases like this."

"Forgive me," I said.

"There's nothing to forgive."

"You were very good to me."

"We're all alike," she said.

"Many thanks again," I said.

"You're welcome."

"Good-bye then," I said.

"All the best."

So far I had been sitting in the front. Now Miklós took my place; he was turning the wheel, pushing buttons like a child. Sanyi was heatedly explaining.

"The first speed has the greatest transmission. I'll sketch it for you at home."

In the rear-view mirror I saw Miklós. His glasses sparkled. Again, he had learned something.

"Are you feeling better?" he asked.

"Will we also buy a car, Miklós dear?" I asked him.

"What an idea! Where would we get all that money?"

They changed places. But first, his face red, he sounded the horn once more. We started. Please, make him get a Goldoni piece for translation. Please make the actors play well. Please make him successful, give him money, a car. He will still remain honest. He is the cleanest man I know. Please, make it so I won't have to cry again. Make him not look back yet. Just one more minute, please.

Translated from the Hungarian by Claire De Poschl

Bogdan Czaykowski

+
\+ +

I

The violent ones, who are they now?
time was
they walked about with a cross, and the cross was violent,
blood soaking the wood, patiently congealing
beside the deathly mask.

Thus I see, of such sights precisely
a night of illusions in explosions of illuminations
rumbled across thunderingly,
I force mutiny on its knees, I violate power,
I compel weakness with force—curbed in a storm
I cannot otherwise.

When he tightened within himself the swing of revolt
(and composed manifestoes), there, at the end of the road
things became clearer, an olive grove, a hill.

Observe, man: I had you in the palm of my hand,
and what could I? kill, send into exile,
tear nets straining with silvery overabundance of fish,
turn Lazarus from his way when he did not walk
but merely in peace lay, perhaps content,
I saw eyelids twitch when people cried:
arise, man. I ordered the blind to look at me
and did violence to a lake with a natural foot—
so I can kill, send into exile, sentence to jail:
so much I can. So why all the illusion?

+
+ +

II

The violent ones,
who are they now?

Translated from the Russian by Adam Czerniawski

Bogdan Czaykowski

Age de la Pierre

In this town they've cleared rubble from squares.
Even built new houses (you can see for
Yourself).
Tidied up cemeteries.
Courts have sentenced both the ones and the others.
Then there were amnesties for the murdered
And rehabilitations for those still alive.
Voluntary outlaws were allowed to return.
But they had abandoned hope.
Others sacrificed themselves for profit.
But repatriations were secured.
Thus some returned to life.
While others could not face the miracle with Lazarus.
Do you ask, what vistas fly open?
You will not clear away ruined thoughts, even when raising statues
Upon each grave.
Until new men arise.
About whom only this is known
That the burden of their heritage will be heavy.

Translated from the Russian by Adam Czerniawski

Piotr Guzy

The Short Life of a Positive Hero

"I'm here to see Comrade Hibisz."

"Really? To see Hibisz? Then follow us."

Good-looking broad—sensual lips, bosom. . . .

"You're here to see whom, Comrade?"

"Comrade Hibisz. I was supposed to be here at nine."

"Your papers, if you please."

It would be sort of risky to start up with a gal like that; first everything would be pretty cozy, but then she'd report you. And then, if only she'd tell the truth, but no! She'll make up stories, cook up incredible stuff about how in a state of intoxication you made some anti-Party remarks, how during sexual intercourse you denounced the Soviet Union, and similar nonsense! I'm sure I'm right; I can always tell when someone's put on a job like that.

"Third floor, please."

Smiles pretty. *We are always pleasant with people*, and if Hibisz had said he didn't want to see anyone, would she then have smiled like that? Exactly! Thick carpets, decorations, walls padded specially so no sound could be heard, silent like a church, neither a telephone nor a typewriter in sight. One person gets to work that way, chauffeur-driven limousine to the office and home, a ten-room apartment on the Avenue of Independence, a summer home at the seashore and another house in the mountains, but I get accused of having lost contact with the masses! Me! Me!

"Comrade Ostuda? Sit down. Comrade Hibisz is busy at the moment, but it won't be long."

A nice birdie, too—Hibisz's mistress? That kind has it made. The guys go abroad, bring them nylon panties, cosmetics, perfumes; next come orgies in country houses, like Woźnicki was saying. He should know, damn it—those revolutionaries!

"Come in, Comrade."

Some peasant from the provinces has come, maybe the doorknob should be handled through a handkerchief so it won't get dirty. One never knows what germs one can catch. Please! Some office! A chapel!

"Come in, Comrade. Why so shy? Have a seat; I'll be with you in a second. Just let me finish what I was reading."

He doesn't remember any more how he used to tramp naked through the fields. Now he feels important, because he's got a big desk—you can even square-dance on it. Where on earth did they get those carpets? They're so thick the foot sinks into them as if it were moss. Good thing they didn't make me take off my shoes and put on my felt slippers. And the curtains on the windows are made of a material I don't even know the name of. Where on earth did they get all that? In Paris? London? The paneling, as it's probably called, on the wall there, what's it made of—Mahogany? Crystal candelabrum, fine and dandy—but how do you interrogate a person in such luxury? It's unthinkable that there should be blood on the carpets; nobody'd ever be able to wash it out. He has a lounge chair here, and when he feels the desire he gets some action on it, five telephones on his desk, the collected works of Lenin—Stalin he threw away; one can still see where those were standing. He picks up one telephone and then another and he thinks that he rules—bureaucratic fart in a chair! I'd show you! He ran naked through the fields, covering his balls with a sack used for German fertilizers, but look at him now! A dignitary! Even the hair at his temples is beginning to turn a distinguished gray, according to the rules. This girlie here is probably one of his. Well, he's got something to impress her with when he can import his suits from Paris and his shirts from London or Rome!

"What mischief have you been up to again, Comrade Ostuda?"

He just looks at a man and already has him sentenced, treats him like a rag that can be pushed around. Nothing will be considered any more. Nothing will be taken into account. It's known in advance that he's guilty. Put him against the wall and put a bullet through his head! You've been up to mischief!

"I've been up to some mischief? I don't understand, Comrade Hibisz."

Is this the way to start a conversation? What have I done? After all, I don't belong to him. What is he, a teacher to scold me like a pupil? And he called me in to see him—let him tell me right away what he has against me, instead of tapping his fingers on his desk and staring at me. He thought I'd come and start confessing to him? Beat my chest? Well, I'll show him! But it's better not to tease him. He might get angry, and then a person would be buried alive.

"You see, Comrade Secretary, you say that I've been up to some mischief. I agree, I have been, but what? Because I don't know myself. I am looking into my conscience and can't find a thing that I should be ashamed of. But something must be there. I know it, I can feel it, some strange things are happening around me. There's such an atmosphere—as if I had leprosy. Don't come near me! Don't touch me! There was a celebration of the October Revolution. Do you think they invited me? Or take my job, for instance. They push me away from affairs that in my department belong only to me. Why? I enter the office and people become silent. My wife has a party and they excuse themselves on account of a lack of time. Why? And when you ask someone they act as if their mouths were full of water. Everybody is hiding something, but what? If somebody has something against me, if there are some objections, please, I'll listen, I'll answer. After all, I do have some kind of a position in the Party, some merits. After all, it can't be done that way."

"Everybody has merits, that doesn't count. Would you like to smoke? I'll be honest with you, Comrade Ostuda. Inquiries have already been initiated in your affair, or are about to begin any day."

It is quiet here, strange, because the windows are open, even the trolleys are running. There is some kind of a smell here. What is it? Toilet water? I have heart palpitations. I should have gone with that broad, put it off a while, necked with her, even if only for a few hours. I have heart palpitations. I swear I'll shoot myself one of these days. I'll have a special role there: right in the forehead and that's the end. Finally I'll have peace. Ran naked through the fields—Jesus Christ! And a moon beam was sliding down his arse, but he did preserve the distance, Comrade! Not you! Or Karl! Oh no, Comrade! In the Committee as well as at the meeting!

"Concerning my affair? What affair? What sort of an affair is it that's supposed to be mine? That I really don't know. I thought that you could tell me something in connection with it, because you above all must know what is going on. Maybe there is some kind of a connection with the Skorosz affair? What kind? Let's be sober about it—what kind? You know yourself how those affairs are handled. The Party demands it, and I, in the best faith. . . ."

"In the best faith?"

"The Party came to the decision that Comrade Skorosz had to be compromised and liquidated. I won't go into the question of whether it was really necessary or not. My personal opinion in this matter is unimportant. I have never questioned and never will question the decisions of the Party."

"I mention the Skorosz matter because I don't know whether you know it or not, but Comrade Niecały was released from jail yesterday and soon, that is, after a few months of treatment, because there seems to be something wrong with his health, he'll return to work in the Party apparatus, perhaps not to the same position he had before, but this is only the start."

"I understand. Niecały has been freed, and I will have to fill his shoes now, right?"

"I haven't said a word about it; I don't even know whether his release has any connection with you. As a matter of fact, I doubt it. I just mentioned it because you were both mixed up in the same affair, and therefore I would like to know how the whole situation looks."

He doesn't know; he's in the Central Committee and doesn't know? Who should know it then? I? Well then, he gave the warning—that bastard conscience of his has moved him—that I have to be on guard, that they're going to crack the whip any moment, as if I didn't know it myself. But for him to lift his finger on my behalf, oh no! Indeed not!

"Comrade Secretary, I don't understand a thing. But it hurts, this persecution. For so many years I have worked, and worked well. I never had any reservations. I was always praised. And now I have to go under the knife? For what? I don't insist that I never committed an error. Lord Almighty, we're all only human. After all, you know yourself the kind of work done in the security section. Nobody wears white gloves on that job. I destroyed people? I agree. Pangs of conscience? None whatsoever! The Party ordered me to do it, therefore it was only my duty to carry out its recommendations. It's like in the war: the soldier doesn't question orders from above. Look through those papers! Those are orders, instructions, circulars. Look at the names. Those are people who presently perform responsible functions in the Central Committee and government. At that time they spelled out the Party line in the sphere of security activities. Of course there was autocracy. Of course there was force used excessively. But you yourself know well that things like that were overlooked. Moreover, things like that were endorsed under some conditions; results that were required at that time had to be obtained. And at present, because of those activities, I have to throw up my hands? Tear my shirt? Shed tears? Act as though I was unaware of those tactics, and how we could have permitted all that? Forgive me, Comrade. This is all a big joke and a hallucination. I really don't understand what the fuss is about. We've loosened the stirrup, fine. Our new tactics demand it. But we all also know that if the necessity arises we'll tighten them again. So what's the big fuss about? The security apparatus is the militant arm of the Party, quite right, and thus we can't demand that it be a school for infants! Here in Warsaw you sign a roll of papers that is sent to our territory, where it ceases to be just a paper and becomes a concrete problem that has to be solved. To solve it means in one way or another forcing compliance. In the final analysis, it means the rod. Don't get upset; I'm simply telling the truth. Comrade Secretary, let's put our cards on the table, all right? If we hadn't had our fist on the rod, we'd have all been devoured or hung on lamp-posts. We wouldn't have survived even half a day. You remember what happened in Poznań? Well! I know it's fashionable today to talk about liberalism, about law-abidingness, and similar crap, but for heaven's sake let's not go overboard. Because if today we practice all that, Comrade, mark my words, we'll pay for it dearly in a couple of years from now. We'll pay for it; you'll see! There'll be revenge! There'll be a bitter revenge! On us! You don't know what it looks like in the field, but I know! I have my fingers on the pulse, I know what people say among themselves, I know what they really think! Just give them the opportunity and we'd have the works! I'm telling you all this, and I don't want to call the wolf from the forest, but you'll see in the future where this will all end up. I repeat, someday there will be a revenge on us! All they are waiting for is to jump on us, to cut our throats!"

"Sit down again, Comrade. You allow yourself to be carried

away by your emotions. You tell such stories as a Party member can't even listen to. Well, what can I do with you, Ostuda? You must control yourself somehow. You're excited. You feel you're being treated unjustly. Fine, but one can't forget himself to such an extent. Well, how should I interpret such an irresponsible outburst?"

"Irresponsible outburst? Irresponsible outburst?"

"Sit down, Ostuda, or we'll have to end the conversation altogether. Well! You're falling apart; you must get a grip on yourself, because otherwise you won't do yourself any good with such behavior. You're concentrating on your own navel and have completely lost the total view of the whole situation."

"I've lost it? I am an old veteran of the Revolution!"

"Again you are carrying on, Ostuda. Why? You don't want to talk to me? Of course I don't deny that in everything you've said there's some truth. However, one can't build a case on it. Force! What kind of language is that? You can't do that. We're talking about the ruling apparatus, about more or less efficient methods. Means of physical action, well, of course sometimes it is necessary to resort to such methods as obviously are unpleasant, but this is not the point. Those are only interjections. Concentrating on these trivialities you lose the main point, you lose the concept of the situation as a whole, you acquire some complexes that overshadow the clarity of your vision. The problem of the rod is not the main question of revolution. You should forget it and push our matter ahead in a different manner, because the times have changed, and the practices with which we are dealing now must also undergo changes."

"Fine, fine, I understand all that, a different phase and so forth, but in this case why do we persecute people who in the past have performed the Party work well, without whom this practice, as you were saying, would not have been changed?"

"Nobody's persecuting them."

"What do you mean, nobody's persecuting them? You yourself just said that I am under investigation."

"Whether it has begun or not, I don't know yet. Besides, even if you are, why should you be afraid? Today these are only gestures."

"For whom?"

"One needs public opinion, to show society that we have abandoned the old methods."

"In other words, public opinion demands some innocent victims, right?"

"I wouldn't make it sound so vulgar. It isn't that easy. All of that has to be viewed in another semantic dimension."

"Screw your semantics! Semantics! The whole issue is about the fact that you need an innocent victim! I don't want to become that victim! I find no faults with me! I have destroyed people; I admit it. I have burnt out their eyes, shoved rats up their arses, skinned dogs, beaten them, tortured them, shot their brains out, buried them alive in pits—yes! Yes! Thanks to that we are running the government today!"

"I beg your pardon! I forbid you! What kind of language is that! What are you allowing yourself? We don't use it here! If you don't calm down immediately, I'll throw you the hell out of here! Well! Understood?"

"Sorry."

"All right. You're lucky, Ostuda, that it's me, because I'm an understanding man. Somebody else in my place would have acted differently."

"Sorry, but if you point a knife at a man's throat. . . ."

"Nonsense! It's all in your sick, dissolute imagination inhabited by some fears, nightmares, monstrous delusions, or hell knows what. You must control yourself, Ostuda, because you might say such nonsense in somebody else's presence and, God forbid, then you'll really be in trouble. Let's smoke. So you say that you have no idea what it's all about? Hmm. I don't want you to go home without any satisfaction. I really don't know what to do about it. Maybe you should drop by to see Comrade Bełszyński at the Central Committee? Perhaps he is better oriented in this issue, what do you say? Would you like to talk with him?"

"If you think it might give some results."

"It won't harm you to have a talk with him. In that case I'll call him. We'll see. . . . This is Hibisz speaking. Listen Frank, I have here Comrade Ostuda from Security. He'd like to meet you. . . . Some business, I don't know exactly what it's all about. Will you have a few minutes to spare him? . . . Ostuda! From Najdrzyc. . . . Yes. He'll explain it better to you. . . . Fine. He'll be with you in a few minutes. Thanks a lot. . . . See, Ostuda, it's settled. I am very glad that you came. I am only sorry that I was not of more help to you. Write me a note, or call me up before you go back to

Najdrzyc. . . . What? A pass? Comrade Belczyński will sign it. Well, so long Ostuda. Chin up, everything will be fine. Don't worry. Goodbye."

Well, what have I accomplished? Nothing. He knows something; he called me because he wanted to find out something and wanted to check whether I'm the one. I don't believe that he doesn't know. It's all the same; Frank, Zenon, or Joe, if one knows, then all of them know it. Wouldn't they tell it to each other? But what? A gesture . . . public opinion? Let them start a trial for Berman or Radkiewicz. Are only a few of them left? No, they've hidden them in the storeroom, with mothballs, assigned to foreign missions, because they might some day prove to be useful again. What about me? I'll go to the pile? Maybe it'd be better if I don't bother with Bełczyński? Stop spreading this stink? Then I'll have to go back and see Hibisz to get my pass, and he'll get offended that I ignored his suggestions, or maybe he'll think that I have some other reasons for not wanting to see Bełczyński? No, I said I'll see him, and I'll see him. Tough luck. Once the word is given one must do it. I've been sentenced. It's all the same. I'll see the judge. Logically speaking, if they've decided to crucify me, they'll do it anyway; it's all the same. Pharisees!

"I'm here to see Comrade Bełczyński."

"Comrade Ostuda? I'll see . . . it's all right, you may come in."

Let them crucify me, this one too, I wash my hands, let this man bleed. Today everyone is washing his hands. No one remembers his own sins. The more they find victims like me for the lions, the better for them, because they were able to hide under the straw themselves. Now what's left is to torture and destroy us, so, God forbid, no one could ask them, "and what were you doing at the time?" Let them crucify me—it will catch up with them too; we are all here lined up.

"Greetings, Comrade. You wanted to talk to me? Please sit down. What did you want to talk to me about?"

"Apparently, there are some charges against me. I wanted to find out whether it's true."

What's he laughing for? Because they enjoy human misery? They've got it good themselves. Because they're still in the saddle I talk like a human being to him, while he—what's that, did I say something funny? He's hysterical with laughter, because some one talks like a human being to him.

"That's dandy! That's a good one! Some charges! I like you, Ostuda. I like sincerity and boldness. I like it when someone poses a question in a straightforward manner. Are you from Najdrzyc?"

"Yes."

"I remember. The incidents in Poznań. You arrested half of Najdrzyc. Of course, I remember;"

"It wasn't half at all, besides, I have already explained the matter so many times, and I was under the impression that the whole business was over with and forgotten."

"Nobody ever knows that, Comrade, nobody every knows."

"Anyway, the investigation committee that dealt with my case has found my explanations satisfactory and the case was dismissed."

"Well, yes, dismissed, but the file remained, right?"

"So what of it?"

"One always can take a look into the file."

"What for? What for, Comrade? You worked in the Party apparatus for many years. You should know that one shouldn't even ask such questions. You made a big mistake, succumbed to panic. You deviated from the Party line. Your subjective appraisal at this point is unimportant. You might have had the best intentions, but it doesn't change the fact that upon your own initiative you undertook steps that brought a lot of harm to the Party. The matter is patched up, that's true, but marks remain—right? Today, if someone opens your personal file, no matter for what reason—right?—and sees all that under the present new conditions, which require a lot of tact, understanding, sometimes even extreme leniency—right?—such a person, like you—right?—perhaps should not occupy a position, if in the eyes of the public you are already discredited."

"Were you at the time in Poznań, Comrade Secretary? You're telling me that I succumbed to panic, that upon my own initiative, etc., etc. If you saw what I did at the time, I doubt that you'd be saying what you are now. I came to visit the Fair. It was in the morning, the city looked normal, nobody would have suspected anything. Well, it was known that the workers were striking in ZISPO. It was also a public secret that, a few days before, the working force sent a delegation to Warsaw, but the news that the delegation was arrested became known only later. But so much for that. I arrived there and went for a walk on the Fair grounds. At a certain moment an unusual commotion occurred among the visitors. Somebody yelled out that a procession was coming. I ran up to the main gate. The main procession was entering the Castle Bridge. You should have seen that, Comrade! Workers, women, children. They carried signs: 'We demand bread and freedom!' 'Long live Poland!' 'We demand a lowering of prices!' This was something so unreal that I could not comprehend it! How was it possible to let it go that far? Why do we have the police? Why do we have the security, the army? And the masses were marching and singing, 'We want God!' and they sang the 'Varsovienne.' The foreigners spilled out of the Fair grounds, and movie cameras swung into action. The next day it was all to be in the foreign press: 'Workers Demonstrate Against Communist Regime!' What could I do? That was the end of the world. I followed the procession. People were running by and screaming, 'Freedom! Freedom!' They stopped me with the words, 'It has come to it! We'll teach you!' That's the way they were talking about the People's Government! Publicly! 'We'll teach you! The whole world will finally learn the whole truth!' On the sidewalks the police stood without any reaction. At the movie-house 'Baltic' the crowd turned to the *Kaponiera* and there in front of the university auditorium a huge demonstration began. Insults addressed to the Government were tumbling through the loudspeakers. 'Demands,' you understand, Comrade, 'demands' were made that the arrested delegates be freed. The crowd was howling. You could hear this erupting volcano; you thought that any moment everything was going to burst, that their hatred was going to inundate us. One was filled with fear, anger, and blind madness. Who was responsible for all that? Why wasn't the army there? Why did the police stand by looking on with arms folded? Where were the authorities and why wasn't anybody trying to bring the situation under control? Those questions were bursting in my mind. Something had to be done. I jumped into the first telephone booth. I called the District Committee; nobody answered. I called the National District Council; nobody answered. Finally, I called the Security Council. They told me to keep calm, that the situation was progressing according to schedule, that we had our own people in the crowds, they knew what had to be done. Keep calm! Good suggestion, but how could one keep calm looking at what was happening in the streets? The business was dangerous, and with every moment it became even more dangerous. The crowd was already pushing itself into the building of the Party District Committee. A few minutes later a white flag was waving from the roof, and from one of the windows appeared the sign, 'We demand bread and freedom!' The crowd went wild, broke glasses. Documents and portraits of our leaders showered down from windows. A mass obsession! You should have seen it, Comrade: that outburst of hatred, that spontaneous madness, that orgy of destruction, that contempt for us. The crowd was stampeding, tearing to pieces and burning everything. On the roof of the National District Council there was also a white banner. Even on top of Police Headquarters! The crowd was pushing itself in the direction of the jail where they expected to find the arrested delegates. I saw how the gate was broken and how this mad rabble was falling inside of the gates. It was horrible, you didn't want to believe your own eyes. It was happening in our Poland, eleven years after we came to power, after all the enormous work we put into laying the foundation of our government structure! There wasn't even an attempt at opposition, no resistance, nobody fired even a shot, complete capitulation. After eleven years of ruling Poznań the People's Government fell in the course of an hour! Do you have any idea how I felt? Of course there were no prisoners there, so they began shouting that they should go next to the Security Office on Kochanowski Street. The Dombrowski Street was already blocked when I reached Theatre Bridge. The first shots came from Kochanowski Street. At last! The crowd will disappear in an hour and there will be peace. But far far from it! It turned out that a child was killed on Kochanowski Street. The news spread with the speed of lightning. It seemed as if all the people were inflicted with madness. Arms appeared. From everywhere trucks were rolling in filled with armed workers. On Theatre Bridge a streetcar was overturned and a barricade began to be built. A car with foreign license plates stopped at the corner, and on its roof stood a man with a movie camera. I ran to him, but the crowd pushed me away. This is exactly what they wanted: to have this publicized abroad. An apparatus for jamming was thrown out the upper windows of the National Security Office. Meanwhile, a complete siege of the Security Department began on Kochanowski Street. An uprising, do you hear, an uprising against the People's Government began! First ambulances carrying the wounded began to dash back and forth. I was armed, of course, but what could I do? They would have massacred me. I went back to the bridge. Just then I saw Comrade Kozlicki coming towards me from the Poznań Security. I worked with him sometime ago in Najdrzyc. I called him and he came to me and said: 'Don't worry, everything is all right. You'll see what'll happen here later; they'll get it up their . . .' but he didn't finish his sentence, because a man stopped in front of us and pointing at Kozlicki yelled out: 'He's from the Security Police!' Immediately several people jumped on him, but Kozlicki got away from them and ran, unfortunately in the wrong direction. People ran after him like a pack of wolves. It was an ugly sight: all those faces glaring with hatred, all those hands scratching the streets to extract stones from them. Kozlicki ran up Railroad Bridge and down the steps to the square in front of the railroad station with the whole mob after him. The crowd was getting thicker, noisier, and was almost at his heels. Kozlicki was dodging all over the square, between the streetcars, between the cabs, ducking the falling stones that showered him like rainfall, but where could he go to once he got out of the square? To the platform! This was the only possibility, to the railroad platform, over the tracks, through the empty cars, to shake off the pursuit, to slip away, to lose them. However, the platforms were also filled with people. He didn't even make twenty paces when somebody stuck his foot out; the rest you can imagine. It's true somebody yelled out: 'People! You are Christians, come to your senses!' but you know yourself, Comrade, what a mob is. When they left him alone on the pavement there were only bloody shreds left. I came out of the station. What happened? How did it happen? The edifice we constructed for so many years fell apart in front of my very eyes. What happened? Nothing. I stood in front of the Fair gate contemplating what to do next. Then suddenly I realized it was unusually quiet around. The loudspeakers, which from morning on had been blaring music, were silent. I got petrified by the thought of what would happen if this mob got hold of the broadcasting system and the news spread all over Poland. A real battle was taking place on Kochanowski Street. A giant column of smoke hung over the spot where the building of the Security Department was located. A few more hours and the Department would collapse, and the whole town would find itself in the hands of the rebels. One had to act quickly. Every moment was precious. I had to return as quick as possible to Najdrzyc. I stopped a German car going in that direction. The Germans fled from the Fair out of fear that with the loss of government control the Poles would give them the works, or perhaps they thought that this uprising would start a new war. In two hours we reached Najdrzyc. The streets were crowded. A single spark was sufficient. I got hold of the Chief of Police and explained the whole situation to him. It seemed that there were already rumors that there was an uprising in Warsaw and that in the Silesian coal mines the Party secretaries were hanged. We decided that the streets had to be cleared, that the possible instigators had to be taken into custody. Within less than an hour the whole city calmed down. We arrested thirty people; some others set up machine guns in the main parts of town. The situation was saved because we acted fast, and decisively. If the same thing had been done in Poznań it would never have come to an eruption."

"Forgive me, Comrade, but before I tell you something, I'll have to have a good laugh. In what kind of world do you live? Do you really believe that if we had wanted to we couldn't have handled the situation in Poznań immediately? Are you really so naive, Comrade, that you think that we didn't know what was happening and what it was all about? We even emptied the jail to make space for the newly arrested. We had our own people stationed all over the city who were taking movies of everything. Who was breaking the store-windows on Dombrowski Street? Our people! Who was instigating the crowd? How do you think it happened that they got hold of the arms so easy? Just think about it, Comrade, in our government structure it is very difficult to organize an uprising. Impossible, I would even say. Of course in some instances we might lose our grip of the situation, for a few moments, but only for a few moments. How long did the strike last in Poznań? Two weeks. We knew very well that sooner or later the workers would come out onto the streets. We could have prevented it but we didn't even lift a finger. Why, dear Comrade Ostuda? Just recall what the entire situation was at that time in Poland. Horrible. There was a lack of goods on the markets, everything was expensive, the waves of strikes were taking on larger and larger dimensions, and after the Twentieth Congress a general fermentation occurred. The situation could not be any worse. Poznań came just in time. Has it ever occurred to you that we purposely created such a situation, moreover, that we encouraged it, added fuel to the flames, so that our enemies would openly crawl to the surface, drop their masks, and make it easier for us to trap them. It would have been enough to send Comrade Cyrankiewicz to make a speech over the radio. He would have agreed to negotiate and promise to free the delegates. We could have done it that way—right?—and the whole business would have been settled immediately. But this would have meant that we would have bent down before force. Thus we waited until the time was ripe, then we threw the army into action with tanks, covered the streets with bodies, and a few hours later there was peace. We taught the working class of Poznań, stirred up by various types of demagogues, respect for the People's Government. After that massacre nobody in Poland will lay a hand on the People's authority. Your mistake lies in the fact that you panicked that day, for a moment you lost faith in the wise, far-sighted policies of the Party. Everything that happened later was the result of this one moment of weakness. Do you agree with my diagnosis?"

"Let's say I agree, but why is all this being held against me right now?"

"Just a second, Comrade, I do not insist at all that it is being held against you now, but it will doubtless, affect, to some extent, the decision of the prosecutor."

"Prosecutor? What is it specifically that I am charged with?"

"I don't know. Undoubtedly you have something on your conscience, because they're interested in you. I only got a letter saying that I have to forward your personal file. This is all I know about your case. At the moment I can't suggest or help you with anything. When the prosecutor finishes his charges, when we know what those charges are, perhaps then one would be able to help you. Perhaps. Meanwhile you must arm yourself with a lot of patience and wait. Why worry? You have such an expression on your face as if the world were coming to an end. Even if it comes to the worst, they will relieve you of your duties as Supervisor of the Security Department and transfer you to a somewhat less prominent position. Is there reason to worry?"

"And what do you consider yourself, Comrade Bełczyński, that you are ready to teach the Polish working class to respect the People's Government? You don't consider yourself a member of the working class? What? Or perhaps you think this is some kind of a clique that with the help of Russian bayonets has come to power and now stirs up the populace with social slogans? Something is lousy there with your ideology. Did you make a slip of the tongue? We'll see whether it was only a slip of the tongue. We'll keep you under close observation now. We'll see what you really have at the bottom of your soul. What other members of the Central Committee think like you? Who? Speak up! Tell me all of them! What do you mean, all of them? Give me their names! Speak up! I'll treat you differently now. I'll find some way. I'll get the rat that for so many years has been chewing away the foundation of the Party, this harmful snake, this blindworm, this flea that has been biting and sucking the blood and poisoning the healthy organism of the People's Government. Oh, wait, Bełczyński, we'll settle accounts with you now! For so many years you were hiding under a mask, and only now have we torn off the mask and seen the horrible face of our enemy, but don't worry, Bełczyński, we'll mask that face again, we'll grind your face through a meatchopper, we'll push you, Bełczyński, through the cesspools, Bełczyński, we'll make you. . . ."

"Take it easy, take it easy, Karl."

"But this bastard has made me mad, this biting snake, this pile of dung, this smelly rat. . . . I must go to the prosecutor, to jail, up against the wall, and this dungpit—for so many years he has been undermining the People's Government, and nobody caught on except me, and I'll remember him, all right. He took too much for granted. He'll learn respect for the Polish working classes. I'll have to make a declaration in writing. Don't you know, Bełczyński, that you shouldn't even formulate such concepts in your thoughts? Not to mention pronounce them orally. You shouldn't be talking that way even to a wall, you understand? Even if the next person were a hundred miles away from you, understand?"

He permitted himself to express himself that way because in his eyes I have ceased to exist. He was already speaking to a ghost. He could permit himself to be honest, because he thinks I can do him no harm any longer. Perhaps he's right, I don't know, my hands are down, my affair is probably forejudged. All that's left is to arrest me, line me up against the wall, bring out the firing squad, a matter of simple formality, please! Please! Arrest me! I am not running away, take me! You'll never see the day! I won't go like a lamb to the sacrifice, out of the question. I'll fight to the end; I'll go and see Wachowiak. He's our man, the same type of a job, all the time field work. With a man like that one can come to an understanding. It's not like this corrupt society who fart in their bureaucratic chairs. I have to get a cab, where can I get a cab? The bastard, he didn't even stop! He should be sent to a workshop for the rest of his life. What a whore, I'll teach him a lesson he won't forget as long as he lives. Well, maybe this one? Aha, he stopped, good man!

"To the Ministry of Internal Affairs."

"Are you going to pick up a passport? It's easier to get one now, so they say. After all, the bastards have learned something, because in the past, sir, there was such misery in getting it."

Today nobody can trust anybody looking at his face. All they have learned is to smile at each other. Say a decent word to someone and he'll take you for his man, and later you can spit, curse, and you have a drinking companion. They've learned; I was always saying that if they had to loosen up a little, these are the results you'd get, but if we continued the old way, some day we'd all wind up hanging on lamp posts. God damn it, they'll ring the bells in the towers and. . . .

"How much? Fifteen zlotys? Here you are."

"This is for the company, and how about me? One zloty? What's the matter with you, man, are you illiterate or something? Aren't you ashamed that a member of the working class has to lower himself and remind you that he should be payed? He did me a favor and threw me one zloty! Look at this peasant! For three miles I drove this peasant and he gives me one zloty! Landowner, son of a whore! Takes a cab to the Ministry and already thinks that he's a big shot and can shove other people around. Two zlotys, did you see that? And I have to remind him of that! Take your two zlotys back, you tramp you, and stick them up your arse! And next time have some idea of what honor is when you ride in a cab! Get the hell out of here, or I'll grab you by the neck and right here on the spot. . . ."

They would have lynched me. What people! First they beg for a tip, then they complain, speak of honor—any shithead talks about honor these days, gives money, throws money. Those people have learned nothing at all. The old habits have so strongly soaked through and through them that it will take years and years. I should have taken his license plate number; I goofed. A fellow like that deserves to be given hell. Damn it, I goofed. It's not because he dealt with me, but generally speaking he should be taught to respect himself, to beat this drudgery out of himself, this servility, to make him carry his head high up, to make him feel that he is a man, a man that sounds proud. Bastard, doesn't he know it himself?

"Comrade Ostuda? I am so happy to see you. Please sit down. We haven't seen each other for a long time. I think I know what it's all about. It's a good thing you dropped by, because I intended to get in touch with you anyway. What was it all about, the business with Wielgocki?"

'Dominik's finished for you. He'll never be able to do it again with any woman.' 'It's all because you could never forgive me that I wasn't a virgin WHEN YOU MET ME.' 'After all, perhaps a man has a right to demand from this filthy life that he be given at least one pure thing. Is that asking for so much?'

"I don't know which Wielgocki you're talking about. There were three of them. The father was sitting behind the bars for economic sabotage, and died in jail. The younger son was put away for a few years for banditry, and if I am not mistaken was released from prison in 1952. The older one is still behind bars for ideological deviation and spying."

"Yes, that's him, Dominik. They say that you castrated him while you were conducting your inquest, is that true?"

"Did I castrate him? You know how it is, Comrade, when one conducts an inquest. It is possible that he suffered some blows on his body that affected him physically, that is, affected his masculinity. It's hard sometimes to keep your eye on everything—it happens, that. . . .

"You don't have to tell me that, Comrade, but you see, one has to keep in mind our good old principle. Once you've got such a man in your grip, once you're already started working on him, you can't muck up the affair. You must do a clean job, or else such a cripple will go running around needlessly giving us bad publicity. You goofed up on this job; now it's dragging. Wielgocki has appealed his sentence. How could you have let it go that far?"

"I'll be honest with you, Comrade. True, occasionally I reproached myself for having blown the case, but, you know, I never thought that he'd last that long in jail."

"Exactly. You see, he's a tough egg, and he'll outlast us all."

"All right, he's still locked up, we could still, you know—well—give him a medical certificate. Very simple, don't you think?"

"I am afraid that it's no longer that simple, not now. A public prosecutor has already been appointed. Everybody's beginning to dig into this case, and that's the worst of all things that could happen because, once they start digging, they'll dig up something in the end. You see, such a trivial oversight, and how it revenges itself now. I always said that one can't blow his job! One never knows how it is with people. Years go by and everything is fine and dandy, but then one day there's a scandal. Especially now when everybody's in a hurry to scream about law-abidingness!"

"Can't we settle this matter in some other way?"

"I don't know. We'll try to bury the whole issue before it comes to something. After all, we're not happy to see one of our comrades being dragged through the courts and have old matters aired again. You shouldn't, however, dramatize the whole issue. We're keeping our eye on it, and if we can, we'll drown it. It's important not to make too much fuss about it. You shouldn't, as you have been doing so far, drag yourself from one comrade to another."

"And how do you know that I . . .?"

"Because I know it; one finds out about such things very fast. Why do you do it? It's better to sit quiet and wait. One begins to wonder whether indeed you do have something on your conscience, the way you're running around trying to prove your innocence. Why do you put yourself in such an ambiguous situation? You shouldn't have come to Warsaw at all. One attracts attention that way."

They must have called him up, Hibisz too. They're looking for reassurance. Bełczyński must have told him everything. Maybe they even called up the prosecutor? If they begin digging now, then I've goofed again, it's my nerves, I must control my nerves. '*Get up! Why are you stretching? Are you sorry to bid farewell to your life? You've lived long enough anyway. It's about time to go against your destiny.*' '*They came to fetch me. I waited for it for so many years. They went to the garage. They're starting the motors. Why have they tied my hands? Will they blindfold me? Stuff my mouth with rags? What for, Comrade? What for? What for?*' Aha, the pass, I must return it, why does she look at me that way? Do I have it written on my forehead that I am a condemned man? Everybody knows it already. They are running back and forth with the files bringing evidence against me, everything to make it rougher for me. For so many years, I never thought seriously that somebody was keeping an eye on me too. I trusted people, I considered them to be my friends, but they were writing reports about me, waiting until I finally tripped, and now everybody knows it, I am an enemy, I must be destroyed—and he tells me I shouldn't worry, we are watching your case. I know how they settle such matters. They shouldn't try to pull the wool over my eyes. Once there exists a file it's not for nothing. Don't I know it myself?

Translated by Vera Von Wiren-Garczynski

Tomasz Staliński

The Funeral

Excerpt from *Widziane z Góry* (*Seen from the Top*).

Borowicz had the distinct impression that someone, standing a bit to the side and yet quite near, was watching the scene. This was a dangerous thing. Feeling uneasy under the persistent stare, he decided to turn around suddenly, so that the rapid gesture would startle the intruder. A strange figure of a man suddenly stood before him: tall, bald, dressed in some kind of denim coat or parka; his face, pudgy and red, seemed to have no outline, as though it were plastered together out of sand or crushed brick, while its general contour contained something monumental, a kind of Mussolini carved in stone. Borowicz did not recognize him, but the man continued observing him with an amused grin. What could this be all about? And suddenly, from the very depths of his memory, or maybe his subconscious, a vague thought started to emerge and slowly take shape: a suggestion of a name. But at that instant the man made his decision, took a step towards Borowicz, and spoke in a very familiar Lwów baritone.

"It's been twenty years since we've seen each other. In Warsaw, remember?"

Borowicz was still straining his memory, but the man continued:

"So, Henry, you now call yourself Borowicz, don't you, old man? And my name has always been Greenbaum, and I'm still Greenbaum. From Lwów, nowhere else. Now you remember, right?"

Arthur Greenbaum! Borowicz was so startled that for a moment he forgot the scene with the President. He even made a move as if he were ready to throw his arms around Arthur, but then pulled them back quickly, seeing that Arthur was not prepared, or eager, for such a warm greeting. What phantoms of the past were showing up today, here at the cemetery! Getreider, in his grave, and now he—Greenbaum.

Arthur Greenbaum had been the inseparable companion of Edmund Getreider while the latter still played the part of troubadour and poet. But Arthur did not follow in his friend's footsteps, for all of his life sport had been his business. Entirely and exclusively. He was a boxer and a ball-player; first he played with the famous Jewish Hasmonea club in Lwów, and then moved on to the Warsaw Polonia. He took a liking to Edmund, and together they roamed the avenues of Warsaw or wasted their time sitting around the cafés. A boxer and a poet—a good pair for the snobs.

Once the memory dam fell open, the information stored within began pouring out in profusion: During the German occupation Greenbaum behaved with dignity and courage. He did not go to the Jewish ghetto, and wanted to join the underground in the forest, but he had a wife whom he loved very much. One day an opportunity came up and Greenbaum bought for her from an agent, a Jew, an American passport, in the notorious hotel on Dluga street. As could have been easily foreseen, it turned out to be a simple provocation: the Germans got all the money they could out of the Jews in hiding and then shot the entire transport on its way, allegedly, to Amsterdam. But Greenbaum did not know all this—he went to the forest. After the war he worked in sports, and later Borowicz heard some talk about a jail term—for financial irregularities, they said. And now here he stood before him, huge, fat, sarcastic, speaking with a deliberately exaggerated Lwów accent. A real "phantom of the past."

Greenbaum was not a person it would be good to be seen with. The people were slowly leaving the cemetery, the rain had stopped, and it was becoming somehow more cheerful—but not for Borowicz, of course; he was still filled with the memories of his unfortunate scene with the President. Knowing himself, he realized that in two or three hours all this would really start worrying him—like a belated toothache after leaving the dentist. In addition, everything was his own fault: he should have tried to telephone, to find the old man at any cost. As yet, he felt merely a slight discomfort about standing there with this intruder from another planet; his departing comrades only glanced from time to time in their direction, carefully, without greeting. My God, what wasted opportunities for conversations, contacts; and that stupid scene with the President, a lot of people must have noticed it, even without actually having to look. Arthur was probably the only person who failed to see anything, and in fact hadn't the vaguest idea about the problems and all the complications around him. He showed no inclination to be gotten rid of, and swayed on his feet standing next to Borowicz, like an elephant. Anyway, after twenty years getting rid of him would not have been too easy. Automatically they started walking toward a more deserted path, where there were fewer graves—the group of people had already begun to fall apart, to thin out, seep into the distance and the moist, slightly rainbow-colored drizzle. So many opportunities wasted—dear God!

"What have you been doing with yourself?" Borowicz asked, although he could not have cared less. But Arthur took up the conversation with great animation.

"Just spent a month in Bulgaria with the boys, at a camp, you know?" Greenbaum had no idea how to speak softly. "Been training the 'Marymont' boxers; really great, old man. Lots of talent. We're sure to rake in the Warsaw championship. 'Legia' is with us all the way."

"And what's new in Bulgaria?" Borowicz felt he was asking a desperately stupid question. What did he care about all this? But Arthur received it well, though with a touch of sarcasm.

"In Bulgaria, old man, same as here: a fucking bore! Socialism, monotony, you know all that!"

"How do you mean?"

"Simple. For the common man, the only diversion—a transistor radio that makes music, or 'totolotek,' namely, their brand of the numbers game. Outside of that, monotony, hopelessness, old man. Same as here."

Borowicz, because of his position, tried to appear indignant, but in a good-natured tone.

"What kind of talk is this, my friend? Bulgaria, why it used to be a backward, agricultural, primitive country, and look at it today. It is building industry, new cities, making up for lost time."

Arthur looked down at him carefully, as if trying to check whether he was being serious.

"Spare me the crap, we've known each other much too long for that! Have you heard the Byelorussian anthem?"

"The Byelorussian anthem?"

"Yes, only changed a little. It goes like this. And Greenbaum started to sing, paying little attention to the graves around them:

We slept for hundreds of years
And they woke us then
And kicked our rears
And they laid us down again.

"So, you see," he continued, "today it is the anthem not just of Byelorussia: it is the anthem of Bulgaria, Rumania, Yugoslavia, and all the rest. And Poland too—here too you've been installing order, imported from Russia."

"Nobody imported me from Russia," protested Borowicz bitterly. Now he understood with whom he was dealing: a Jewish reactionary, a very characteristic type. Well, and why not? But why was he letting himself become involved in the discussion? Luckily they now came to some deserted section of the cemetery, overgrown with weeds and full of little crosses: some white, made of birch, others just plain, simply two pieces of wood nailed together. Arthur arranged his two-hundred-pound body on a low, rain-drenched garden bench, somewhat blackened by the weather, and Borowicz felt obliged to sit down as well.

"Nobody imported you, you say? But he over there, Edek (he pointed in the direction of the more important section of the cemetery), he was imported, dropped from an airplane, wasn't he? He used to be a great guy, only later on he lost his senses. A group of the surviving Jew boys are messing around with the whole business, just to spite the people: you're having fun, and the people get knocked around!"

"What's this, anti-Semitism?"

Greenbaum really lost his temper.

"Now don't be an idiot and stop pretending—to yourself too. Jews should not be ruling, because they're too nervous, they're too hysterical. They have reasons to be, big reasons—but who cares about that. In a country where the Jews rule, normal Jews cannot live. Greenbaums, like me, cannot live, because everyone thinks that they too are guilty. You heard the story about the cab-driver?"

"No."

"A visitor arrives in Warsaw, takes a cab at the station, but he sees that the cabby is a Jew. The visitor stares and stares at him, so finally the cabby says: 'I know, you're surprised that I'm not in the government!' You see, old man, I am that cabby. You're in the government, and I, do you know where I've been? In the clink! Four years, old man. In the clink. And they really let me have it! You want to know what for?"

Borowicz thought that he knew: for stealing, and now he'd probably start giving him the patriotic bit. He kept silent, but Arthur, excited, did not wait for a reply.

"They locked me up for the Pobianice Bicycle Association, old man. Does that strike a familiar note?"

"Not in the least."

"Ah, well then! (Arthur began explaining, slowly, patiently, as if lecturing a somewhat slow-witted student). The Pobianice Bicycle Association, old man, was in existence as many as sixty years before the war. In Russian-occupied Poland it played, you see, a really important role, because they not only taught you how to bicycle, but also how to think and speak and feel in Polish and, next to the sport, or maybe under cover of it, they were doing many, many other things—all the poor people of Lódź flocked around them, you see, because they were a truly democratic group, no question about it. They had great traditions, old man, and much wealth, because whenever a more enlightened guy, either from Lódź or among the landed gentry, would kick the bucket, he'd leave them his dough or some other stuff; it was, I tell you, old man, a big thing. And what treasures they had, what documents, you wouldn't believe it. . . ."

He stopped for a moment; Borowicz sat rather bored. "So what happened?" he asked, to be polite.

"I'm just giving you the highlights, though it's a whole long epic. But after the war, when that Bolshevik order of yours set in, all hell broke loose: there was no room in our country for such bourgeois (bourgeois, mind you) organizations, and, as everybody knew, in pre-war Poland there had been nothing but hunger, filth, and misery (the fact that we actually got along rather nicely didn't count, it wasn't true, who ever heard of such a thing?). And so they took the Association under their own wings, they started preaching that brother Stalin was our sun, until the members, in private, had to hold on to their bellies, they laughed so hard, and finally the whole thing was shut down and liquidated. My pals there, they asked me to become the liquidation officer: they thought I had some pull; they hoped I could at least help save some of their treasures. I lived in Lódź at the time, so I agreed. Meanwhile all that stuff started rotting, falling apart, and then I heard that an inventory would be taken and everything put into storage at some warehouse, which would be the same as throwing it out. Think of it! Such treasures, flags, medals, documents, all kinds of trophies, signed photographs, priceless stuff, old man, the entire history of sport in Lódź—and more. So I thought to myself, don't be a fool: I took what was most valuable and distributed it among the people, for myself I kept the photographs, it's nice to be able to look through such things once in a while. And—you can guess the rest, my friend: arrest, a long hearing, the whole rigmarole, and ten years to boot."

"Ten years," Borowicz shuddered slightly, interested in the story despite himself, "why so long?"

"Because it was a military court, the charge—counter-revolutionary activities, get it? Ten years was a minimum with them. And they sure gave me a whipping, to punish me for the fact that, although a Jew, I refused to join them. I ended up at Wronki, and after four years came October and they let me go, even apologized. But four years were gone! Six years wasted under Hitler—that makes ten altogether; I got my own one way or another, ten years of living, down the drain. Yes my friend!"

"Why didn't you come to me?" asked Borowicz without conviction (after all, he had very little influence in those days).

"Hell, old man, I'm just a cabby! My name has always been Greenbaum, and Greenbaum it will remain, and you are Borowicz, you're in the government. Don't get angry, you're not a bad guy, but you're in the government!"

Borowicz controlled his annoyance and decided to fall back on principles. "So there's nothing that you like in today's Poland?" he asked. And then again: what about the education, the schools, industrialization, investment, hard work, rich peasants, the end of the police methods after October, and the new Western territories and the long sea coast, and that a different Poland would now be impossible, that they had saved it, saved it through transformation and adjustment. In vain! Arthur shook his head sadly to everything he said.

"Save your breath, friend," he said at last. "You know what you know, and I know what I know. Poland's not a pin that it should be lost. Hitler couldn't do her in, neither could Stalin. You are building, that's true, but the people don't love you. Because, you see, it's like this: new buildings are rising, new glass buildings, block after block, but inside them there's no life. And there's no life anywhere under communism. You asked me about Bulgaria, and, you know, it's curious: lots of sunshine, wine, the sea, yet everything's sad as hell. And if you gave it to the West, then you'd see real life! What have they done to be suffering so much, what have we done?"

Again it started to rain, the wind was now howling through the tree branches. Borowicz looked around him, as if for the first time: they were sitting in some deserted, little-known part of the cemetery, alone, among weed-grown graves, some with crosses over them, others without—lonely, anonymous mounds, with not even a name-plate. There was no point in continuing the discussion with Greenbaum; he obviously cared only about his youth and the terrible years under Hitler, with the mass murders, the misery, the unbelievable humiliations. Fascinated with his past—good and bad—he would never be able to participate in the new times, he was too weak, too broken; the unjust—if one could believe him—jail term did the rest. It would have been pointless to go on with the discussion, since he seemed incapable of looking at the world from a fresh perspective, unbiased, not tinted by the past events.

Greenbaum seemed to guess his trend of thought, for he rose slowly from the low, black bench. It was now raining heavily, water ran down his bald head, his old fashioned coat became drenched and darker.

"We'll then, so long, old pal. I'm sorry—forgive me for stopping you and giving you such an earful. You have your own troubles; I guess it's not too easy for you, either. I came here because I remembered about old Edek, I read in the papers that you'd be burying him here today. He was a great guy, even though at the end he lost his senses. You remember Sophie, remember when you warned me that the hotel on Dluga street was nothing but a trap? I didn't want to listen to you. You were smart, and I was stupid. That's right."

His huge hand was making curious maneuvers in the vicinity of his eyes—wiping away tears, or what—he turned away for a moment, and then, as if apologetically, turned again toward Borowicz. They shook hands in silence and he walked away down the cemetery path, stepping clumsily between the weed-grown graves.

"It is my past walking away"—thought Borowicz.

Translated by Barbara Vedder

Leopold Tyrmand

A Cocktail Party

THE host and hostess had decided to give a cocktail party in classic style. But as everything in Poland gives in to the national bent, rather than endure standing with their glasses spleen-high the guests sat comfortably in sofas and chairs. The conversation was monopolized by a few eager and agile tongues. Individual private conversation was obliterated by the terror of a collective show—the eloquent and venomous indulging themselves at the expense of the shy, the delicate, and the duller ones to the frightened approbation of the others. Malice governed every impulse. "What lovely drapes," said someone. "Where ever did you get them?" Knowing glances were exchanged behind the backs of the host and hostess, reflecting contempt for their hideous taste. "In London," the host or his wife replied, "At Liberty's. We bought the very last lengths of the material. . . ." A representative of an international pharmaceutical concern, the host had, of course, been granted his position with the permission of the Polish authorities; hence his permanent passport, his cordial relations with the foreigners living in Warsaw, his house in the diplomatic quarter, and his bath and toilet straight from America. It was no secret how he acquired them, but how had he transported them and how had he obtained the required customs exemptions? The toilet was enthusiastically displayed as the great acquisition of his life. His wealth and usefulness conditioned his small extravagances, such as his inclination to frequent intellectuals. He paid for that weakness by giving sumptuous receptions and ignoring the sneers at his little snobberies. When a certain Hojda said: "It's awful what they've hung on their walls! A giant dressing gown . . ." the host and hostess had to pretend that they hadn't heard.

"I had a little bar in my library at the beginning of the Six-Year Plan," Larbiński was telling Elizabeth, but Hojda corrected him: "The truth of the matter is that you already had one under Stalin, made by a private carpenter." "Perhaps a little cup of crayfish soup?" the lady of the house asked with studied sweetness. "Crayfish soup at this time of the year?" Elizabeth marveled meekly. "Canned crayfish," the hostess admitted, "but the cream turns out quite tasty." "What a genius Rybicki is," said Hojda. "I ran into him yesterday at the *Pod Gwiazdami* Café with a brand-new kitten, seventeen years old, with legs, eyes, hair and teeth, believe me, good enough to export." Kostkowski said, "What do you think you're up to, Rybicki? I know that number; she's engaged." To which Rybicki replied, "I'm not jealous. . . ."

"Rybicki," Andrzej laughed tightly, "has been hopping around the embassy cocktail parties lately like a foreign cultural exchange officer, passing judgment on books, on films. The other day he said to me he couldn't understand why artists weren't able to create a positive hero out of our times, and the country was wasting its money on them if they couldn't." "Maybe he'd like to offer himself as a model," Hojda laughed. "Nothing surprises me anymore."

"Andrzej Felak!" Klara Onyx came over. "I haven't seen you for ages. What's new?" Andrzej told her, and thought about his conversation with Malecki. That day in the editorial office, Malecki had asked, "Did you see *Die Welt?* Day before yesterday?"

"No," said Andrzej, alarmed. Malecki usually portended trouble.

"They wrote about you. A lot. And so did several other German papers. Especially in West Berlin. The way they went on about you! It's enough to make one burst with pride, that Germans could write that way about a Pole. . . ."

Nausea gripped Andrzej's breast. He wasted no time before checking. In the past few days, the German papers referred to Grohmann's despatches from Warsaw about the persecutions and sufferings of the well-known Polish journalist Andrzej Felak, who had dared speak a bit of truth in his new book about Germany.

To be sure, one journalist commented, he had read Felak's book carefully, and had not found that objectivity which Germany so longed for when considering their controversial problems. But he had reports from Warsaw, nevertheless, that Felak had been rapped for such a book, so the book's import must be more positive than it appeared at first sight. In one Berlin paper, there was a specific invitation to visit West Berlin, the front-line city, where the dialogue about the conflicts between East and West took on the shades of authenticity, stating that an honest and penetrating journalist like Felak could make use of the occasion for the good of troubled mankind. This perfidious sentence was dragging Andrzej into a catastrophe. This affair, not based on a semblance of truth, was turning into a disaster. It had to be counteracted, but how, in what way, against whom, with whom?

From the open doors of a large room, panelled in light wood, Grohmann entered, a German press ephebe adorned in an Anglo-Saxon elegance elaborated by the great department stores of the Economic Miracle. Behind him the voice of Ella Fitzgerald could be heard, cut to the obligatory half-tones; crushed into the stereo, Ella underscored Grohmann's greeting with sterilized, sadness-proof blues. "Hi," Grohmann addressed Andrzej in English, "may I ask you: *zadowolony? Zufrieden?* Happy?"

Andrzej smiled wryly. "That wasn't so shrewd."

"What?" Alertness appeared in Grohmann's face, like one magic lantern slide replacing another: easy amusement.

"You know what."

"My dear friend," Grohmann defended himself, "in one day you have become a hero, at least in Germany. You can't have everything."

Andrzej thought perhaps one could, but you don't know that, you idiot; you and those like you stuffing your ice boxes with crayfish. The idea of service, patronage to worthy people in world history, what do you know about it, you golden-haired elephant! Those who really know themselves to be villains and fools pay best!

"I don't understand," Grohmann continued with slight irony, "how you can expect to criticize official moves and still enjoy the love and favor of the government? You have to make up your mind one way or the other."

"And you will never understand," Andrzej smiled, "because you make a wrong assumption. I criticize nothing. I never violate inviolable lines. I simply have my own outlook, my own working tools. You won't find a single word or thought in *Spiked Helmet* that violates the dictated interests of my country and its leaders."

"Just a minute," Grohmann said, taking out his ball-point and note pad, "I'll write that down at once—so there won't be any misunderstanding in the future."

"Have you gone mad!" Andrzej gasped. "Here, in front of everyone!" Andrzej panicked, realizing that anything he said could be turned against him. "For some," Grohmann whispered, apologetically and confidingly, "you became a champion the day before yesterday, a champion of progress and liberty under communism. . . ." He seemed slightly alarmed at what he had done; Andrzej's reaction surprised him.

"Don't play the fool, Grohmann," Andrzej said quite sternly, as if to warn him not to push his jokes too far.

Grohmann floated away in the eddies of the cocktail party. Elizabeth said, "Andy, what are you so depressed about? Has something happened?" Her words were drowned by the flood of remarks from all sides. Larbiński was smiling wryly, and saying "*Ça va?*" which showed that he used French on impulse. Hojda was talking with the hostess, whose face was so covered with paint and make-up that it suggested a beige death mask. Hodja liked the brand of beauty produced by heavy industry: cosmetic casting, the triumph of modern chemistry, distilling beauty from brown coal, sulphur, and animal fats. But then Hojda was unspoiled. He still delighted in the brilliance of neon lights reflected on wet asphalt. Larbiński navigated toward Elizabeth, finally moored her in the corner of the overdone library and spoke to her. Elizabeth grinned like a half-wit. Andrzej didn't like that smile. He knew the concentration behind it, systematically a chain of events which could not possibly make him, her husband, happy. His consolation was that in Warsaw people mistakenly believed she screwed with anyone, after exchanging only a few words. But he alone knew the truth. That frigid old bag only reached a climax at the prospect of a new pair of square shoes straight from Paris. I'm the only one who's ever gotten anywhere with her, he thought, while others. . . . In any case, that was long ago; now her only passion is showing off. That stupid prick Larbiński is kidding himself if he thinks he'll get anywhere! He suddenly felt disgust for Elizabeth, a deep repugnance. He had never thought so ill of her as he did at this moment. He wondered whether instinct dictated that he spit on her and drown her in abominations.

He ran into Lavertisse. Fear floated on the surface of Andrzej's thoughts like grease spots on water. He was worried. Who was informing the police? He could imagine the report on him. Again, he thought, I must talk about it in front of everyone. Lavertisse was not easy to avoid. His broad shoulders were covered with crumpled tweed, and the pipe stuck in his fluffy sandy beard amplified his voice like a microphone. "I was hoping I'd run into you, *cher* Felak," Lavertisse said and rubbed his rarely washed, festering eyes. He was exceptionally slovenly for a Swiss, which probably had something to do with intelligence, for he was considered a star in his profession. "Tell me about Mikołaj Plank. What's the story? First the startling news in the *Wieczór Warszawy* and then the attack in *Teraźniejszość?* Why are they trying to grind him into the ground?"

"Plank . . .," Andrzej said evasively, "a charming man. The darling of the tables at the *Spatif*. But basically. . . ."

"The world is interested in him," Lavertisse remarked rather casually. "It would be even more interested if Plank did something—wrote books or made films."

"Laziness is his ideology. He doesn't want to do anything, so he simply does nothing."

"Perhaps they won't let him do anything; perhaps they make it impossible for him. It's a waste! Any other countrv would be earning foreign currency on him."

"You believe in fairy tales. Who won't let him? In any case, I'm not a Plank specialist. Ah, here's Lorant. He can tell you something."

Lorant approached, smelling of Old Spice. "I'm late," he said. "I'm sorry." "Why tell us?" smiled Andrzej. "Apologize to the host and hostess." "One only apologizes to people who really matter," Lorant said. "What terrible hors d'oeuvres. They feed you here like in the ministry mess." Andrezej felt better now. As a threesome with Lorant, they formed a group a little better than the rest, one not liable to suspicions. "Lavertisse has been after me about Plank," said Andrzej. "Tell him something, will you?" "Plank?"

Lorant lightly asked. "A charming bum. You tell me, Lavertisse, who in your opinion is the more genuine and useful ally of freedom—the notorious Plank or our friend Felak?"

Andrzej thought this a slimy joke, a kind of patronizing scoffing, to make him a bit of an ass. Lorant shouldn't pull this sort of thing. He was supposed to be an ally. Andrzej thought of a neat ploy, but decided to pass for the time being. Lavertisse buried a sly, contemptuous smile in his beard. "Of course," he said, "our dear Felak." For a moment he seemed to be struggling with himself, but then he fired. "Those who prosper in the bosom of communism are always the best allies of freedom and . . . of America. Which means, of course, of Coca Cola, limousines, superhighways, and the California beaches."

Lorant nodded agreement adding, just to be on the safe side, "It's not so simple . . . Plank, in any case, considers us," and he gestured around the room, "common swine. If let in, he'd get drunk and offend everyone. That would put him in your good graces, Lavertisse. Isn't that so?"

For a moment unchecked repugnance flooded Lavertisse's eyes. He could not bear Lorant, but he tried to hide it. "Why should we take our bearings from your Polish moral reckonings?" He asked. "They're so complicated. And difficult. And boring."

Andrzej thought: "Actually, you know shit and that's better for you and for us. Why do you have to meddle in matters that don't concern you to find out what's what?" He wanted to slip away unobtrusively, but Lavertisse had him by the elbow, while Lorant drifted off into the ceaselessly flowing stream of guests. "I have news about your trip," Lavertisse said softly. Andrzej maneuvered him as far away as possible. Known for his contacts with the American Embassy, he was the only foreign correspondent in Warsaw who mattered. Andrzej knew the arrogant representatives of Western wire-services, bored nose-pickers, sly and narrow-minded, hanging around the Grand and the Bristol and the inter-country games, looking for signs of hostility in the camp of peace. He knew their run-down offices, cluttered with cigarette cartons and old statistical yearbooks they ransacked to find out who was who and what was what. They knew nothing about the simplest subordination of one man by another, nothing beyond stock universal slogans, which did occasionally fit. Lavertisse was different. He was penetrating, and powerful in his way. He represented some influences: uncoordinated, but nonetheless real and far-reaching.

"Well?" Andrzej asked nervously when they stopped in a corner of the vast library, a safe distance from Larbiński and Elizabeth.

Lavertisse smiled indulgently. "They're probably arranging your giant trip for you," he said.

"Did someone tell you that?"

Lavertisse smiled, still more indulgently. "You overestimate my capabilities, *cher* Felak. I simply imagine that in one of the rooms far back from the street in the United States Embassy in Warsaw, several *gentlemen* met to discuss the awarding of fellowships, aid, gifts, and scholarships for citizens of this country. The name Felak came up and the following remarks were made: "Well dressed," "New generation of Communists," "Always clean-shaven," "A man of Western civilization," "A very elegant wife," "Everyone in Poland reads him," "Recognition from all over," "What else is he writing, what else does he say. . . ."

"The last remark is yours, Lavertisse, not the Americans'." Andrzej flashed a hard smile.

"In other words, you deny the Americans even elementary perspicacity, not to mention intelligence?" Lavertisse shook his head. "That's not nice. And that's why you want to hit them for such a fat bankroll. . . . Perhaps you're right after all? Perhaps they say: 'He can't do otherwise. He must. He is too liberal, too forbearing, too tolerant to be dishonest, so that if he writes shameful things about us, well, that's just because he has to. . . ." He sucked his pipe with obvious excitement, as if watching tiny animals in furious combat.

"You don't understand the delicacy of my position," Andrzej said calmly. "Within the limits of possibility, I do all I can to bring us together and not to divide us."

"Us?"

"Us!" I mean reasonable, enlightened people of good will throughout the world, on both sides of the great trench. . . ."

Lavertisse reflected that a hitherto unknown caste of people had been bred in this country, who imitated Americans in behavior, dress, and ambiguous statements. The stupid Americans fed them, refreshed them at cocktail parties, and showered them with gifts through their foundations. On their return home, these Poles churned out old-fashioned, shoddy accusations with charming smiles on their lips—because they had to. At least, so they claimed. But what compelled such baseness, except their own innate greedy cunning? "You know," Lavertisse remarked, "Pakowski said the very same thing to me about himself. That he is enlightened, reasonable, loaded with good intentions for filling the trenches that divide men of good will."

Andrzej bit his lip and lit a cigarette, his fingers trembling slightly. The Pakowski case was unpleasant, foul-smelling. The young editor-in-chief of a weekly had been invited by Lavertisse's newspaper to Switzerland, where he had been fêted splendidly as a representative of the new, promising generation. He had delivered utterances dripping with liberal humanitarianism and declared his towering admiration for the achievements of modern Swiss democracy, calling it a watchmakerly perfect system of social life. Then he returned to Poland and published a series of articles depicting Switzerland as a dump of degenerate inter-personal relations, an oasis of moral depravity organized with the financial chicaneries of prosperity. "I had letters from him," Lavertisse said, "written in Geneva and Zurich, dripping with praises for our institutions. 'It's like a wonderland here' . . . he wrote. A few weeks later, I opened his magazine. The same old invectives, but how spendidly turned out! Of course, the very next time I saw him, he clasped my hands and said, 'You do understand! I couldn't do anything else! They forced me. Otherwise I'd have lost my job!' I replied, 'Surely, they didn't hold a gun at your back. This is Poland, not Russia, and Polish Communists insist it's not the same.' He cried, 'They almost did!' I decided then he was a common scoundrel, but Switzerland will not go bankrupt just because one bugger screwed it out of a month's good living."

Andrzej thought how stupid they all were, even Lavertisse. Soon his paper would call him back, and everything would be patched up. And two years from now Pakowski would make another trip, with all expenses paid by his hosts, to Denmark for a change, to fill in the trenches cutting off the Danes from people of good will. And rightly so. It's the way it ought to be. Let the fools pay. . . . "Do you know what Lewinson said about Pakowski's articles?" Andrzej asked ironically. "That they were schematizations, pure and simple, and that Polish society expects better of its journalists. What do you think of that?"

"Lewinson is a decent fellow."

"I think so too. But even the most decent can make mistakes; isn't that so?"

Lavertisse glanced distractedly at the silhouettes of the guests gorging on hors d'oeuvres, hovering in the background. "What are you thinking about?" he cautiously asked Andrzej.

"The fun that Grohmann has created in Germany. It looks as if I can kiss the trip to America good-bye. You guys fixed me just fine. Do you think Lewinson will let me out of the country now, me, the authentic spokesman of critical sentiments?" The proud bitterness of the sorely-tried herald of the true and beautiful reverberated in Andrzej's voice.

"*Cher* Felak," smiled Lavertisse, "we can put an end to your fresh-baked career as an oppositionist with two telegrams. I've read *Spiked Helmet*. All I'd have to do would be to write the truth about it, and Lewinson would beg you to go to America. Would you like me to do that? Me, Grohmann, and a few others?"

Andrzej dragged deeply on his cigarette and slowly sipped the cognac in the fat bubble glass. Looking deeply into Lavertisse's eyes, to create an effect of subtle perception, he said, "Don't do it."

"No, no," Lavertisse shook his head in sincere admiration. "You're playing a great game, *cher* Felak."

Andrzej feverishly assured himself that his frankness must somehow have put Lavertisse under obligation to him. But if not, he thought, I pay dearly for it! "But when you read my statement in the papers tomorrow," he said calmly, "about how the West German hacks used my book for provocation and attributed thoughts to me I never had, remember that I wrote it under pressure and in terror—that I was forced to do it."

Lavertisse's admiration took on a semblance of respect. He bowed his head as if before a masterpiece. He thought: That's an enormous enterprise, demanding talent and pluck. To reap profits from servility and opposition at the same time, for both selling out, and for non-conformism. Who in Poland today were the real allies of the West, the men of ideas, or the swindlers and clever careerists? "So you are eroding communism from within, *cher* Felak," he smiled warmly. "It's difficult to be ungrateful to you for that. . . ." He vacillated, as if avoiding too overt an offense. "I think the Americans understand. . . ."

Andrzej knew immediately how to react to a caustic openness he hadn't seen before. Lavertisse had made an offensive and dangerous statement with a nonchalance none of them had ever indulged in before. Yet Andrzej also knew that this particular assault was an expression of weakness. It masked anger—anger because they had to pay dearly for something they did not care to pay for. Andrzej smiled superiorly, "The West is withering from a lack of ideology. You haven't managed to elaborate your own slogans, so you feed on a hope glued from obstructionism and negation. Oh yes, Lavertisse, it is too bad, but as you have nothing to fire the imagination, nor any conscientious program, you are forced to rely on me, and build on my desire to consume and make profit. . . ."

"Yes, yes," Lavertisse readily agreed. "That is what we want after all, people without complications. À propos, why doesn't Mikołaj Plank take his films to Paris with Larbiński? They say they're revelations."

"How should I know?" Andrzej smiled. "He probably couldn't get a passport."

"Why not?"

"Perhaps he stole something? Or perhaps he embezzled? He always has some complications. But why should you care about him. After all, you prefer people without complications."

Lavertisse was accosted by the hostess, and beat an awkward retreat. Andrzej was sopping wet. His shirt stuck to his back, his heart was beating irregularly and loudly. He thought feverishly, but soberly, that it was pointless—he had to reach an understanding with Lewinson! How could he possibly establish his moral authority when everyone was senselessly knocking him for not seeking an all-out struggle? Was it a sin to try and make constructive peace with everyone? How could he defend himself when enemies were everywhere, lying in wait for a man? After all, Andrzej asked himself, why should I bother harvesting on both sides of this chasm which divides one half of mankind from the other? The pit gives off fumes and an ugly stench, and everyone runs away from this scar-infested gash to find shelter in some safe, chosen spot of earth. And he alone, Felak the just, Felak the brave, is left stooping over the dizzying abyss and looking for something. What was he seeking? Certainly not shallow gain. He was seeking his greatness, a moral monument that one day would rise adorned with golden words of praise and favor from both sides.

Lorant approached again, free and easy. "Andrzej," he said,

"I've a hunch that I've finally fixed that trip to America, from which you will return in glory."

"Ah, that's fine," Andrzej remarked off-handedly. "I always knew I could count on you." Not for an instant did he believe that Lorant had fixed anything. Someone had probably told him that Andrzej's trip was on, so he immediately made a point of taking the credit for himself.

Translated by Ronald Strom

About The Authors

ANDRZEJ BOBKOWSKI was born in Wiener-Neustadt (Austria) in 1913. He was educated in Cracow, and studied at the Higher School of Commerce in Warsaw. The outbreak of World War II overtook him in France, where he stayed during the entire war period working among and caring for Polish factory workers. His diary and literary sketches, published by the *Institut Littéraire* in 1957, are a priceless study of the German occupation in France. After the war, Mr. Bobkowski was a frequent contributor to *Kultura*. In 1949, he left for Guatemala, where he settled and started a shop for model aviation, his life-long hobby, which soon made of him a well-known and highly popular person among the youths of Guatemala City.

Mr. Bobkowski died in 1961 after a long illness.

IOSIF ALEKSANDROVICH BRODSKY was born in Leningrad, in 1940, into a Russian Jewish family. He has been writing poetry since 1958. He left school at age fifteen, but has since taught himself Polish and English, and has read widely and deeply in Polish, English, and American poetry, as well as classical mythology, religious philosophy, and the like. In March, 1964, he was sentenced as a "social parasite" to five years at hard labor in the remote Arkhangelsk region of Northern Russia. He was quietly released in November, 1965. He has since been living in Leningrad, writing poetry and doing translations. Four of his poems were published in 1966 and 1967 in Leningrad anthologies, but most of his work remains unpublished in the Soviet Union. He is currently engaged in a large-scale translation of the English metaphysical poets, with special emphasis on John Donne.

JÓZEF CZAPSKI was born in 1896 in eastern Poland. He was educated in St. Petersburg, where he witnessed the Russian Revolution of 1917. He took part in the Polish-Soviet war of 1920, after which he returned to his art studies at the Cracow Academy of Art, and then in Paris. As a successful *avant-garde* painter, he exhibited in Paris, Geneva, New York, and in Poland, collecting many prizes and awards. He published essays and articles on art theory and was highly noted as an art critic.

In 1939, he fought against both the Germans and the Russians who invaded eastern Poland. Subsequent to his capture by the Russians, he was one of the 79 survivors of the massacre of 4,000 Polish officers in the Katyn Forest. After escaping from the Soviet Union, he served with the Polish forces in Egypt and Italy. His book, *Memoirs from Starobielsk,* a detailed description of his imprisonment in Russia before the notorious slaughter, was published in Italy in 1945. It has since been translated into many languages, including English. His second book, *The Inhuman Earth,* which appeared in Paris in 1948, was also widely translated.

Mr. Czapski, who presently lives in France, is a contributor to French journals and magazines, and is considered an outstanding expert on Russian culture and literature. He is one of the leading figures among the Polish intellectuals gathered around *Kultura.*

BOGDAN CZAYKOWSKI was born in eastern Poland in 1932, and deported to northern Russia in 1940. He reached England via Persia and India in 1948, and studied modern European history at the University of Dublin and Polish Literature at the University of London. His publications include four volumes of verse and a book (jointly with B. Sulik) on the Polish community in Britain. At present he is Associate Professor of Slavic Studies at the University of British Columbia in Vancouver, and is preparing a study in English of modern Polish poetry.

ADAM CZERNIAWSKI, who was born in 1934 in Warsaw, writes poetry, short stories, and criticism. He has also published translations, and is now preparing English-language editions of poems and plays by Polish poets, and of papers on aesthetics by the Polish philosopher Roman Ingarden. In 1966, Czerniawski was awarded an Abraham Woursell Foundation grant by the University of Vienna, and this has enabled him to devote all of his time to writing and study. He is currently attending a graduate course in philosophy at Oxford University.

YURI M. DANIEL was born in Russia in 1925 as (according to official Russian sources) "a Jew." After university studies, he worked as a teacher and translator of poetry from the other Slavic languages of the U.S.S.R. (Byelorussian, Ukrainian, and Georgian). He has never published anything in the Soviet Union. In the early 1960's Daniel's writings, mainly short stories, were transported to the West and published with his consent by the *Institut Littéraire* under the pseudonym of Nikolay Arzhak. They first appeared in Polish, then in several Western European languages. In 1966 he was sentenced in the same trial as Sinyavsky to five years of hard labor.

WITOLD GOMBROWICZ was born in Poland in 1904. He studied law at Warsaw University. Before World War II he published only a volume of short stories and a novel that aroused considerable controversy and interest among literary critics for its off-beat ideas and form. He spent the war years in Argentina working in a bank and writing. Although banned in Communist Poland, his novels, plays, and diaries were published by *Kultura* and the *Institut Littéraire*. A decade ago French critics took an intense interest in Gombrowicz's work and hailed him as a major contemporary European writer. His books were translated into fifteen languages and his plays presented in European capitals. In 1967 he won the *Prix International de Littérature* for his novel *Cosmos*. Mr. Gombrowicz last lived in France. His novels published in English are *Ferdydurke* and *Pornografia* (Grove Press, New York, 1968).

Witold Gombrowicz died in 1969.

PIOTR GUZY was born in Zawadzkie, Lower Silesia, in 1922. He was educated in Poland, and took part in the Polish–German war in 1939. After escaping from a prisoner-of-war camp, he joined the Polish army in the West, and was wounded during the Allied landing in Normandy in 1944.

After the war, he studied economics at the University of London. He then returned to Poland in 1949, where he worked as a journalist and wrote mystery stories. In 1958, he was accused of anti-Communist activity, and was forced to defect. Since then, he has been living in England. The *Institut Littéraire* published his novel *The Short Life of a Positive Hero*, which won wide recognition among Polish readers and critics.

ZYGMUNT HAUPT was born in 1907 and brought up in eastern Poland. He studied architecture at the Lwów Polytechnic and urban planning at the University of Paris. However, he abandoned technical studies for painting and writing. When World War II broke out, he served as an officer in the Polish artillery corps from 1939 through 1946. He has lived in the United States for the past twenty years. Much of his writing, which he himself translates into English, has appeared in such American "little" magazines as *Accent, Furioso, Perspectives,* and *The Chicago Review;* several were also published in *The Paris Review*. Some of his work was included in a *New Directions* anthology of new writing. His book *The Paper Ring* was published in Paris by the *Institut Littéraire* and shortly after he received the 1962 *Kultura* award for literature. He has also translated into Polish various poetry by Robert Frost, W. H. Auden and Robert Lowell, as well as fiction by Henry James, e. e. cummings and James Agee.

GUSTAW HERLING-GRUDZIŃSKI was born in Kielce, Poland in 1919. The war interrupted his university studies in Warsaw, and after the fall of Poland, in 1939, he and his firends founded one of the first Polish underground anti-Nazi organizations in Warsaw. After fleeing to the Russian-occupied sector of Poland, he was captured by the NKVD in 1940 and spent two years in a Soviet slave labor camp on the White Sea. His experiences there are described in his book *A World Apart* (with a preface by Bertrand Russell), which was translated into many languages, and included two American editions in 1952.

After his release by the Russians, in 1942, he joined the Polish Army organized in Russia, and went to the Middle East and then to Italy, where at the battle of Monte Cassino he was awarded the highest Polish military honor. After the war, he lived in London and Munich and finally settled in Naples. His new book, *The Island: Three Tales*, has been published recently in America (The World Publishing Company), and also in Italian and German translations. He contributes regularly to *Kultura* in Paris, and to *Tempo Presente*, *La Fiera Letteraria*, and *Il Mondo* in Italy. Some of his articles have been reprinted in America by *The New Leader*, *Atlas*, and *Dissent.*

I. IVANOV is the pseudonym of a Russian writer. His real name is Remizov. He was born in Russia in 1925. The *Institut Littéraire* published, with his agreement, his play *Does Life Exist on Mars?*, which was smuggled out of the U.S.S.R. in manuscript form. Little is known about Mr. Ivanov, except that he was Andrey Sinyavsky's friend, and that he has done translations from French into Russian. None of his work has been published in the U.S.S.R.

WACŁAW IWANIUK, poet, literary critic, and translator of modern American poetry, lives in Toronto, Canada. He studied economics, took part in World War II, and has traveled extensively in Europe and both North and South America.

ALICJA IWAŃSKA was born in Poland in 1918. She studied in Warsaw, Brussels, and at Columbia University. During World War II she took part in the Polish resistance movement and was an instructor at the underground university in Warsaw. Since 1950 she has been teaching sociology and socio-anthropology at various American universities. At present she is with the State University of New York at Albany. She edited a monograph entitled *Contemporary Poland* (published by the University of Chicago for HRAF, 1955) and contributed to *Sociologus, America Indigena,* the *Journal of Inter-American Studies,* and others.

LEO LIPSKI was born in Zurich, Switzerland, in 1917 and educated in Cracow. After the outbreak of World War II, he was imprisoned by the Russians in Lwów, and later sent to a concentration camp. After he was set free, he managed to escape to Iran. Since 1945, he has been living in Tel-Aviv, Israel. His most acclaimed novel, *Piotrus,* was published by the *Institute Littéraire* and has been translated into German. In English, Mr. Lipski published *Roads to Nowhere* (Modern Writing, New York, 1953).

JÓZEF ŁOBODOWSKI was born in northeastern Poland in 1909. He studied at the Lublin University, then in Warsaw. He took part in World War II in Poland and France, tried to escape to England but was imprisoned in Spain where he lives still and works as a broadcasting commentator. Before the war he published poetry and novels. As a long-time *Kultura* contributor he is best known as an outstanding translator from Russian.

JÓZEF MACKIEWICZ was born in 1902, and studied philosophy at Warsaw University and mathematics at the University of Wilno. He was a well-known journalist, columnist, and writer in pre-war Poland. He participated actively in the Polish resistance movement during the German occupation. An ardent anti-Communist, he went into exile after the war and has been living in West Germany. His political essays and articles have appeared in Polish, Russian, Lithuanian and Ukrainian émigré publications, and in numerous translations in English, German, Italian, Swiss, Belgian, Dutch, and Spanish periodicals. His books published in English are *The Katyn Wood Murders* (Hollis & Carter, London; The World Affairs Book Club, London), and *The Road to Nowhere* (Harvill Press-Collins, London; Henry Regnery, Chicago).

CZESŁAW MIŁOSZ was born in Lithuania in 1911. He completed his high school and university studies in Wilno (which belonged to Poland at the time), and in Paris. He entered the diplomatic service of Communist Poland, and in the years 1946–1951 held posts abroad (New York, Washington D.C., and Paris). He broke then with the Polish government in Poland and emigrated to France. In 1953, he won the *Prix Littéraire Européen* for his novel *La Prise du Pouvoir.* Since 1960, he has lived in Berkeley, California, where he is a Professor of Slavic Languages and Literature at the University of California. Although the author of several prose works, he considers himself primarily a poet and a translator of poetry. His volume of essays, *The Captive Mind* (Knopf, 1953), brought him international attention and was translated into a number of languages. Other works published in English include: *The Seizure of Power* (Criterion Books, 1955), *Postwar Polish Poetry* (Doubleday, 1965), *Native Realm* (Doubleday, 1968), and several studies on Polish literature.

TADEUSZ NOWAKOWSKI was born in Olsztyn, Poland, on November 8, 1920. He studied philosophy and literature at Warsaw University. Arrested by the Nazis in 1939, he spent the next five years in German prisons and concentration camps. From 1946 to 1954 he was a journalist and writer in Italy and in London; since 1956 he has lived in Germany, where he writes for radio and TV. Among his best-known works are his novel, *Camp of All Saints* (New York: St. Martin's Press, 1962), and his essay *The Radziwills* (New York: Funk & Wagnalls, 1968).

ISTVÁN ÖRKÉNY was born in Hungary in 1912, and studied chemistry at the University of Budapest. Before the war he contributed to the periodicals of the Hungarian Socialist Left. As a prisoner of war he spent several years in Russia, returning to Hungary in 1947. In 1955 he was awarded the Attila Jozsef Award for a volume of short stories entitled *In a Snowstorm.*

ANDREY D. SINYAVSKY was born in Russia in 1925, and studied literature and history at Russian universities. He was an associate member of the World Literature Institute (the Maxim Gorky Institute) in Moscow and a renowned literary critic and contributor to various Soviet magazines, chiefly the highly regarded *Novy Mir*. He was known as an expert on Boris Pasternak and the Soviet poets of the 1920's. His works, transferred clandestinely with his approval, to the *Institut Littéraire,* have been published under the pseudonym of Abram Tertz, first in Polish, then in twenty-four languages around the world. He is now widely acknowledged as one of the most important, talented, and influential Russian writers of our century. His novels (*Lyubimov, The Trial Begins*) and essays (*What Is Socialist Realism?*) won serious recognition in intellectual and literary circles in Europe and America. In 1966 he was sentenced, in the now notorious writers' trial in Moscow, to seven years of hard labor in a Siberian concentration camp for exceptional criminals, where is now serving out his term.

TOMASZ STALIŃSKI is the pseudonym of an unknown author of a novel *Seen From Atop* which the *Institut Littéraire* received clandestinely from Poland.

LEOPOLD TYRMAND was born in 1920 in Warsaw, and educated there. He studied at the l'Academie des Beaux-Arts in Paris. During World